GET ME
TO THE ABBEY

a memoir

LISA AVELLEYRA

LITTLE CREEK PRESS®
AND BOOK DESIGN
MINERAL POINT, WISCONSIN

Little Creek Press.
5341 Sunny Ridge Road
Mineral Point, WI 53565

ORDERING INFORMATION
Quantity sales. Special discounts are available on quantity purchases by corporations, associations, and others. For details, contact info@littlecreekpress.com

Orders by US trade bookstores and wholesalers.
Please contact Little Creek Press or Ingram for details.

Facebook @ Get Me to The Abbey

Printed in the United States of America

Cataloging-in-Publication Data
Names: Avelleyra, Lisa, author
Title: Get Me to the Abbey, A Memoir
Description: Mineral Point, WI: Little Creek Press, 2022
Identifiers: LCCN: 2022912468 | ISBN: 978-1-955656-28-3
Classification: Biography / Personal Memoirs

Book design by Little Creek Press and Mimi Bark

Cover image of glass by © Roman Sigaev/Shutterstock Images
Cover image of sky by © Evgeny Karandaev/Shutterstock Images
Cover image of Abbey: Farragutful, CC BY-SA 3.0 <https://creativecommons.org/licenses/by-sa/3.0>, via Wikimedia Commons

Dedication

This book is for those still suffering the stranglehold and despair of addiction. May they find an Abbey.

Chapter One

I didn't care about anything. Except vodka. About whether or not I had enough. On that last trip to get more, I made sure to get enough. Two liters. Doubling up.

After a three-week bender, I was so weak I had to psych myself up to go and get it. Kum & Go was more expensive, but also the least amount of walking from car to checkout compared to my other two regular places. I pulled a red Wisconsin stocking cap over my ratty, snarled hair and walked out the door. It was nine o'clock in the morning.

"You can do this," I said to myself, as I walked gingerly to my car.

I rested my forehead on the steering wheel. Fifty yards from my front door to my car and I felt faint. *That's ok. You can do this.*

At the gas station, I had to grab the seat and door frame to hoist myself out of the car. My legs were so weak. I focused on walking steadily into the store. *Can I carry two bottles?*

Back in the car, I rested. I had done it. Relief washed over me. At home, I went straight to the fridge. One bottle in the freezer, the other on the kitchen counter. My hand shook as I screwed off the cap. I took a long swig and wretched. I stumbled to the bathroom and heaved into the toilet. It was all liquid spotted with a couple droplets of blood. I returned to the kitchen and tried another swig. This one stayed down, soothing my mind and insides. *Ahhh, Smirnoff.* I was so glad I splurged on the better stuff.

This was it. I was done. Not with drinking. With living.

I poured half a glass and carried it to the bedroom, set it on the nightstand, and lay down. Periodically, I propped myself up to take a drink until the glass was empty. *Fuck! I have to get up to get more!* Why didn't I just bring the bottle to the bedroom? I believe I was grasping onto a fragile shred of dignity, not wanting to be found with an empty bottle next to me. I made a couple more trips to the kitchen for refills, weaker with each trip. I hadn't eaten a meal for days. A spoonful of cottage cheese here, a slice of cheese there. But that was it.

During that last trip to the kitchen, I gripped the counter after pouring, dizzy and lightheaded. I took a long drink and started to walk back to the bedroom, but I was so weak and so tired. I lay down on the kitchen floor, the glass of vodka near my outstretched hand. So much for dignity. I wanted to sleep and never wake up again. I wanted to die.

I awoke to a circle of faces looking down at me. Among them were my sister Martha and her husband. *What the hell are they doing here? And who are these other people?* Gradually, it registered that they were in uniforms. They were EMTs.

"Why are there so many of you?" I murmured woozily.

There were four or five of them, all jostling for position while prodding me, Martha plying them with questions. *She loves a man in uniform.* I heard a rattling—the sound of shaking metal. I was lifted onto a gurney. I neither protested nor resisted. Martha walked along with the EMTs, blathering on. We rattled out to the parking lot, past my car and to the open rear door of the ambulance, where another EMT awaited.

"Why are there so many of you?" I repeated. Still no answer.

Next, I found myself in a hospital bed, a blood pressure band around my arm. I had always found the sensation unsettling, your arm pumped up almost to the point of bursting. When the nurse moved away, I could see the rest of the room: Martha and her husband, Dennis, had been joined by my other sister, Paula, and her husband Mike. They were all staring at me, rigged up to a machine, fluid flowing into my arm. My stomach hurt, but mostly I was weak and very tired. Paula pulled up a chair next to the bed.

"How are you feeling?" she asked.

I shrugged. "Tired. Weak."

"Brian found you on the kitchen floor. Do you remember how you got there?"

Brian? Brian was an old friend who had broken my heart years ago. My listless mind swirled. He had been checking on me. He was in cahoots with Paula. I had let him in yesterday and he had brought soup after I declined to go out to lunch.

"I lay down. I didn't fall."

"How long were you there?"

"What time is it now?"

"About three."

I shrugged again. "I don't know. A couple hours."

We looked at each other. I looked away first.

Then a nurse, or a nurse's aide, or a candy striper—I don't know what she was—came in and asked me a bunch of questions. Name, address, phone number, social security number.... I couldn't remember it. I couldn't remember my own *social security number*.

"I...I can't remember it." I looked imploringly to my sisters.

"Don't look at me," Martha snipped. "I don't know it."

The hospital staffer, with her clipboard and admission forms, was more kind. "That's alright. We can get it from you later." She left.

Paula was looking at me. I could tell she wanted to say something. I waited.

"Your temperature was really low," she said. "The EMTs were really concerned. They think part of the reason was because you were on the cold floor."

I nodded slightly. So?

"The doctor said your blood-alcohol level was one-third. One-third alcohol. He said most people die with that."

I looked at her silently.

"Is that what you wanted?"

I deliberated about what to answer. Should I act like this was just an old-fashioned bender that got out of hand? Should I pretend I accidentally drank too much and apologize profusely for worrying everyone? I knew I was cornered. I told the truth.

"Yes," I replied softly, my mouth trembling.

Paula looked back at me unwaveringly, her eyes brimming with tears.

After a couple of bouts of dry heaves, during each of which Martha rushed over with a plastic barf bag, a doctor entered. He was dark-haired and handsome and folded himself smoothly into the chair Paula had vacated. His voice was kind, but his words were tough. He told me about my high blood alcohol level and how close I was to dying. *Not close enough.*

I sensed my sisters watching me intently. I was too sick and weak to express any emotion. And then came the question I would hear frequently in the upcoming days.

"Are you having thoughts of harming yourself?" he asked.

Well, not right at this moment, I wanted to quip at him. "No," I said instead. Which was the truth if I would've been under oath. Through the fog and pain, I realized I was pissed. *Just a few more hours, another day, it would've been over. Damn Brian! Damn all of them!*

I tossed and turned as the pain in my belly grew worse, moaning aloud. My sisters watched anxiously. Withdrawal symptoms can last 72 hours. I didn't usually get the shakes, although there were times my handwriting looked different when signing my name or writing a check, jerky like I had some kind of palsy. My primary withdrawal symptom was an inner shudder, an intense disquiet that was only quelled by a drink. This disquiet was accompanied by spinning anxious thoughts. *It's time to get up. I have to get ready for work. I don't want to go to work. What am I going to wear? I'll just lay here a few more minutes. I have to get up.* Ordinary tasks seemed insurmountable.

Once I was up, my feverish thoughts modified to a different whirling loop. *How am I going to get through the day without a drink? Why can't I have a little sip? Why does it have to smell? Do I smell from the night before? Should I call in sick to work?*

I'd open the freezer and gaze longingly at the bottle of vodka lying there. I'd pick it up and check the level of liquid—kind of like checking the oil in your car—to see if I had to stop somewhere after work to get more. Sometimes, I'd get some over my lunch hour, allowing me to drink even sooner after work, making sure it was covered up in the back seat of my car in the parking lot so no one would catch a glimpse of it through the car window. It was comforting to know I had enough vodka waiting for me. Sometimes I'd swig Listerine in the morning to quiet the shudders. I'd never hallucinated. Lucky me.

Everyone left for the night. The pain in my belly was now constant, making me want to curl up into a ball. But I couldn't because of the IV machine—lying on my side with my arm bent under my head set it off, resulting in a loud, incessant beeping that only a nurse could turn off. This machine, from which several bags of liquid hung, was replenishing me and undoing my handiwork. It was a long night of writhing, groaning, and beeping. I had to pee and fumbled around for the call button. Too late, I found it. I peed myself and lay there in my wet clothes, beyond caring.

I listened to the chatter at the nurse's station, the stomach pain and mind-gnawing restlessness keeping me awake. I rolled fitfully back and forth, mindful not to bend my arm, thereby setting off the goddamned beeping. My groans turned to cries. Then shouts, the mental and physical anguish clawing at me. A nurse rushed in.

"Lisa, what's going on?"

"I'm in pain. I can't sleep."

She checked my vitals. What she saw caused her brow to furrow. "I'll be right back."

I was slightly curious, but only slightly. She returned with reinforcements. "We're moving you to the ICU."

Move me wherever the fuck you want. I watched indifferently as the nurse disconnected the IV machine and the two reinforcements clicked and clacked parts of the bed. Apparently the whole bed was going to ICU, the three nurses maneuvering it out to the hallway. The first nurse took it from there, pushing me through seemingly endless corridors, into an elevator and then more fluorescent lit hallways. She pushed a red button on the wall and the double doors before us swished open.

A fresh team of nurses greeted us. I overheard snippets exchanged. *Electrolyte levels...withdrawal...low blood pressure.* All I wanted was to sleep, to crawl into a gray place away from thoughts or noise. I rolled away from the nurses and saw a clock on the wall. It was 4:45.

The bed was pushed behind a curtain next to another bed, the fresh team and my escort surrounding the two beds, getting into position to transfer me from one to the other. I lifted myself slightly, offering to help, feeling like a worthless slug. I thought maybe I could roll onto the new bed. The nurses assured me they could manage it, they do it all the time, and before I knew it, using the bedsheet as a lift, they had hoisted me onto the adjacent bed. The nurse who delivered me left and three new faces looked down at me. They were young and kind. They prepared me for IV machine hook-up, searching for a vein and plunging a needle into it, which bothered me not at all. Vitals were checked. At least when they take your temperature now, it's just a poke in the ear—no more thermometer under the tongue. But the blood pressure arm band! What the fuck! That hasn't changed at all! The Velcro! That tearing sound! I totally get it, Morty Seinfeld! (Seinfeldians will get this. To everyone else, Google it.) After that round of vitals I was left alone.

A couple of hours later, I heard new voices, familiar voices. The curtain swished and billowed. I lay there helplessly, the lameass booby prize behind the curtain like on the game show Let's Make a Deal. But it wasn't Monty Hall or Carol Merrill on the other side of the curtain. It was the sisters.

"They moved you!" Paula exclaimed. "I told them to let us know if there was any change!"

Ah. Dear, lovely, bossy Paula. I couldn't help but grin.

Paula grilled one of the nurses while Martha looked on, listening carefully. *Electrolytes, hemoglobin level, withdrawal.* The nurse disappeared behind the curtain, thoroughly grilled. Paula looked down at me.

"They were supposed to tell us if there was any change," she repeated.

"Well, you found me," I said.

We smiled at each other.

The sisters pulled up chairs next to the bed. Their vigil had begun.

Chapter Two

The daily interrogations began.

"What's your name?" a nurse asked.

"Where are you?"

"What day is it?"

"Who's the president?"

Even though I felt like shit, this last question got a rise out of me. I rolled my eyes and groaned, "Donald Trump."

The sisters laughed and the nurse chuckled softly.

"A lot of people have been answering that way," she said.

With the nurse gone, the clean-up began. I knew I looked awful. I didn't really care but certain things were bugging me. My lips were cracked and rough. I could feel the lump of matted hair on the top of my head. My fingertips and palms were peeling. I was a dehydrated mess.

Martha got up and stood over me, critically, but compassionately, inspecting me. "Is there anything I can do for you?" She frowned. "Do you want some lip stuff? Your lips are really dry."

I touched my rough lips with my peeling fingertips. "Sure."

Martha gently dabbed the gel on my ravaged lips. We have long made fun of how she applies lipstick—dabbing on rather than a couple of strong swipes back and forth. Dab, dab, dab, dab, dab. Now Paula was eyeballing me. She either wanted to do something to me or talk about something. I could tell. Martha fussed over my pillows and bedding. I was so weak, it took great effort to drag myself to the head of the bed. "Do you want to sit up?" she asked.

"Yeah. I think I do."

Martha dug around on the side of the bed for the controller. She found it and started pushing buttons, the whole bed slowly rising like Linda Blair's bed in The Exorcist.

"I don't think that's the right one," Paula noted dryly.

"Ok, ok. I'll get it." Martha pressed another button and the head rose. "How's that?" she asked, fussily rearranging the pillows.

"That's good." That small amount of activity had exhausted me. I rubbed my aching belly while Martha returned to her seat, Paula still eyeballing me.

"Do you have a brush?" she asked.

"Yeah, in my purse." I looked pointedly at her. "But I don't have my purse." They had whisked me away without grabbing any of my belongings.

"Oh. That's right."

"Let's ask the nurse," Martha suggested helpfully. "They probably have one."

"I could use some water too," I said. "I'm really thirsty."

Martha got up and grabbed the controller. "Be sure to push the right button," Paula needled.

"Bitchacho," Martha muttered loudly enough for Paula to hear. We all chuckled.

This was our dynamic. Martha and I united against Paula's bossiness while Paula and I ganged up on Martha over her indecisiveness and chronic dawdling. We were always waiting for Martha, whether it was for a food choice at a restaurant or just getting out of the car. We stewed while she dilly-dallied. When it came to me, Paula and Martha joined ranks over my youngest child ineptness and irresponsibility. Hence my landing in the hospital. But we all made each other laugh.

Martha found the right button and a crackly, echo chamber voice emitted from the controller, startling me.

"Nurses' station."

"Could I please get some water?" I asked.

A nurse appeared from behind the curtain carrying a plastic glass of water. I couldn't take my eyes from that glass, couldn't wait to put that straw to my lips. She dangled it before me. "Only small sips," she said.

I sipped deeply and quickly. The nurse pulled the glass away and set it on a cabinet, out of reach.

"Why only small sips?" I asked.

"Because of your pancreatitis. When you drink or eat, it puts pressure on your pancreas and we don't want that. It needs to heal."

I gazed at the out of reach glass of water. "But I'm still thirsty," I whimpered.

"Small sips," she said, firmly but not unkindly.

"Do you have a brush we could use?" Paula asked. "We want to brush her hair."

The nurse glanced at the bird's nest on top of my head. "I'll get you one."

She came back with a small brush, one of those types from the '70s that were designed to be gentle on the hair, so gentle that the snarly underlayer was left untouched. Paula had her work cut out for her.

"Can you sit up?" Paula directed. "We'll just do it for short periods of time."

I sat up and Paula walked around to the other side of the bed. I could feel her scrutiny. "Oh Lisa. This is worse than I thought. It's gonna take a while."

I hadn't brushed my hair for days. Like eating, it just wasn't a priority. I had stopped looking in mirrors. When I ventured out for more vodka, I wore a stocking cap.

Paula began the long arduous task of unsnarling my hair. She yanked, I grimaced.

"I'm sorry," she said after a particularly hard yank. "Did I hurt you?"

I shook my head. "I am getting tired though."

"Ok. We'll take a break. I'm gonna have to do small chunks at a time."

She cleaned out the brush and took her seat. The brothers-in-law emerged from behind the curtain. Followed by a doctor. The parade of professionals had begun. This one was from the psych unit.

Dr. Connelly asked if I wanted to speak to him alone. I mulled it over briefly. I had been found out, exposed. My drinking wasn't a not-very-well-kept secret anymore. I had nothing to hide. My plan to die had been foiled. "They can stay."

He reviewed what got me here. I corrected him when he recounted that I fell in the kitchen. I lay down, I corrected. I didn't fall. I don't think the doctor cared about the distinction.

Now my drinking history. Here we go, Sissies! Fasten your seatbelts. It's gonna be a bumpy ride. "How much a day?" the good doctor asked. Half a bottle—the big plastic one. I held back that I wasn't even mixing drinks anymore. Straight out of the jug! Half a bottle was all I divulged. Do you suffer from depression? That's hard to say. It's the old chicken and egg conundrum. Do I drink because I'm depressed or does drinking make me depressed? Were you suicidal? he asked. A pause. Silence. I held the doctor's eyes, mindful of the eyes on me. Yes, I murmured, annoyed with my own trembling lip. Goddammit! The astute Dr. Connelly moved on. He outlined the havoc I had wreaked on my body. Again the thought flashed: *Not enough havoc.* My electrolytes were out of whack, hence the multiple IV bags. I had pancreatitis, hence the stomach pain. Liver damage was unknown, hence more tests. Martha jotted down notes in the notebook she always carried with her. Paula asked what's next—the plan moving forward. *Oh boy. Here we go.*

The plan included tests—an ultrasound, an esophageal scope (why did I have to mention there was blood when I puked? It was just a couple of drops) and an MRI. As they attended to my physical recovery, he continued, they also wanted to start on my mental health. When my physical condition stabilized, I would be moved to the medical/psych unit.

My stomach lurched. Psych unit. I didn't like the sound of that. My mind flashed back to "the intervention" two and a half years ago. After the deputies had hauled me off to the Fort Dodge emergency unit, they transported me up to the Mason City hospital psych ward for detox since the Fort Dodge detox beds were filled. I had spent a couple of days in a cinder block-walled room with a slab of a bed and a locked bathroom, the raving and cursing of my fellow inmates echoing up and down the hall. And my condition was much worse this time around.

Dr. Connelly told us that the head of the med/psych department would be in later that day to explain (sell me a bill of goods) the dual treatment philosophy. He left. The post-visit analysis began.

"I like him," said Martha, who gushes over any man in a uniform, lab coats included. "He had nice shoes."

"What did you think of him, Lisa?" Paula asked.

"I liked him," I replied. "I couldn't see his shoes...." I looked pointedly at Martha. Everyone chuckled. "He was no nonsense and straight forward. He made me feel comfortable."

"What about what he said?" Paula followed up. "About the med/psych unit.

What do you think about that?

I paused before answering, gazing at the curtain through which the doctor had just exited, choosing my words carefully. "It makes sense, I guess. But psych unit talk makes me a little nervous." I looked directly at Paula. "But I don't have a choice, do I?"

"No, you don't," she said softly *and* firmly, if that's possible. With Paula, I guess it is.

A nurse entered. It was time to check vitals, which meant a poke in the ear and puffing up the arm. "Would you like to clean up?" she asked. "I have a toothbrush and some wipes for an overall wash."

"Sure," I said. I quickly sniffed my armpit. I was pretty stinky. God knows the last time I showered. I had brushed my teeth fairly recently before one of my treks outside for vodka. It did feel good, refreshing, to brush my teeth. The nurse brought over the glass of water, holding the straw to my lips so I could rinse. I sipped greedily, sucking in as much water as I possibly could. She pulled the glass away.

"Still only small sips," she gently chided.

I looked at her as she unwrapped a wipe. She was beautiful. She gently wiped down my arms, that simple act of being touched, not poked or prodded, amazingly soothing. I looked at her badge. Her name was Jackie. Her skin was creamy, light brown, her eyes dark brown and luminous. *Mexican? Is she one of us?* She was achingly young—probably in her 20s. She lifted my hospital gown and wiped my belly, my breasts, my legs. It felt so good, so relaxing.

"Thank you. I feel better."

She smiled brightly. "Good. Let us know if you need anything." She disappeared behind the curtain.

"Better?" Paula asked.

"Yeah. My stinkiness was starting to bug me."

"Do you wanna work on your hair some more?"

"Sure. Let's get some more done."

The untangling continued.

The curtain undulated. A distinguished looking man appeared, accompanied by three underlings carrying clipboards. The bigwig had arrived. One of his entourage grabbed a chair and set it next to the bed for him. He sat down and looked at me through his stylish tortoiseshell eyeglasses.

"I'm Dr. Sharma." Dr. Sharma had a slight accent, I guessed from India. He was dark-skinned with salt and pepper hair that is so maddingly attractive on middle aged men—this from one who battles the relentless creeping gray roots every few weeks. He talked about the neurological aspect of alcoholism, the brain's role in the compulsion. He said something that not only struck me to the core but also struck my non-alcoholic sisters.

"This is not a moral issue. This is a neurological issue," he said.

"Could you repeat that?" Paula asked. "I'd like to hear that again."

"Me too," chimed in Martha, scribbling madly in her notebook. "I want to make sure I get it down right."

He paused and looked at each of us, knowing the import of these words.

"This is not a moral issue. This is a neurological issue."

A murmur of assent, and even some surprise, rippled around the room. I had never heard it put that way before.

He looked directly at me. "You should not be ashamed or embarrassed. You are sick. You have a disease."

I liked this guy. He deserved to have an entourage. I was so glad my sisters were here to witness his words. I knew they tried to get it, to understand my drinking. But I don't think they fully did. I'm not sure that I did. All of us in the room had heard the "alcoholism is a disease" concept before. Paula and her husband were social workers, Martha's husband was a recovered alcoholic who came from a family full of alcoholics. We'd all heard it before. But not like this. Not in this solemn, non-judgey fashion. This pronouncement had a different impact on me. It had taken this doctor, saying it this way for it to click, for it to sink in. Better late than never? I had come awfully close to never.

Chapter Three

It was Oscar night. The brothers-in-law were gone, leaving the Avelleyra girls together again. The last time we three had been together was the night our mother died three months ago. We had spent the night in our mother's hospice room, her last night of life, even though she was unconscious. She died that morning, gasping her last breath with us around her. I kept my shit together that week, not drinking at all. As soon as I headed back to Iowa City, I stopped and got a small bottle of vodka and a Diet 7-Up, mixing a road cocktail in my car. Fearful of being spotted at a liquor store, I waited until the first town out to get it. We alcoholics are so sly.

The sisters and I had always been Oscar watchers, and the event included pre-ceremony interviews on the red carpet and Martha's Joan Rivers impression. On Oscar day, I expected a call from Martha speaking as Joan. "Who are you wearing? She looks like a tramp!" In my hospital room, we critiqued the gowns and rolled our eyes at the vapid interviews. It was fun.

Paula continued to unsnarl my hair, a piecemeal, tedious chore. She worked on a small section at a time and took breaks when we both got tired. It wore her out, too. For me, just sitting up was exhausting.

It became clear that La La Land was the frontrunner, much to our dismay. Paula had seen most of the nominated films, I had read about them, Martha doesn't like going to movies. But we all had favorites. We agreed that Jimmy Kimmel was doing a great job as the host. We agreed that the Indian actor from Lion was adorable. We agreed that La La Land was winning too many awards. Near the end of the show when they hand out the best awards, Paula started yawning. Best actor and actress awards were handed out with unanimous sister approval for Casey Affleck in Manchester By the Sea, a movie I particularly wanted to see. During a commercial, Paula stood up. "We gotta go. I'm exhausted. I need to go to bed."

"There's one award left. The big one," I lamented. "You can stay for one more award."

"Yeah, you can make it through one more," Martha agreed.

"Alright," she said reluctantly but remained standing.

Just as The Best Picture nominees were being read, a nurse walked around the curtain.

"Do you need to do something?" Martha asked. "We're just about to go."

"No. You're fine," she said, another young, fresh-faced girl. She looked up at the TV. "Is this for best movie?"

We all turned to watch as Faye Dunaway and Warren Beatty recited the nominees.

"She's been under the knife," Martha commented.

"Yeah, but not too much knife. She looks good," Paula added, then chanted, "Moonlight, Moonlight, Moonlight."

"I think they look really good," I said, referring to Bonnie and Clyde.

"Anything but that La La Land," Martha said.

I nodded. "Yeah. Anything but that La La Land."

"I'm sick of that La La Land," Paula muttered.

"And the Oscar goes to..." began Warren before handing the card over to Faye. Dramatic pause (of course), "La La Land!" she announced with a flourish.

We all groaned. Martha clicked off the television. The nurse chuckled at us.

"That's it," Paula said. "We're outta here. We'll see you tomorrow."

There was a flurry of good-byes and Paula hustled Martha out of the room. I was left alone with the nurse who checked my vitals, still clearly amused.

"You guys are really into it," she commented.

Her tasks were completed, and she left me alone.

Another restless night loomed before me.

I just couldn't get comfortable. Keeping my right arm straight while lying on that side wasn't working. The pain in my gut was still there, a dull constant reminder. How can you be so tired but still not sleep? I'd learned to call the nurse at the onset of the urge to pee so I wouldn't wet myself. I just couldn't hold it while the bedpan was being adjusted beneath me. I was still that weak. But I wasn't embarrassed or self-conscious at all; I was resigned.

Toward morning, the nurse who had watched the Oscars with us came in, but without any instruments or devices to poke and prod me with. "Did you hear what happened with the Oscars?" she asked, clearly excited about whatever information she had.

"No," I answered, brow furrowed, puzzled.

"La La Land didn't win! They read the wrong card!"

"What?"

"I saw it later after the show was over and thought of you and your sisters. Wait. I'll go get my phone and show it to you."

We huddled over her phone, the miniature image flickering on our faces in the darkened room. The actual winner was Moonlight.

"I can't believe this!" I exclaimed. "What happened?"

"They had the wrong card," she explained.

"Wow," I whispered.

"Your sister's movie won."

"And she didn't get to see it because she was in such a big hurry to leave."

"Do you think they know?"

"I don't know. But I can't wait to tell them."

We smiled at each other.

A couple of hours later, the sisters arrived. I was happy to see them. Paula looked pretty and casually chic, as always. The woman knows how to wear a scarf. I looked longingly at Martha's bottle of water. I was still confined to sips.

"Water?" I begged.

Martha hesitated. "Just small sips." She looked around nervously before handing over the bottle. I managed a few glugs—heh, heh, heh—before she snatched it away from me. Today I was scheduled for an ultrasound.

"Did you guys see what happened with the Oscars?" I asked them, then relished their blank expressions. They didn't know.

"What are you talking about?" Paula said.

"What happened?" Martha said.

"La La Land didn't really win. Moonlight did." I explained the mix-up with the cards and how the nurse who watched the end with us fetched her phone so I could see it.

"She was really excited to tell me," I recounted. "She said she wondered if you guys knew."

Martha and Paula were pleased with that—that she thought of them, too— as I knew they would be. "That's funny," Martha said.

We discussed the Oscars a little bit more, then Nurse Jackie walked in, fresh and bright. I was so glad it was her! She checked my vitals followed by the daily itinerary of questions to test my sanity. Where are you? What month is it? What day? This one was tricky since I hadn't been keeping track for the last couple of weeks. But now I knew. Who's the president? A groan and an eyeroll was acceptable. What is your pain level on a scale of 1 to 10? Still 7.

"What time is your ultrasound?" Paula asked.

I shrugged and looked at Nurse Jackie. "I think around 10, but I'll check," she said, adjusting my pillows and IV line.

"And can I get some ice water?" I asked, plaintively.

"Yes. But still only small sips," she said, smiling as she left.

I looked over at the sisters. Paula was looking at me in a certain way. Her way. Her soft, yet stern way. Her "I'm about to suggest something" kind of way.

Suggestion #1: "Do you want to work on your hair?"

Suggestion #2: "Don't you think you should call work?"

Suggestion #3: "I think you should talk to the social worker today about the Family Leave paperwork."

The thought of calling work caused me instant anxiety. I was so lucky I hadn't gotten fired. At the end, I was calling in sick. Then I just stopped calling. I got busted when human resources contacted Paula, my designated emergency person. On the day before ending up on the kitchen floor, I finally answered my phone and Paula badgered me into calling work so I wouldn't be fired. She told me what to say, to request FMLA time off. Being drunk, I didn't really understand why I was calling but knew it had something to do with not getting fired. So I did it. On some level, I must have known my plan might not succeed. I had tried to sound somewhat coherent during the call. Afterwards, I got back to drinking.

There were deadlines to meet for the family leave paperwork, so I had to call work again. This was the kind of shit I hated dealing with. And I knew Paula wasn't going to make the call for me. Tough love bullshit.

"She doesn't get in 'til 8:30," I said.

"Ok. You can call her at 8:30 then. Do you want me to work on your hair?"

I touched the shrinking snarled nest on the top of my head. "Yeah. Let's do it."

Paula resumed the tedious process, one chunk of hair at a time, untangling with her fingers and the brush.

"I wish we had a better brush," she said.

"I have one at my apartment." My place was not far from the hospital.

"I can go get it," Martha offered. Apparently, she had my keys.

"Okay. Go get it," Paula ordered, prompting Martha and me to exchange a look. *Geezus, she's bossy.* Paula caught it and grinned. When I had reached my untangling limit, I leaned back against the pillows and whimpered for more water, savoring each sip. Martha returned with the better brush, but I wasn't ready for more desnarling. It was 8:32.

"Do you wanna call work now?" She was relentless.

"Sure," I mumbled without enthusiasm. Paula handed me her phone, which reminded me about my phone. "Where's my phone?"

"I have it," Martha said sternly. "And your purse." I didn't understand the stern tone but also didn't feel like pursuing it. What did she think I was going to do? Send crazy texts? Strangle myself with my purse? Paula read me the number. As I listened to the phone ringing, a nervous gnawing joined the ache in my stomach. Click. A voice.

After the call, a wave of relief washed over me, the nervous gnawing dissolved. I had spoken to someone on the outside. At work. Sober.

"How did I sound?" I asked the critic's corner.

"Good," Martha said, giving a thumbs-up.

"What did you find out?" Paula inquired.

"More than I expected. But it's good." I explained how not only would I be on the Family Medical Leave Act or FMLA (I hate acronyms) but also on short term disability, which meant I would get 60 percent of my earnings. This came as a complete surprise to me; I'd had no inkling that such a benefit existed. There was more paperwork and new deadlines, but the knowledge of financial support brought relief. That's why Paula had pressed me to make that phone call to human resources before the kitchen floor. She knew about the benefits. I laid back and closed my eyes. For the first time in a very long time, I felt a glimmer of something that relaxed my insides. And I think that thing was hope.

A technician hauled in another contraption for the ultrasound. The hospital hallways must be filled with machines passing each other like ships in the night, maneuvering around each other, barely avoiding collisions. The technician twisted dials, pressed buttons, and adjusted the display screen. Then she began to work me over. For the next half hour (silly me, I thought it would take a couple of minutes), she pummeled and pressed my torso, high, low, on the sides. And not with a gentle touch like Nurse Jackie. I believed all modern medical technology should be like what Bones used in Star Trek, a handheld device hovering over the body, gathering data. I winced and tried not to cry out but a couple of groans escaped. She stopped and fiddled with the machine. I let out a breath of relief.

"Now we'll do the other side," she said.

Are you fucking kidding me? That was only one side? I laid there, helpless, powerless as she continued to work me over. *Doesn't she realize my stomach already hurts?* For another 20 minutes she poked, pressed and manhandled my belly. I looked at her face. It did not flinch or soften whenever I expressed discomfort. It was all business. I wondered how many people she beat up a day. After she left, I looked over at the sisters, who looked a little stunned.

"She was kind of rough," Martha said.

"Kind of?" I said. "That was brutal."

The afternoon agenda was about getting ready, getting ready to move from ICU to the Med/Psych unit. I was still too weak to feel any real apprehension, but it was there, lurking.

The hospital social worker arrived. He was around retirement age but full of vigor—a seasoned veteran who had seen it all but was not beaten down by it. I liked him instantly. He was pleased I had talked to my employer and told us to have them fax the paperwork to him and he would handle it. He had an east coast, no-nonsense gregariousness about him even though I didn't know where he was from. He bonded with Paula over their shared social work background. After he left, we voted our unanimous approval of him.

We settled in for the afternoon, and Paula continued to work on my hair using my brush, which considerably sped up the detangling progress. During my bender, I had not only stopped brushing my hair, I had ground it into the pillow as I tossed and turned in bed, not really sleeping except when I passed out. The nest on my head had taken two weeks to build. It wasn't going to deconstruct easily.

Nurse Jackie was still on duty and the Avelleyra girls, being curious by nature (some might call it snoopy), started asking her questions. But we were also perceptive. If any of us had sensed she was uncomfortable with our queries, we would've stopped.

Jackie had just gotten out of nursing school; this was her first job. Her family was originally from Texas but moved up to southwest Iowa when she was young. Her parents still lived there, in the small town of Atlantic. And she was Mexican, as I'd suspected. She had gone to school at Mount Mercy and now lived with a guy who was not her boyfriend. She didn't have a boyfriend, she stated without a hint of remorse. *Good for her.* My sisters had other thoughts, but I'll get to that later. She had always wanted to be a nurse. How cool to be so self-aware and certain at that young age. Self-awareness came to me late. Hell, I wanted to go into forestry and I don't even like camping or being outdoors. I'm a city girl. I'm perfectly content to be inside with the windows open. Taking care of people suited Jackie. Kindness and gentleness flowed from her. You felt it in her touch and saw it in her brown eyes. You heard it in her girlish, lilting voice. Beautiful inside and out.

We got the word: I would move to the Med/Psych unit tomorrow morning. This was my last day in ICU. Just when I was feeling a little better and more comfortable. Disquiet awoke and stirred inside me. *You may be feeling a little better, but you got a long way to go, Sister.* My gut had always been my moral and stress barometer. "You shouldn't have said that, Lisa." Gnaw, gnaw, gnaw. "You shouldn't have done that, Lisa." Churn, churn, churn. Often after a night of drinking, I would wake up and my first conscious thought would be accompanied by a lurch in my belly. *I yelled at someone. I made a phone call I shouldn't have. What the hell did I say? Where did I leave my car?*

My gut also signaled joy but less explicitly, more like an absence of anything rather than a presence. It was an opening up inside, a fullness, but not a heavy fullness like after eating too much. It was light, airy, easy to breathe. Laughter came easily, sometimes wracking my entire body until my ribs ached. But I hadn't laughed that hard in a very long time.

The last afternoon in ICU passed with intermittent sips of water, hair brushing, and daytime TV talk shows. The pompous Dr. Phil was resoundingly rejected (though I admit I like him) and Ellen was wholeheartedly approved. The evening was the same. With the sisters gone, I spent the night between near sleep and navigating the bed pan, worry about the psych unit gnawing at my edges.

Morning arrived and so did the sisters. Nurse Jackie was also there, which brought unexpected comfort to me on this pivotal day. We asked her about the med/psych unit. I would have my own room. I could have my cell phone but had to cover the camera lens so I wasn't able to take pictures. *Darn. No selfies with my fellow crazies.* And visitors had to buzz in for security purposes. I felt a little uneasy about the rules but decided it didn't sound too Nurse Ratchety. And hearing it from Nurse Jackie helped. She left the room and we looked at each other.

"I love her!" Paula exclaimed.

"I do too!" Martha echoed.

"I'm gonna miss her!" I added.

"She would be perfect for Augustine!" (Paula's son)

"What about Andrew?" (Martha's son)

"Augustine's in physical therapy. She's a nurse...." I said, ignoring Martha. "He likes Iowa City."

"Andrew likes Iowa City," Martha tried again.

Nurse Jackie returned and Paula pounced, phone in hand. "Jackie, you would be perfect for my son. Here's a picture of him." Paula whisked through the photos in her phone, finally coming upon one that satisfied her. Jackie was startled and a little embarrassed. Then she saw the picture. "He's cute!" she cried, looking closer at the photo.

"He's tall and athletic and he's in school for physical therapy and he's a really nice guy," pitched Paula.

Martha stumbled forward with her phone. "Here's my son. He's tall, too. And he's an actuary."

As Paula made plans for Jackie and Augustine's future, I laid back and allowed the new trepidation to flow through me. With the sisters here, it was not as intense. And the move not as daunting.

Chapter Four

It was a long wheelchair ride through the halls, and the architecture changed as we entered the older part of the sprawling hospital. Nurse Jackie stayed after her shift so she could take me. She really was an angel. She picked up a phone outside a set of double doors. There was a buzz and the doors parted and she wheeled me through. *Hello psych ward! I'm here!*

It was brighter and cheerier than the dark, dank institutional atmosphere I had imagined. We passed the nurses station, manned—actually womaned—by warm, friendly faces. We passed a sitting room, furnished with comfy chairs and bright with natural light from a window with a nice view—no metal bars or wire. Folksy paintings hung on the corridor walls.

It was a big room, one bed, no roommate. My own bathroom. Unencumbered by the IV machine, I gingerly got out of the wheelchair and walked to the toilet. My legs were still so weak. After I was done—I made it just in time—I realized I could not get up. I grasped at the handrail to push myself up. It took both hands and a lot of effort. I hobbled to the bed and collapsed. A new nurse entered and hooked me back up to the IV behemoth. It had felt nice being unhooked.

The sisters arrived, oooing and ahhing over the size of my room. They got excited when I told them I had used the bathroom. I was excited, too. Once again, they picked their spots. Paula chose the comfier chair against the wall next to the bathroom (she does have back issues—a rebuilt spine justified her spot) while Martha chose a less comfy chair on the other side of the bed, which she proceeded to drag to a far corner by the window.

"Why do you want to be all the way over there?" Paula asked.

"I like to observe," Martha replied. Paula and I exchanged a look, not unnoticed by Martha.

"What?" she said to us.

A new parade of visitors came through my room. New faces, more vitals checking, continued orientation testing (Where are you? What month is it? Who is our president? Ugh! Quit asking that!). And interviews. The first interview was with the med/psych social worker. She was young and pretty with long, dark, sleek hair, a chic dresser. She asked if I wanted to talk in front of my sisters. I looked at them, then the social worker. I had nothing to hide anymore.

"They can stay."

I told her about my drinking history. It had started in high school at a summer dance before my freshman year. Junior and senior year, I drank a couple of times a month. Funny, even back then, I revealed, I was a secretive drinker, sneaking a couple of swigs from my dad's liquor stash before my friends picked me up.

"It was more than a couple of times a month," interjected Martha, the gatekeeper. "It was every weekend."

Following up on Martha's comment, I talked about how she would let me in the back door when I came home. "You smell like a brewery," she'd say. "Get up to your room." I didn't think it was every weekend, but I wasn't going to quibble over my drinking thirty years ago.

I described the official launch of my drinking in college and how it had become a centerpiece of my life and remained a constant in my adult years. Because of its social acceptance and pervasiveness, I was able to navigate a drinking life for years, keeping it under the radar. I knew my family had concerns about it but instead of cutting back, I merely curbed drinking with my family and talking about drinking.

The questions turned to suicide. I squirmed. Had I attempted suicide before? I had. The first time I got sober, it had started with me leaving my ex and fleeing to Fort Dodge, back to Mom. Before fleeing, my intent was to go out in a blaze of drama, or a haze of carbon monoxide drama. I wanted to hurt my ex, really wound him. I wanted to be found dead in his beloved Saab. But it didn't work out that way. Sitting in the Saab, starting to feel nauseous from the fumes, I had noticed a crack in the garage ceiling. I don't think this is going to work, I had told myself. The fumes were getting to me but I wasn't getting peacefully drowsy before falling permanently asleep. Instead, I was getting sick and coughing. I turned off the car and came up with plan B. I would leave and not tell him where I was going, which was what I ended up doing. I had been drunk when I came up with these plans. Admittedly, it had been a lame attempt.

"What about that time in high school?" Martha piped in.

"What time in high school?" Paula asked.

"I took a bunch of aspirin," I said, trying to minimize it. "It was actually after the first time that I drank at that school dance. I thought dad knew and I was afraid of what he would do. It was also lame."

"Do you remember what I said to you?" Martha asked. "I've been thinking about it and it really bothers me."

I sighed. "No. I don't remember." The social worker stopped taking notes.

"It was upstairs in mom and dad's bedroom," Martha continued. "You'd just gotten off the phone with one of your friends—"

"Gina Gerdes," I murmured.

"I was mad at you. And I said, 'I hope you die.'" There were tears pooling in her eyes.

"Martha," I said, "first off, I don't remember it. And if I did, I wouldn't hold it against you."

"I know. But I've been thinking about it." A hushed pause. "I don't want you to die, Lisa. I want to grow old with you."

The room was quiet. I wiped a tear. The social worker shifted in her chair.

"Tell her about the gun, Lisa," said Paula, breaking the silence. Leave it to Paula to keep us on task.

"I looked into buying a gun," I intoned. "But gun laws here are way too strict. It would've taken too much effort." That's when I had decided to drink myself to death. I was thwarted by the very laws I so strongly support. Is that irony? I'm not sure.

The session with the social worker ended and I had a brief respite. There was more noise and activity in this part of the hospital—rattling carts, footsteps, some heeled, some cushioned, passing conversations. And shouting. From the room next door and a little further down the hall.

"Mama! Mama! Mama!"

The second voice wailed without words. My sisters and I exchanged glances. I tried to calm an inner alarm.

We heard several sets of footsteps shuffle down the hall and stop outside my room. There was a knock on the open door. A team of doctors walked in. There were six of them and two who did the talking. The guy talked about my physical recovery and the tests to learn what damage the drinking had done to my body. The other one who spoke, a woman, talked about treating my mental health and about what was going to happen after my physical health stabilized and I left the hospital. Gnawing churned in my belly. *What the fuck did I get myself into, not dying?*

After they left, a young good-looking upbeat guy came in to talk about the hospital library which also had DVDs. I told him I would like some books—I was ready to read again—and that I liked mysteries. Mysteries were a good way to return to reading—nothing too thought-provoking. My thoughts didn't need to be provoked. I had plenty to ponder.

Next an attractive middle-aged woman entered to make her pitch. She was the occupational therapist, and she talked about daily activities offered in the community room at the end of the hall. There were games, crafts, and mild exercise, she said, which were all important for mental healing. I nodded politely. *There's no way in hell you're gonna see me down there, lady. No offense. I know you're just doing your job but it ain't gonna happen.*

The woman doctor from the earlier group returned. She apologized that she wanted to go over what I had already told others, but it was necessary to hear it from me. She had a strong, steady gaze. Paula and Martha could have stayed but I wanted to be alone with this doctor. I'm not sure why; I wasn't hiding anything from my sisters anymore. They left, and she pulled up a chair next to the bed, clipboard in her lap.

I had been transparent up to this point about my despair and my plan to die, but with each telling, I had become more matter of fact. Dr. Laura quietly looked at me and a wave of emotion that had been out to sea, surged to shore like high tide. She asked the same questions but this time they hit me harder.

Dr. Laura asked about my childhood. I unflinchingly talked about my dad and his hair-trigger temper, how we were all afraid of setting him off. I was always on edge, I told her, when he was around. After leaving home, my relationship with him changed, becoming less fearful and much more loving. He had expressed remorse, sometimes after drinking, during emotional speeches at family reunions or on the phone; he'd apologized for being mean to me. I had forgiven him even if he could not forgive himself. There was much fear and tension growing up, I told Dr. Laura, but I had made my peace with it. What still hurt was that my mother never did. My second oldest sister, Cindy—yes, I have four sisters—had told me once about Mom telling her that Dad had never said he was sorry. He had expressed that public remorse at reunions when he had also acknowledged and praised our mother, but apparently he had never apologized directly to her. My dad was a reactionary hothead, my mom cool, even-keeled. Sixty-plus years they stayed together. I would've been okay with a divorce, I said.

Dr. Laura asked about my drinking history. I recounted how I started in high school and increased during my college years. Post college, it continued, mostly confined to weekends. During this time, I had shifted to vodka drinks— beer was too filling and, let's face it, didn't get the job done fast enough. I even drank scotch with a boyfriend for a while, and that was a total disaster. I learned to stay away from the brown liquors. The daily drinking started during a relationship in which we drank together every day. After that relationship fell apart, I continued the daily drinking on my own. Except for that year and a half of sobriety and the week of my mother's death.

"And what brought you here," she asked. "What brought you to lying on your kitchen floor and then the hospital?"

I looked directly into her calm, bespectacled eyes. "I was trying to drink myself to death."

"And how do you feel now? Now that you didn't succeed."

We held each other's gaze.

" I wish they'd never found me."

Chapter Five

It was not a good night. I could not get comfortable with the damn IV being so temperamental. And the screamer and the wailer apparently couldn't sleep either. They were quiet until about one in the morning. Then they were quiet no more.

"Mama! Mama! Mama!"

"Aaaaaaghhhh! Help me! Someone help me! Aaaaaaghhhh!"

I wasn't frightened by the painful sounds, but they made it difficult to ignore what I'd done to end up here. And this was just the beginning. Again, that dark thought fluttered across my mind: *Why did they have to find me?*

I finally drifted off to sleep after "Mama" and "The Wailer" had quieted. I was roused awake for a vitals check and the daily quiz. The white-erase board was updated with the names of the nurse of the day and the nurse assistant. Footsteps and cheerful voices wafted in from the hall. A knock on the open door and the sisters entered. My spirits immediately lifted at the sight of them.

"How did you sleep?" Paula asked.

"Not good," I answered. "It was kind of noisy..." A nod to my hallmates. "And I just can't get comfortable with this damn IV thing."

Martha fretted over me, fluffing my pillows and straightening the covers. Paula sat in her designated chair, texting busily. The library guy dropped off some books and the med/psych wing hummed with activity. During The Young and the Restless, there was a tap on the door and the dream team entered. Martha sprung from her chair and muted the television. The tall, younger guy in the scrubs was the spokesperson today. He went over the plan, the schedule of procedures to check for damage. He was boyish and awkward but clearly intelligent. He avoided extended eye contact but was not shifty-eyed. The dream team left and the post-visit analysis began.

"I like that young guy," Martha started. "Do you think he's a resident? The color of scrubs means something."

Paula and I nodded in assent. "So residents wear scrubs?" I asked.

"I think so," Martha continued, showing off her hospital garb hierarchy knowledge. Martha has peculiar areas of expertise and we were about to be enlightened by one of them. "Dr. Laura—I can't remember her last name—was wearing regular clothes and the young guy was in green scrubs and the others were in maroon."

"So what's maroon mean?" I asked.

"They're interns. The nurses have different colors too."

"And what do regular clothes mean?" Paula asked. "Dr. Laura."

"She's a full-fledged doctor," Martha replied.

Paula and I exchanged an amused look, not unnoticed by Martha. "Wow, Martha. The things you know," I said.

"I saw that look," she said. "I know you're making fun of me."

"No. It's very interesting," said Paula, smirking.

"Shut-up, you bitchachos," Martha retorted.

"There's something about that young intern," Paula said. "Like he has Asperger's or something."

"You mean the resident," Martha corrected.

"Pardon me. The resident," Paula said.

"Like some kind of autism maybe?" I suggested.

"Yeah, I noticed that too," Martha agreed.

Martha and Paula were hungry and decided to go to lunch. Still no food for me but they were letting me drink more than little sips of water. The pain in my belly was subsiding but still there. Martha and Paula left and I got up to go to the bathroom, dragging the damn IV machine with me, an annoying and exhausting task. Afterwards, I collapsed.

Martha and Paula returned, brimming with excitement and bearing gifts. They'd had lunch in the hospital cafeteria and then visited the gift shop, where they had picked up a lovely spring flower arrangement and Aladdin-like bedroom slippers.

"You'll never guess who we ran into!" Martha exclaimed.

My mind catalogued the possibilities. Someone from Fort Dodge? One of the EMTs? A celebrity athlete? "Patty Knoblauch," Martha revealed. "She works here. She looks just like a Knoblauch."

Patty was the sister of Kitty, one of my best friends during the college years and beyond. The Knoblauchs had moved to Fort Dodge when Kitty was a junior. She and I got close after high school and were roommates our first year at Iowa. We had gone on several Ragbrai bike rides together and shared a rich drinking history.

I swung my legs to the side of the bed so I could try on the slippers. My feet and ankles were so swollen, I'm not sure why, but the brightly striped slippers fit and were comfy. I lifted my thick, swollen ankles and modeled them. I told them it was still difficult to get up from the toilet. "It isn't pretty."

"You're lucky we found you when we did," Paula said.

The dark thought bubbled up. *Am I?*

The flowers were lovely and emitted a subtle aroma, but I began to feel a tickle in my nose and a tightness in my chest. My asthma and allergies were kicking in. The flowers had to go.

"You guys, I love the flowers, but I can feel them," I said, gesturing to my nose and chest. They understood, having grown up with their baby sister's ailments. I watched with gentle amusement as they apologized and gushed their concern.

"We can't return them to the gift shop," Martha said. "They'd look at us like we're nuts."

"Yeah. We can't walk in and say 'Hi. Can we return these? They made our sister have an asthma attack,'" Paula added.

"Someone can enjoy them," I said. "We're in a *hospital.*"

Martha came up with a scathingly brilliant idea. She suggested they take them to the ICU. "Nurse Jackie will know what to do with them."

I dozed after they scampered off, imagining them putting in another plug for their sons. My light sleep was interrupted by vitals taking and afternoon bellowing.

"Mama! Mama! Mama!"

"Aaaaaaghhhh! Nurse, nurse! Help me! Help me!"

The sisters returned and we settled in for afternoon television. News commentators were still talking about the Oscar kerfuffle and, of course, that Big Tweet in the White House. Unfortunately, the latter wasn't a hallucination cooked up by my booze-soaked brain. I was sober and he was still president. Paula finally finished brushing out my hair. I touched it and ran my fingers through it. It had been a while since I had done either.

Early evening, the young resident we liked popped in, boyishly shy but businesslike, cute and sweet in his mannerisms. Dr. Michael outlined the tests they were scheduling and reiterated the concern with my out of whack electrolytes. He asked about my pain and how I was doing in the new room. On cue, one of my hallmates started up.

"Nurse, nurse, nurse! Aaaaaghhh! Help me! Help me someone!"

I grinned before I answered. "Everything's good but sometimes it gets a little noisy."

Dr. Michael grinned back. "Er, ah, one of your, ah, vocal neighbors," he stammered, "will be leaving tomorrow." The sisters and I giggled.

"Oh, that's unfortunate," I said. "I'm gonna miss him."

His grin widened. "You're funny."

It felt good to be funny again, to make—or almost make—someone laugh. After he left, we, of course, discussed.

"I really like him!" Martha exclaimed. "He said you're funny."

"He really is cute," Paula said.

I laid back against the pillows, rubbing my belly. The pain was still there but it was accompanied by something else. A loosening, an unfolding. It was something good.

I had another restless, sleepless night. I just couldn't get comfortable. I repeatedly adjusted the bed—head up, head down. I adjusted my position. Right side, left side, on my back. My feet kept getting tangled in the covers. My elbows were raw from dragging myself to the top of the bed.

The night nurse was chatty but I welcomed it. She was near retirement, having worked in this unit for a decade. And she had an anecdote for everything. She had an uncle who was an alcoholic and had been in and out of hospitals and was still drinking. She noticed my new slippers and upon telling her I got them from my sisters, she launched into a story about her own sister with whom she doesn't get along. I laid back and smiled to myself as she chattered away and fussed over me. Her kindness was soothing. Sometime around four in the morning, I fell asleep, awoken a couple of hours later for the morning vitals check. It was a milestone to be deeply enough asleep that I had to be woken up. *Where are the sisters?* I was impatient to see them.

They arrived around 7:30—we had kind of fallen into a routine—again bearing gifts. New underwear, a notebook, and lotion for my parched skin. We turned on Morning Joe, groaning and lamenting the latest faux pas committed by this cartoon character of a president. We listened intently when our favorites commented. Mine was Mike Barnacle, Paula and Martha's Eugene Robinson, and we all adored Willie Geist. Joe and Mika annoyed us.

The Dream Team arrived during The Young and the Restless. Martha got up and muted the sound. Dr. Michael asked me about the stomach pain, told me my blood was still out of whack, and updated me on the upcoming tests. "When can I eat something?" I asked, trying not to sound desperate. Not until after the esophageal scope which they were still trying to schedule, he told us. I think he was a little peeved that it wasn't scheduled yet.

Now it was Dr. Laura's turn. She looked at me with that calm, steady, slightly unsettling gaze. "It's time to start talking about a plan for when you leave the hospital."

It was? Already? I just got here. I instantly felt a lurch of foreboding. I knew I had to go back into treatment. There was no getting around it. I knew I couldn't just leave the hospital and go back to my life, to my apartment. "I'm going to have to go back to treatment." Saying it aloud shook me.

"Yes, you are," Dr. Laura stated. "We have to discuss where."

I was a little confused, having assumed I would be going to the facility in Iowa City. I didn't think there were any other options. "Well, ah, that place here in Iowa City," I stammered. "I can't remember what it's called—"

"Prelude," piped in one of the interns. "But there's usually a waiting list."

"We may be able to get around that," said Dr. Laura, giving the eager intern a stern look. "There's someone here who is also on the staff at Prelude. And there's a place called The Abbey, which has a great reputation and has a holistic approach."

The Abbey? Never heard of it. And the name triggered my dormant, Catholic hostility.

"Where is it?" Paula asked. I looked over at her. She looked interested. Too interested.

"Bettendorf," Dr. Laura replied, looking right at me.

"Bettendorf!" I cried out. "I want to stay in Iowa City."

"It's an actual old monastery," the dark, swarthy intern added, stepping forward to hand me a computer printout. "And they have great, gourmet food!"

I set aside the printout without looking at it. Why are they pushing this place?

"But I thought I'd be staying in Iowa City..." I weakly repeated.

Another intern chimed in. "There's also a place in Council Bluffs," she said.

With that, I shut down. "I'd like to talk to the person from Prelude."

"We can arrange that," said Dr. Laura, sensing I was done for the day. "But look through this information about The Abbey." She touched the printout I had set aside on the tray table. After the Dream Team left, there was silence.

"I don't want to leave Iowa City," I stated flatly. I saw the sisters exchange a look. They were closing ranks.

Martha got up and looked at The Abbey printout. She read the pages, her face showing increasing interest. She looked at me, holding the printout toward me.

"You need to look at this."

"Why when I can stay in Iowa City? I don't want to go to Bettendorf." I could feel myself getting warm with emotion. I was digging in.

"It doesn't hurt to look," said Paula, trying a gentler approach.

I had accepted I was going to treatment. The sisters wouldn't have it any other way. I wouldn't have to be committed this time. But I had been picturing myself in treatment here in Iowa City, where Brian and Kitty and work friends could come and see me. Nobody was going to come and see me in Bettendorf.

"I'll look at it later," I said, picking up the remote and unmuting the television.

The social worker, again fashionably dressed, returned that afternoon to discuss treatment options. I asked about Prelude and meeting with the doctor who was on staff there. Kayla agreed to contact her. Then, of course, Paula asked her about The Abbey.

"It's a great facility," she replied. "It's in a beautiful setting and has a holistic approach." *Here we go again.* Paula and Martha were lapping it up. "And I hear the food there is great!"

"I want to stay in Iowa City," I stated.

"There's usually a wait list for a bed," she answered, "but I'll check."

After she left there was a silence, a charged silence. Paula broke it.

"What do you think will happen if there's a wait list?" Paula started.

"I don't know," I stammered. "How do you know there's not a wait list for that Abbey place?"

"You're not going back to that apartment," Martha interjected.

"What difference does it make that it's in Bettendorf?" Paula pointed out. "It's not like you'll be going anywhere."

I shook my head and smiled softly at Paula, who smiled back. "What difference does it make?" was one of our Mom's pet phrases during particularly vexing arguments.

I picked up the computer printout. "I'll look at it." I gave it a cursory look to appease the sisters. Yes, it was in a monastery. Yes, it was holistic, offering yoga, art therapy, and music therapy. Yes, it claimed to have healthy, gourmet meals. But it was in Bettendorf, an hour's drive from Iowa City. I set the printout aside on the tray table.

"It looks nice," I stated flatly.

Martha and Paula exchanged a look but said nothing. They let it go. For now.

That afternoon, the doctor from Prelude visited. She had read my file, so I didn't have to go over my history. I had to go to treatment—that was the consensus. Inpatient, not outpatient. And there was a weeklong wait to get into Prelude.

"I don't think you're gonna be in here for another full week," Paula said after the doctor left. "We'll have to ask them where you could go in the meantime."

"You're not going back to your apartment," Martha repeated.

Ok, Martha. You've made your position on that quite clear. I remained silent. Apprehension rustled in my belly. I was starting to feel the pressure to think again, to make decisions, to participate in life. I didn't like it. Again, the dark thought flickered across my mind.

"I suppose we could check at The Abbey," I said reluctantly. "I mean about a wait list."

"Let's ask Kayla about it," Martha suggested.

"I'll give her a call," said Paula, reaching for her phone in her purse. She left a message.

Kayla walked in about an hour later. There was no waiting list at The Abbey. How it worked, she told us, you made an appointment, go in for an assessment, and you're admitted on the spot. I was instantly alarmed. I had to go there for an assessment? Couldn't it be done over the phone? No. Facetime? Skyping? No. It had to be done in person. And I had to find out if they took my insurance. There was a lot to consider. Thankfully, my sisters didn't harangue me, and the evening passed quietly. Even though we had been at odds most of the day, I did not like seeing them leave at night.

It was another mostly sleepless night. I had started a book, so I passed some of the time reading. I also spent some of the time thinking about The Abbey. The idea of going to a place that was an old monastery was not unappealing. I dropped off to sleep sometime just before dawn, and the sisters arrived during the morning interrogation. After the nurse left, we turned our attention to Morning Joe. We all agreed Jeff Sessions is a weasel and should step down. We groaned when Joe talked over people, and when Mika tsked and simpered while looking prettily at the camera. Let Willie and Barnacle speak! Let them talk about sports, Mika! Jesus!

"Have you thought anymore about The Abbey?" Paula asked. "We looked at it online. It looks really nice."

There was no way I was going to tell them that I had been thinking about it.

"Do you want to see?" asked Martha, a little too casually. They'd rehearsed this. I went along with the performance.

"Sure," I said. I scrolled through the images, many of which were the same as in the printout. But these were in color. It really was an old brick monastery, started by some Franciscan nuns. Something stirred in me, but I tamped it down.

"It does look like a cool place," I grudgingly admitted, "but I have to go there just to talk to them."

"Give them a call," Paula casually offered, following the script.

"I don't see a number here," I said, squinting at the phone.

"I have it," Martha offered. "The person to ask for is Karen."

If nothing else, a call would get them off my back. Martha handed me my phone, that unwelcome conduit to the outside world. I dialed the number. A soft voice answered. Karen wasn't available so I talked to the soft voice. I explained that I was in the hospital in Iowa City and needed to go to a treatment facility. I asked if there was a waiting list. There was not. And the soft voice was off to the races. She talked about the stuff on the website— holistic, great environment, great food. Then her tone shifted. It got stronger, warmer. She talked about the people there. The dedicated staff. The people who had gone through the program. Good people, a variety of people, the special relationships that are built there. The soft voice reverberated with passion and serene conviction. Something quivered inside me. And it wasn't my pancreas.

"So I have to make an appointment?" I asked, my voice quavering.

The soft voice told me that first they had to check my insurance to see if it covered treatment. Did I have my insurance information? I gestured to Martha to hand me my purse and pulled out my billfold. I read the numbers from my insurance card. The soft voice told me to call back tomorrow, and the phone call ended.

"Well?" Paula asked.

I hesitated before speaking, trying to come up with fancy, descriptive words. I failed.

"She sounded so, so *nice*," I answered. "She talked about all the good people who have been through there. She just sounded so nice. I can't come up with a better word."

"You have Blue Cross, right?" asked Martha about my insurance.

"Mm, hmm. Do you think it'll cover treatment?" I didn't even try to hide the hope in my voice.

"We'll find out," Paula said.

"But what else did she say?" asked Martha, who always wanted details.

I gave a brief synopsis, that voice still in my head. Something was opening up inside me. And because I'm an Avelleyra, I started to worry about the insurance coverage.

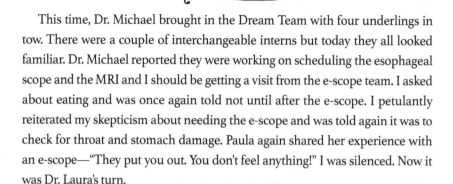

This time, Dr. Michael brought in the Dream Team with four underlings in tow. There were a couple of interchangeable interns but today they all looked familiar. Dr. Michael reported they were working on scheduling the esophageal scope and the MRI and I should be getting a visit from the e-scope team. I asked about eating and was once again told not until after the e-scope. I petulantly reiterated my skepticism about needing the e-scope and was told again it was to check for throat and stomach damage. Paula again shared her experience with an e-scope—"They put you out. You don't feel anything!" I was silenced. Now it was Dr. Laura's turn.

"Have you given any more thought to a plan after you leave here?" she asked.

I felt a little smug. "I called The Abbey," I said, almost defiantly. "They're checking my insurance."

There was a murmur of assent among the Dream Team, but Dr. Laura just looked at me with that steady gaze, saying nothing. I guess I'd expected a pat on the back, but I didn't get it. The visit wrapped up quickly and after they left, I thought of something I wanted to ask.

"They still haven't filled out that paperwork for FMLA," I said. "There's a deadline."

"I know. I've been thinking about that," Paula said. "It's these doctors who are now responsible for it. We'll talk to Kayla about it after we hear from The Abbey."

The afternoon and evening passed quietly. I spent another fitful night rolling from side to side and untangling the covers, my elbows raw from dragging myself around in the bed. My mind whirred with brand new worries. What if The Abbey didn't accept my insurance? When would the doctors fill out the paperwork? What if I don't qualify for FMLA and short-term disability? The dark thought made an appearance. Reading a book kept these anxious thoughts at bay. Just before dawn, I drifted off to sleep.

A nurse awoke me for the vitals check. Anxious thoughts immediately rose to the surface of my groggy mind, like bubbles in a glass of beer. The sisters were late. I was hungry. I really wanted to eat. When was I going to have those goddamn tests?

I laid back and listened to the sounds in the hall, tuned in for a couple of particular voices. I dozed. Sounds filtered through my light sleep. I opened my eyes. A voice. Footsteps approached. A light knock on the door. There they were. My heart lifted, my angst melted. I had come to depend on their daily presence, much like my body depended on the IV. They were bickering. Martha had left behind her favorite lipstick at the hotel because Paula had been rushing her. Left to her own devices, Martha would still be getting ready, Paula stated. Martha grumbled and plopped down in her chair. She knew Paula was right.

We settled in for Morning Joe and morning exasperation. That Jeff Sessions really did look like a little elf. Willie Geist asked strong questions, Mike Barnacle got pissed, Mika preened, and Joe talked over everyone. We relished it all.

During The View, my phone rang, the Notre Dame Fight Song playing over the voices of Whoopi Goldberg and Joy Behar. I looked at my sisters, then at the phone.

"Well, answer it!" Martha demanded.

I did. It was the same peaceful voice. My insurance had been accepted—I gave the sisters a thumbs up—but there was a fee of $1,500 for room and board. The sisters were nodding excitedly. I had to make an appointment for the assessment, but I wasn't sure when I'd be getting out of the hospital. "We'll ask Dr. Laura and Dr. Michael when they come around today," Paula stage whispered.

The call ended and I set down the phone. I wasn't ready to speak, to express how I was feeling, which was relief tinged with excitement. Why was I excited? Had I decided to go to The Abbey?

"What are you thinking?" Paula prodded.

So much for not being ready to speak. I paused, choosing my words carefully. "That voice," I attempted to explain. "There's something about that voice."

"How does that voice make you feel?" Paula asked.

"Comforted." A pause. "Relieved." Another pause. "But how will I get there?"

"I'll take you!" Martha exclaimed.

I began to cry. It started with tears streaming down my cheeks, then turned into gulping, gasping sobs. Where had this emotion come from? It blindsided me, like being t-boned in a car at an intersection. Something long held tight had been unleashed.

Martha jumped out of her chair to comfort me. "It's okay to cry," she said, petting my hair. "You're feeling a lot of stuff."

"But why am I crying? Why now?" I looked over at Paula who stayed in her chair. She looked back at me, tears welling up in her eyes. Seeing her tears made me cry harder. Martha kept gently petting me, her eyes dry. Martha was a weird crier. It happened unexpectedly, out of nowhere. Like when our Mom died, she would start crying during a non-sad discussion. A random memory would trigger her, taking everyone else by surprise, sometimes making me giggle. But now, no tears.

"It's a lot," she said. "A lot is happening."

I nodded, my sobs subsiding. "I guess I'm going to The Abbey."

I had a plan. Not the plan I had planned, but a plan, nevertheless. A plan from out of nowhere to go to a place I had never heard of before.

Chapter Six

I was excited for the Dream Team to arrive. When they did and I told them the news, I was again disappointed in their lack of response. Dr. Laura matter-of-factly acknowledged it and launched into AA propaganda.

I was irritated. "I'm not a big fan of AA," I interrupted. "The emphasis on God and religion. It's too much like a bunch of Bible beaters. I don't like it."

Unstoppable, Dr. Laura continued. "Well, The Abbey is based on the 12 Step principles and you will be going to meetings there."

I leaned back against the pillows and crossed my arms over my chest, knowing full well what that body language conveyed.

"AA in Iowa City is really diverse and progressive," chirped the intern who had suggested Council Bluffs as an option. She pulled something from her clipboard and handed it to me. It was an AA meeting schedule. My arms remained crossed so she set it on the tray table. "There's a group, The Misfits, that's like an offshoot rebel group," she continued. "They broke off from the main, traditional group. You might like that meeting."

"A rebel group," said Martha, trying to be helpful. "You'd probably like that, Lisa."

My crossed arms tightened. "Can I just get through treatment first?"

Dr. Michael apologetically notified us about the lack of updates on the two tests and in response to Paula's question about when I would be discharged, they agreed that Monday seemed likely. It was now Wednesday.

After they left, Martha picked up the AA schedule and looked at it. "You know, you were kind of rude."

"I don't care!" I spat out. "Can I please get through treatment first before they start ramming AA down my throat?"

Ever the Sarge, Paula steered us back to practical considerations. "Now you need to call The Abbey and make an appointment. And you've got to get that FMLA paperwork into ACT."

"I know." I laid my head back on the pillow and closed my eyes. I was hungry. Dr. Michael had said I could eat. The e-scope people were dawdling and they would just have to deal with it. Hunger and nerves wrestled around in my belly. Plus, it was time to take a shower. Such a commonplace task was going to be a challenge with my weakened condition. I really wanted to wash my hair, but dreaded the process.

During my spiral, I'd showered less and less. The water pressure in the shower of "that apartment" sucked and it took forever to rinse the shampoo, then the conditioner, out of my hair, so I began to wash my hair under the tub faucet. As the spiral gained momentum, any cleanup had been reduced to a "cowboy" shower now and then. Also, as I had become weaker, I got dizzy while standing. It just wasn't worth the effort, and it interrupted my drinking.

The nurse's aides were sympathetic, and they placed a chair in the shower. Having unhooked me from the contraption, they carefully taped over the IV insertion points on my arm. I shuffled to the bathroom, where the shower had already been turned on. The hot water felt good, but I was wobbly and had to sit on the chair between shampooing and conditioning my hair. I was unable to turn off the water, too weak to turn the knob, so I left it on while I dried off and put on fresh hospital pajamas. I gripped the sink, glanced briefly at myself in the foggy mirror and walked slowly to the bed, on which I slumped. I lay there for a while before summoning a nurse, relishing being unhooked from that machine. I sat up and started combing my wet hair. It felt so good to be clean.

The sisters returned while I was still combing out my hair. Paula noticed that the shower was still running. "I couldn't turn it off," I said. "You try."

Paula disappeared into the bathroom from where we heard thumping and banging, then loud grunting and groaning. "Aaaahhhhh, Iiiiiiiiiiii can't get it," she called out just as a nurse's aide walked in. Martha and I giggled. The nurse's aide ducked into the bathroom and we heard more banging, then the water diminishing to a drip. They came out.

"It is really hard to turn off," the nurse's aide said. She gathered up the damp towels and dirty pajamas and left. Without rehooking me. I wasn't about to remind her.

"Why don't you sit up in the chair for a while?" Paula suggested. "If you lay down with your wet hair, it's gonna get all messed up again. I'm not going through that again."

I sat in Paula's chair. Another commonplace task accomplished. Paula and Martha were smiling at me.

"What?" I said to them.

"It's just nice to see you up and all cleaned up," Paula said. Martha nodded. Tears stung my eyes and emotion clenched my throat. I got it. I was becoming more like myself again, less a bedridden patient. But I was still easily fatigued. A nurse's aide came in, pleasantly surprised to find me in the chair.

"Look at you!" she exclaimed. "All cleaned up and out of bed. And you get to eat tonight."

"Eat?" I squeaked. "Tonight?"

"Yes. A limited menu but you get to eat something."

I get to eat. I took a shower. And I sat up in a chair.

Every once in a while, it struck me how sick I really was. Mostly it happened when I had to grip the handlebar to pull myself up from the toilet. Now that I knew where I was going after the hospital—the number one concern— secondary concerns surged to the forefront. *Gotta get the FMLA paperwork done. And when am I gonna have those goddamn tests?*

That night, I got what I wished for. After the sisters left, a male nurse and a female nurse entered. The man pushed a wheelchair and the woman unhooked me.

"You're going down for your MRI," she said cheerfully.

"Wha-what?" I stammered. "Now? Right now?" It was nine o'clock. And let's be clear. This was not something to be cheerful about. This was serious business.

"Their schedules open up at night for inpatients," the male nurse explained. "They're usually booked during the day."

I clambered out of bed and plunked myself down in the wheelchair. The male nurse, Brad, draped a blanket over my lap. "It gets chilly down there," he said.

"Where's down there?" I asked, my voice a little sharp.

"We're going to the basement. And there's one stretch that's pretty chilly."

Brad was talkative. Was this my first MRI? They weren't that bad, he said. You just lay back, keep your eyes closed and not think about it. They give you music, he pitched. I was annoyed. I would've liked to have had some forewarning, for mental preparation. This was so abrupt. My stomach churned. He pushed me up a long ramp—*Brad's in good shape!*—and we descended in an elevator. The doors opened onto a windowless corridor. He wasn't kidding about it being chilly down here. At the end of the Arctic passage was our destination—Radiology.

Two women were waiting for us in the outer room. Brad said he'd be right outside to take me back. My agitation grew. I could see the machine in the adjacent room through the glass—a science fiction monster. The technicians indicated that I sit on the conveyor belt next to the opening of the gaping, metal maw that waited to swallow me whole. While they gave their spiel, my mind wandered to an episode of Star Trek, the original with William Shatner and Leonard Nimoy, in which they encountered a giant, electrically charged tube hovering in outer space, sucking in spaceships with its magnetic force. In the end, guest star William Windom sacrificed himself, diverting it away from the Enterprise by flying his ship right down its throat. Are you claustrophobic? I didn't think I was, I answered. What kind of music do you like? I glanced at the gullet that was about to consume me. *How about the Star Trek theme? Or the soundtrack from Jaws?* My mind went blank. Anything but country, I told them. Finally they got to the pertinent stuff, like how to use the panic button and how long I'd be in there. The communication button (I dubbed it the panic button) would be lying right next to my right hand. I could press it if I became uncomfortable and wanted to discontinue. *Good to know.* And it would take 25 to 30 minutes.

"25 minutes?" I squealed. "That long?"

"It's not that long," one of them assured me. "You just lay there and listen to music. It's over before you know it."

It was go time. I lay down on the conveyor belt, adjusted the headset they had given me, placed my arms at my sides and made darn sure the panic button was under my hand. I caressed it with my index finger—*nice panic button*—familiarizing myself with its curves and edges and the outline of the button, my lifeline. It was the size and shape of a computer mouse. A whirring sound, then I slowly began sliding into the throat of the beast. The din was horrifying. No music was going to drown that out. You were engulfed by it. The close metal quarters magnified the sound and sent it reverberating along the tube. I opened my eyes—big mistake—and shut them quickly. But the damage was done. The ceiling of the tube was right above my face. Panic stiffened my limbs and froze my brain. I tried to suppress it, but I felt like I was suffocating. My index finger pressed the button. And kept on pressing.

"Are you ok?" a disembodied voice asked over the headphones.

"No. I need to get out."

"Just relax. Take some deep breaths."

"No! I need to get out now!"

The conveyor belt slowly slid me back out. I popped up.

"Wait. You can take a few minutes and we can try it again," one of them said.

"No. I want to get out of here."

"We have a larger machine for just such situations," the other tech offered. "We can try that one."

They didn't get it. I had to get out of here now. It was a completely visceral response. My basic animal instincts were telling me to get the fuck out. Fight or flight? Flight. But I might have to fight in order to flight. I had been possessed by this survival response one other time, shortly after I moved to Madison, Wisconsin, and was living with Paula in an apartment located in a not-so-great part of the city. Upon coming home from shopping, we had walked in on scuffling and crashing sounds, finding a busted-out screen in the bedroom. Without a moment's thought, I turned and rushed out into the hallway, standing frozen and shivering against the wall. Meanwhile, petite Paula had grabbed a butcher knife from the kitchen and beelined to the open window. From the hallway I heard: "Come on! I've got a big fucking knife! Come on back! I dare ya! I've got a big fucking knife and I'll use it!" I wasn't proud of my response in that frightening situation, but I couldn't help it. And I was feeling it again, the overwhelming need to remove myself from this place. *Where the fuck is Brad?* I scurried out to the waiting area.

On the way back to my room, Brad assured me that this happens all the time. Next time I should get something to relax me, he said, and now I know what to expect. I listened to him in silence. I was shaken but I was also mad. They had sprung it on me and hadn't offered me any drugs.

My mind seethed. *Why did I have to have all these tests? Don't I have any say at all? These tests cost a lot of money. Don't I have any rights of refusal?* I laid awake and stewed. When the night nurse came in and asked me how I was doing, I didn't give my pat answer.

"Not good," I answered.

She tilted her head and looked at me. "What's going on?"

I vented. I told her about the botched MRI and my misgivings for all these tests. I repeated my skepticism about the esophageal scope and its necessity. She nodded sympathetically, tall and lovely with thick brown hair and a steady, no-nonsense gaze, not unlike Dr. Laura's. She spoke with a slight accent, Eastern European I think, and her name was Natalia. I told her, my voice quavering, that I felt like a guinea pig with all these tests. She agreed they should've given me something to relax me before the MRI and assured me she would make sure they did next time. Bonus sympathy, she said she would say something to the Dream Team about my misgivings. It felt good to have an ally.

Chapter Seven

The next morning, I was antsy to share my MRI drama with the sisters. They knew right away that something was up.

"What happened?" Paula asked. "You look like you want to tell us something."

"I had an MRI. Or rather they tried to give me an MRI."

"When?" Martha exclaimed. "Last night?"

"But they didn't say anything yesterday," Paula said.

"Nope. They just came in about nine with a wheelchair and whisked me away."

"Just like that?" Martha asked.

"Just like that. No forewarning."

"Did they give you anything?" Paula interrogated. "Did they give you any drugs?"

"They didn't even offer me anything."

"Maybe they can't give her any drugs," Martha speculated.

"What?" I yelped.

"They can give her drugs for that," Paula interrupted. "I can't believe they just came in here and took you down there with absolutely no warning. Did they talk to you before they stuck you in there? About what to expect?"

"No, not really. They asked if I was claustrophobic and I said no, because I really didn't think I was. Then they talked about how it works and a bunch of jargon and about how important it is to stay still." A beat. "It was awful. So I pressed the button." I could see Paula was trying not to smile.

"What did you say?" asked Martha, the detail sponge. "What did you do? What did *they* say?"

"I told them to get me out of there. They tried to talk me into trying again and said they have a bigger machine, but I said no, I'm getting out of here. I needed to leave. The guy who took me down in the wheelchair said it happens all the time."

"What was so bad about it for you?" asked Martha.

I closed my eyes, remembering. "The closeness to my face, the loudness. And having to be in there for twenty-five minutes!"

"You have to close your eyes..." Paula advised.

"I did! But then I opened them. And the damage was done." I put the palm of my hand in front of my face. "It was right there! It was visceral, pure instinct."

"So it was like..." Paula started. I knew where she was going with this.

"Yes, it was like when we got broken into," I finished. "My instinct was to get away, to remove myself."

"Oh," said Martha who was very familiar with the break-in story. "So it was just like running out into the hall. You had to get out of there. I get it."

Although amused with my MRI attempt, Paula was irritated with how it was handled. She was a great one to have in your corner. "They should have prepared you better about what to expect," she said. "And they should've given you drugs. We'll talk to them."

I laid back, the MRI stress temporarily abated. But there was another apprehension lurking. *We have to get that FMLA paperwork done. And now a brand new one. I have to pack for The Abbey.* There was always something. *You got a long way to go Lisa, a long way to go.*

We had an unexpected visitor that morning. Dr. Michael tapped softly on the open door and shyly entered, prompting Martha to move faster than usual to mute the TV. He stood next to the bed and looked down at me. "I heard it didn't go so well last night," he said.

Emotion fluttered in me. His solo visit took me by surprise. "No, it didn't,"

I said thickly, tears gathering behind my eyes. He crouched down so we were eye to eye, a simple shift in his posture so touching in its humility.

"I also heard how you feel about all the tests," he continued. "That you feel like a guinea pig." A beat. "We don't want you to feel that way."

I felt like a big baby, but I just couldn't help myself. "The MRI is bad enough," I said. "But I have to get the scope too. I don't see why I need it. There was just a little blood." I could feel myself becoming unhinged—residual effects from the botched MRI, the prospect of going to The Abbey, the lack of good sleep—but I didn't want to blubber in front of this man. So I shifted to defiance.

"I don't see why I can't say I don't want a certain test. It's my body!"

Dr. Michael was unfazed and still sympathetic. "I'll see what I can do." He straightened up effortlessly (goddamned young whippersnapper), nodding at Martha and Paula as he walked out.

"That was so sweet," Martha gushed. "You know, it's not easy for him to do stuff like that, with his shyness and everything."

"Yeah, that was pretty sweet," Paula agreed. "But you're not gonna get out of having the scope done."

"But he said—" I attempted to argue.

"Mm, hmm, I'm just saying," she replied. "And you're not gonna want to hear this, but you have to call The Abbey to find out what you can bring. And you should call work."

I frowned and rolled my eyes. "You're right. I don't want to hear that."

"And after you talk to The Abbey," Martha piped in, "you need to make a list and then I can pick up the stuff at your apartment."

I rolled my eyes again, but inwardly I smiled. Another day with the sisters had begun.

I made the damn phone calls. From The Abbey I found out I could bring pretty much anything, all the clothes I needed, my own pillow and blanket, anything that made me more comfortable during my stay. What about cash? Minimal amount of cash—drinks and snacks were provided. Cell phone? No cell phones. Ouch. That one stung.

I decided to call my boss rather than human services. I told her I was in the hospital and I would be going to residential treatment so I wasn't sure when

I would be back. She was kind and sympathetic, triggering the tightness in my throat. She told me not to worry about anything and to work on getting better. I thanked her, my voice quavering. After hanging up, enormous relief washed over me.

The Dream Team got an earful that morning. Paula started with the lack of preparation for the MRI, including no drugs, then launched into the inaction on the FMLA paperwork.

"We need this so she has a job when she gets out of The Abbey," Paula stressed. *In this corner, in purple and gray, her shoulders draped in a paisley scarf, we have Paula Avelleyra. And folks, she came out swinging! Go Paula!* I watched my lovely advocate do her thing.

Another unrelenting force, Dr. Laura, notified us that the esophageal scope was scheduled for Thursday. Dr. Michael quietly stood next to her. Sensing his discomfort, I caught his eye and smiled softly at him. I didn't want him to feel bad. His visit meant a lot to me.

"It's not that bad, Lisa," Paula chimed in. "They knock you out just enough so you don't feel anything."

Fine. Slide me into a big fucking tube and ram another one down my throat. I can't stop you. The swarthy intern, Dr. Mariucchi (not really his name, but that's what we called him), suggested that I start taking short walks, that I get out of bed more. *But I've gotten accustomed to the helpless, bedridden life, Dr. Mariucchi. Why do you have to ruin that?* I glared at him before I could check myself. The sisters pounced.

"That's a good idea, Lisa," Martha agreed. "Getting up and moving will help you get your strength back."

"We can take a short walk down the hall this afternoon," Paula added. "We'll help you."

After The Young and the Restless, the sisters went to lunch and I waited for mine. The food here was pretty good and the menu extensive. I ordered over the phone and it arrived about 45 minutes later. But I still couldn't eat much. My hunger was larger than my belly could handle. I soon reached a point where I couldn't eat anymore. It wasn't nausea. It was a lack of appetite. I was learning to order less so I wouldn't waste so much food. After lunch I dozed until the sisters returned with a proposed itinerary for the afternoon.

"We got you a notebook," said Martha, pulling an old-school ringed tablet from a bag. "You can start your packing list and you can use it when you're at The Abbey."

"Do you want to go for a walk?" asked Paula eagerly.

"Jesus, you guys! One thing at a time!"

I got up for a walk, admittedly curious about how my body would respond. I shuffled down the hall in my Aladdin slippers, the contraption on one side, Paula on the other, Martha trailing behind. I started to feel woozy halfway to the nurse's station but didn't say anything until we got there. We turned around. It did feel good to move but I was again dismayed at how quickly I tired. I crumpled on to the bed.

"You'll sleep good tonight," Paula said.

"No, I won't," I replied.

"Ok, maybe you won't."

Later that afternoon, word came down: MRI, round two. It was scheduled earlier this time, eight o'clock, drugs around seven, and the sisters could accompany me. Things were happening fast.

A nurse who had heard about the botched MRI delivered the magic pill. She was into yoga and offered breathing tips. I wasn't in the mood. I just wanted the drug to kick in and to get this over with. Knowing the sisters would be with me alleviated some of the fear. The drug started kicking in. I felt lighter and a little spacey. *Where's the wheelchair guy? I'm ready! I don't want the drug to wear off!*

"What kind of music do you want to listen to?" Paula asked. "You said you couldn't think of anything last night."

"Earth, Wind and Fire!" I answered immediately. "I had this one album, it had 'September' on it and 'Shining Star' and 'Boogie Wonderland.'"

"I don't think they have albums," Martha said. "Probably music genres like Motown or R & B."

"If you say Earth, Wind and Fire, they'll probably play similar songs, like on Pandora," Paula added.

Brad arrived with the wheelchair. He tucked me in with a blanket and wheeled me out to the hall, sisters in tow. We wound through the halls and descended in the elevator. I warned them about the chilly stretch. Having the sisters along was like a tonic for my nerves. Or maybe it was the drugs. And then we were there. There were different torturers this time, but I had my posse with me. The technicians had been briefed—I was going into the bigger machine. Pep talks ensued.

"Don't look at it," Martha advised. "Don't look at the machine. Look at the floor. That's what I did."

"Do you have something to cover her eyes?" Paula asked the techs. "She needs to have something over her eyes."

I had envisioned those velvet eye covers that movie stars wear to bed but instead I got a plain, thin, old washcloth. "You don't have anything else?" I whined. "Like eye covers?"

No fancy eye covers. The sisters assured me the washcloth would work, it would block out seeing anything and would stay in place. It was time to lay down again on the conveyor belt, washcloth covering my eyes. The sisters would be right outside in the waiting area. Their absence was palpable. My heart beat faster as I slowly slid into the larger, but not nearly large enough, metal gullet. Since I knew what to expect, the noise wasn't so shocking. I took deep breaths, listening to the bright, brassy sounds of Earth, Wind and Fire. They asked me how I was doing, and I said fine. I didn't want to talk for fear of the washcloth falling off. They asked a couple more questions and I answered quickly. The din of the machine overpowered Philip Bailey and Stevie Wonder. I relaxed a bit and forced myself to lie still and keep my mind blank, no easy feat. I was going to do this. I was going to stick it out.

"Ten minutes to go. How are you doing?" a disembodied voice spoke through the headphones, interrupting Marvin Gaye.

"There's still ten minutes?" I asked, willing my voice to sound dispassionate. I calmed my thoughts so the stirring anger wouldn't turn into raw panic. I had to get through this. I didn't want to go through it a third time. *You're almost there, Lisa.* I played a mental game with myself to get through the last few minutes. *Ten minutes is half the time it took you to drive to work. That's not very long and it goes by really fast.* So I drove to work in my mind, ticking off landmarks along the way. Finally, the magic words: "Ok, Lisa. We're done. We're bringing you out." I slowly slid out into the light, ripping the washcloth off my eyes and springing off the conveyor belt as soon as I cleared the tunnel entrance.

"You did great," one tech said. "We got a lot of good pictures."

"Slow down," the other tech said. "You might be lightheaded."

Without responding, I scooted out to the waiting area and my sisters.

"I did it. It's over." We embraced in a three-way hug.

Chapter Eight

MRI down, one scope to go. I actually slept a couple of hours, despite the fact that my room was freezing. I usually run warm, but I had to ask for a blanket. The night nurse agreed it was unusually chilly and checked the thermostat but was unable to adjust it. He left and returned, reporting that there was something wrong with the heat and covering me with another blanket. I slept for another hour but was awake when the sisters arrived, anticipating their reaction to the room temperature. They greeted me then settled into their respective chairs.

"Is it cold in here? Or is it just me?" Paula asked.

"I think it's cold," Martha said. They both looked at me.

"The heat isn't working."

Timing exquisitely perfect, one of my hallmates agreed. "Where's the fucking heat! It's fucking freezing in here!"

Martha's mouth dropped; I stifled a guffaw. And Paula? She leaped out of her chair, pressing her mouth shut and scampering quickly to the bathroom. Hearing her muffled laughter through the wall, increased ours. "Oh my God!!" Martha exclaimed. "Right when you said the heat wasn't working! I feel bad laughing."

"Oh, man. I don't," I said between paroxysms.

Paula emerged, still laughing. "That was close." She collapsed in her chair and we laughed some more.

The scope was scheduled for 10 o'clock and shortly before that a volunteer arrived with a wheelchair. A few minutes later, we arrived at the scope department, a large room filled with beds occupied by patients—but there were no beds available, which was not uncommon, the volunteer explained, because it was always busy. *Jesus, there are so many sick people. How many don't have insurance?* My own situation again triggered worry. *They've got to get that paperwork done and we won't be there for the Dream Team visit to remind them.* My stomach roiled. Martha scooted off to an appointment and soon after, a bed opened up. We settled in, Paula and the volunteer taking seats against the wall while the nurse hooked me up to another IV. The beds were separated by curtains, but only on the sides, so I was able to observe my fellow guinea pigs across the aisle and the many staffers scurrying around. Despite all the staff activity, there was no patient movement, no beds changing occupants across or next to me. A half hour turned to an hour with no status update. Jan, the volunteer, told us about a flower nursery south of Iowa City and about commuting from Kalona. When she heard I was in the hospital because of drinking, she launched into a story about a relative with a drinking problem and recited the platitudes of AA—one day at a time, go to meetings, blah blah blah. Her chattiness was getting on my nerves.

"Where's the nurse?" I interrupted. "When am I gonna get in?" Jan offered to find a nurse and bustled off.

"She's starting to bug me," I said to Paula. "She's a very nice person but I really don't want to hear about AA from her."

"I know. She's starting to bug me too. Pretend like you're asleep. Then maybe she won't talk so much."

I closed my eyes and tuned my ears to approaching voices, willing them to stop at my cubicle. Jan returned and talked softly to Paula—I guess she saw that I was "sleeping"—informing her it could be another hour. Outwardly I dozed, but inwardly I railed. *Fuck an A! Another hour? We're gonna miss "The Young and the Restless!" They better not take a break for lunch!* Eventually, I did actually doze, the myriad of voices drifting around me.

Finally, it was my turn. They wheeled me, bed and all, to the scoping room, which to me looked like a mini operating room based on watching "Grey's Anatomy." There were cabinets, machines, instruments and tubing. *Let's get this mother fucker over!* They prepped me with another IV which was to deliver the magic elixir to render me oblivious. The woman technician/scoper explained the procedure, showing me the tube, which was actually a catheter, that would be slid down my gullet. *First I'm slid into gullet, now something's going down my gullet. Too many gullets!* I could tell the elixir was kicking in. Irreverent thoughts swirled. "What about my gag reflex?" Oops. I said that out loud. "I have a strong gag reflex."

"The scope is thin enough that it won't trigger a gag reflex," said the scoper, snapping me out of my thoughts about other activities that make me gag. "Are you ready? We're about to start."

I nodded. *But I'm still awake!* The scoper hovered over me, gently opening my mouth. I stared at the ceiling. *Don't look! Don't look at that thing!* She slipped it in while I continued to stare at the ceiling and before I knew it, it was over. *Phew, another milestone behind me.* There was another one coming up, one I hadn't allowed myself to think about. And it was a big one.

A lifeline was being yanked, as crucial to me as the IVs dripping nourishment into my veins. The sisters were leaving tomorrow, Martha to Dubuque 60 miles away and Paula to Madison, 110 miles further east on Highway 151. We often referred to ourselves as the Sisters of 151. My chest felt heavy at the thought of them going. Martha was coming back Sunday to pack my things, but the magic of the triumvirate was coming to an end. For the rest of the day, I got quiet and found it hard to look at Paula. How sterile and hollow it will be without their presence, their companionship. And most of all, their laughter.

Swarthy Dr. Mariucci entered, a welcome reprieve from the ache opening inside me. The FMLA paperwork was complete, he announced. I thanked him profusely, relief joining my other jumbled emotions. I took a couple of walks up and down the corridor then we spent the evening in quiet companionship, watching TV. It was Paula's bedtime so it was time to leave. I spent another fitful night, this time in a state of heavy dread.

When the sisters arrived in the morning, I did not feel my usual uplifting of spirit. Instead I felt vulnerable and heavy sadness. We were all more quiet than usual. They stayed until the Dream Team visit, making sure the loose ends were tied up and we were still on schedule for a Monday departure. The Dream Team left and the moment I had been dreading for a day was here. Martha was trying to keep it light, repeatedly emphasizing how she would be back Sunday and how it was only one full day that I would be alone. One day, but what a bleak and quiet day it will be without them, my precious sissies.

Paula told me that she had been in touch with some of my friends, including Brian, and she would contact them if I didn't feel up to it. I said I would text them but wasn't ready to call. My two other sisters had also been asking about me. "You should call Cindy and Patty," she said. "And you have to work on your packing list." I knew what she was doing, deflecting with tasks, and I appreciated it. But I didn't trust myself to speak. Or look at Paula, who was quietly looking at me. I met her eyes and mine instantly filled with tears as did hers. Petite, beautiful Paula, the smallest of the Avelleyra girls but oh so strong. We hugged and sobbed.

"You can do this," she whispered in my ear. "I love you."

"I love you too," I said thickly through my tears.

And they were gone. I caught a faint whiff of Paula's perfume. I filled the day by starting a packing list, taking a couple of walks up and down the hall, and staring blankly at the television. The sisters lifeline had been pulled and I had to adjust. There would be many adjustments in the upcoming days.

Saturday morning, I got a text from Kitty, a simple "Hi" accompanied by a selfie of us at the Iowa-Wisconsin tailgate, which I had hosted. I stared at the photo. I had been drinking that day. Tailgating is perfect for alcoholics. We're not the only ones drinking right away in the morning. She and her husband Tom had helped me set up in the parking lot at Brian's reserved spot. Of course, I had started drinking even before they got to my place that morning. *Oh, Kitty. What do I say to you?* I started to text her then stopped, pressing Call instead. It rang once, twice.

"Hello?" that familiar voice answered.

"Hi Kitty. I got your text. I was just going to text back, but I thought, no, I'm gonna call."

"I'm so glad you did! How are you doing?"

I sighed. "Oh, better every day but I have a long way to go. How are you doing? How's Tom?"

"We're good." A pause. "Lisa, I'm in a rest stop bathroom halfway between Des Moines and Iowa City."

"What? What are you doing there? Are you coming here?"

"I'm coming to drop off a care package—just some stuff I thought you might need."

"Drop off at the hospital?" I was caught off guard.

"Yeah. And I thought I'd come up to see you if you're up to having a visitor. I understand if you're not."

My mind whirled. I wasn't sure. Talking on the phone rather than texting was one thing. But seeing someone in person? From the outside? My world had shrunk to hospital personnel and the sisters. Was I ready for someone from the outside? I looked like hell, but with Kitty, it didn't matter. "Sure. Come on up."

"Ok. See you in about an hour."

I was nervous. I brushed my hair, but the image in the bathroom mirror was a disappointment. I lay in bed and reminisced. Kitty had been there for a lot of my firsts. First brush with Johnny law (we got caught letting the air out of a guy's tires). First Ragbrai and the meeting of Brian on that Ragbrai. First roommate at college. And now, first friend to visit after almost killing myself. I laid back, closed my eyes, and listened to the hospital sounds. My eyes opened. Familiar footsteps, pounding footsteps. Kitty was a hard walker, something I had become familiar with while roommates. There was a light tap on the door, then Kitty peeked into the room, a wire basket over her arm.

"Hi Lisa," she greeted me timidly.

I smiled broadly, I couldn't help myself. It was good to see her. "Hi Kitty." She went by Kate now—I understood why—but she would always be Kitty to me. And she was okay with that.

"I brought you a care package, or I guess a care basket," she said. "I'll just set it over here. You can look at it later." She set it on the table next to Martha's chair.

She was leggy and chesty, so naturally we always gave her shit about her boobs. She didn't flaunt them, but she didn't hide them either. I think she was a little self-conscious of them. Fresh-faced and freckled, she had always kept her curly hair short. And blonde. And lately straight. And those eyes! She had the bluest eyes! Limpid pools of indigo blue, her dad used to say. He also said they were bedroom eyes. Her dad had been gruff and very funny and died too soon when we were in our early 20s. In the unforgiving light of the hospital room, her eyes were startling in their blueness. And comforting. Comforting and familiar. She pulled up Paula's chair close to the bed. We looked at each other a moment.

"I really did it this time, Kitty."

"What was going on? What happened?"

I told her. I didn't have to sugarcoat anything with her. "I tried to drink myself to death. And obviously, I didn't succeed," I added wryly. The unvarnished truth poured out, how I didn't care about anything except getting drunk and not being alive. I summarized the events leading up to it, Brian's involvement, being brought to the hospital, and how I was going to The Abbey.

"Have you ever had an MRI?" I asked.

She had, and she understood the horror of it. "They have a partial one now, where you don't have to go all the way in."

"Why didn't I know about that? Why didn't they tell me?" We laughed.

While talking, I recalled another Kitty first. When I had gotten sober the first time, my first social outing where drinking was involved had been with her and Tom. I had gone with them to the Iowa-Minnesota game in Minneapolis, where we stayed with another high school friend. They had been wonderful and understanding. The friend we stayed with had not, throwing drinking into my face at every opportunity. I don't think that friend is unkind, just oblivious. The trip had marked another milestone in my friendship with Kitty.

I told her about the hopelessness and the lingering disappointment from not getting back with my ex. I told her about how I was sick of being surrounded by couples, the preponderance of couples in everyday life, on TV, in books, in my family—something I hadn't discussed with the sisters. It was a constant reminder of my aloneness. And Kitty understood. Tom was Kitty's second husband. She had lost her first husband, Joe, to cancer. She told me how after Joe's death, couples they had hung out with still included her, but that it gradually dwindled. They stopped calling. And it hurt, she said. She'd see the neighborhood couples walking to each other's homes, carrying coolers. She had felt left out. Recently she and Tom had taken a trip to Mexico with a bunch of couples and one of the women was a scheduler. At night, she had insisted they all stay in, cooking and hanging out at the condo. When some of them wanted to go out at night, she had gotten upset.

"Never again," Kitty said. "I was sick of couples!"

When our visit had run its course, we both knew it, but not in a bad I can't-wait-to-get-out-of-here kind of way. We were so comfortable with each other, it was instinctual. She looked at me with those eyes, filling with tears. I much preferred it when they were filled with tears of laughter.

"I don't want you to die, Lisa," she whispered, lowering her head and setting it on my arm. I petted her hair, tears falling from my eyes. She lifted her head and looked at me. "You're important to me. I can't imagine you not being here."

I was deeply moved. Kitty was stoic. I was the expressive one, and I didn't know what to say. I kept it brief.

"I'm not going to die," I whispered back.

After Kitty left, I lay there quietly. For the first time, another first, I think I really was okay with not dying.

I called the other sisters. Patty is a phone talker. You can easily be on the phone with her for an hour. She was effusive about hearing from me. She had looked up The Abbey online and was excited. It also reminded her of something—the campus from the movie The Trouble With Angels, one of the Avelleyra girls' favorite movies. She informed me that there was a M*A*S*H marathon on WGN—one of the Avelleyra girls' favorite television shows—and that it was the older ones with Henry Blake and Trapper John.

Cindy was not a big phone talker. Conversations with her were informative and under fifteen minutes. She had also looked up The Abbey online and was also excited for me. It wasn't like I was going on a vacation, but I understood the enthusiasm. This was a completely different setup than the rehab in Fort Dodge. Cindy had been very supportive the first time I got sober, sending me nice AA anniversary coins during that year and a half. When I say nice, I'm comparing them to the ones they gave you in Fort Dodge AA which were colored poker chips. The ones she sent were medallions with the serenity prayer on one side and the AA triangle on the other. We spoke often when I was sober but once I started drinking again, our talks waned. Cindy was going to Spain in May to hike the Camino de Santiago, and she was dedicating a couple of legs of the hike to me. My throat tightened with emotion, but I had to speak. I was on the phone after all. There was no way to hide the tears in my voice.

"That means a lot to me, Cindy. That's really special."

"Oh, don't cry!" Cindy was not a crier. "It's something I want to do for you!" She was a cool cat, the polar opposite of Patty, who was as volatile and unpredictable as a tornado. You never knew when Patty's emotions were going to touch down or what path they would take, not unlike Martha and her weird crying. We wrapped up the phone call with my genuine thanks for her gesture. Phone calls done, I started on my packing list.

I wanted to make it effortless for Martha, so I described each item, then the location in the closet or dresser drawer or medicine cabinet. Martha had come up with a scathingly brilliant idea (a Trouble With Angels reference), texting me she would take pictures with her phone when she had questions. I heartily approved. I took some jaunts down the hall, extending my distance past the nurse's station to the community room where I had never gone for occupational therapy activities. With sleep still elusive, I spent awake time that night mentally packing and rechecking my list of things to do.

Sunday dawned and a sister returned. But not until noon. Without Paula, Martha was operating on Martha time—leisurely, fraught with indecision. Departure time kept getting pushed back and finally I got the text I was impatient for: *On my way.*

For the next hour and a half, I finetuned my packing list. Earrings. A necklace Paula gave me when I first got sober. I figured I was going to start caring about how I looked at some point, which meant wearing jewelry again.

She arrived. It was weird seeing her without Paula. She wanted to know about the visit with Kitty. I summarized the highlights, gesturing to the basket on the table. "There's a lot of good stuff in here," she gushed, inspecting the basket. "This is really good lotion. Look at this cute cat mug. And earrings! Look at these earrings! They're so you!"

Dear, wonderful Kitty. I felt myself getting emotional just looking at the earrings, silver hoops with a silver, dangling fringe. They were me. Thinking of Kitty picking out those earrings warmed my heart.

"Good snacky snacks, too," said Martha, still digging.

I looked over the list, adding a couple of toiletry items—tweezers, razor— hair removal returns! The list was ready and I tore it out of the notebook. "Here you go," I said, handing it over.

She read it, nodding occasionally. "That's good. You put exactly where to find everything. How do you remember that?"

I shrugged. After every clothing item, I had written which drawer, right or left side of the closet. For toiletries, either the medicine cabinet or hall closet. I liked to keep my stuff orderly. I told her where to find the big suitcase and duffel bag. She was ready to go and I was ready for her to go. She left, promising to text questions and pics as needed. I figured she'd be gone an hour or so; she was gone for three. During that time, I got several clarification texts. *Brown boots, tall or short?* That's right. I do have two pairs of brown boots. The taller ones I don't wear very often so I had forgotten about them. *Short ones,* I texted back. She sent pics of a couple of tunics. *Yes. That one.* I'd forgotten about that one. *Yes. That one, too.* When Martha took photos, she displayed the items artfully, using the bedspread as the backdrop. For a jewelry pic, she displayed the earrings on a solid background along with a beaded jewelry case I had also forgotten about. Yes and yes, I texted. We had agreed all clothing would go in the suitcase, along with hangers, and the duffel bag would be for socks, underwear, leggings, and shoes. She was taking longer than I liked, but I knew she was being thorough. Alone, she worked at her own, plodding pace, which was okay. I took a stroll down the hall, carrying my phone with me.

Back in my room, I watched the Real Housewives of Beverly Hills without really watching. It didn't take a lot of concentration to watch and keep up with the storyline. Two of them go to lunch—leaving their yummy looking food untouched—and talk about a third one. Then the third one finds out what was said about her and brings it up over cocktails with all of them. Alliances form and the botoxed broads square off in alcohol-fueled tirades, the fight rehashed for the rest of the season. It was mindless and ridiculous, exactly what I needed to keep me from thinking too much. My ears perked up at an unfamiliar sound, the clickety clack of uneven wheels on linoleum. The clickety clack grew increasingly louder and Martha entered, pulling my big suitcase, a duffel bag hanging over her shoulder.

"I think I done good," she said.

I set the suitcase flat on the floor, unzipped it and inspected her work. She had done good. It wasn't packed the way I would've packed but it was all there. This is what I would be wearing for the next month. I had chosen my favorites, based on comfort and how they looked on me. Refolding and rearranging the clothes soothed me.

"Do you know what you're going to wear tomorrow?" Martha asked.

"I do," I said, fingering the clothes. I looked up at Martha. "I'm scared."
"I know."

There were still things to do. Since I couldn't have my phone, I had to copy down phone numbers in my notebook. And I had to pack up shit that had accumulated in my hospital room. Once I started gathering the stuff, I was surprised at how much there was. Books, lotion samples from Paula, two folders of hospital paperwork. Ugh! Anticipating this, Martha had also brought up a couple of shopping bags. They were perfect for the miscellaneous crap. I kept busy. I took a walk up and down the hall with Martha accompanying me. A week ago, we had watched the Oscars in the ICU. Tomorrow I was going to a place I hadn't even heard of a few days ago. *You really did it this time, Avelleyra.*

Chapter Nine

It was gray and dreary driving east on Interstate 80. Perfect. I felt gray and dreary. I was wearing gray. The roots of my hair were turning gray. The sky was an unbroken tableau of gray. Not even shades of gray, like the Monkees song of the same name by Peter Tork. I stared blankly out the car window. Not much to see—just the brown dormant cornfields and ditches lined with dirty, old snow. I was quiet, partially from fatigue, partially from turning inward. Which meant away from Martha. I was getting ready, psyching myself up for the unknown—strangers, a city I had never seen before, a foreign place where I would live for a whole month. Sure, I'd been in residential treatment before, but it was in my hometown next to the hospital where I'd been born. On our daily recreational outings, we had walked to the tennis courts where I played as a youth. I had even played tennis again. We had taken walks to a park where we held family reunion picnics. There had been comfort in that familiarity. This time I wouldn't have that.

Martha was acting upbeat without being obnoxious about it. I appreciated it. "What kind of music do you want to listen to?" she asked, pulling out a CD folder from between the seats. "Barry Manilow? Carole King? Bruce Springsteen? Did you know Bruce Springsteen had depression issues? Whitey read it in his book."

"Was he a drinker?"

"I think when he was younger. Not sure about later in life."

"Hmmm." I continued looking out the window. "Barry Manilow."

"Good choice." She pulled the CD out of the folder and slid it into the player.

It was a good choice. Barry was comfort music. Barry was nostalgia. I recognized each song and knew the words. They ranged from poignant to lively so I could wallow a bit with "Weekend in New England," then be pulled out of the wallow with "Beautiful Music." It was as soothing as anything could be at this point. Besides Martha's presence. I was pulling away, but I still needed her. She was wearing her big sister hat, looking after her baby sister, taking up the gatekeeper role again. Only this time, she wasn't protecting me from our father's wrath. She was protecting me from myself.

She had appeared that morning with new pajamas from Target—soft, plaid, flannel bottoms accompanied by a comfy, gray Johnny Cash t-shirt. The shirt had a "I Walk the Line" gold record disc printed on the front. Martha had calmed me when I got prickly and impatient with the nurse who brought the sheaf of checkout paperwork. "Just let me out already!" I cried after the nurse left the room. "She's just doing her job," Martha gently reminded me.

Then there was the final visit from the Dream Team. I sat proudly in a chair, clean, dressed in regular clothes, no make-up but gussied enough. Dr. Laura was warm and encouraging. Dr. Michael was professional but he had a glint in his eye. I could tell he was happy to see me dressed and ready to go. And he was going to be my primary physician post-treatment! The tightness inside me loosened slightly at that news. *Something to look forward to!*

Dr. Laura had looked at me with that unwavering and slightly unsettling gaze. "How are you feeling about all this?"

I paused, choosing my words carefully. "Ready. And in a weird way, excited. But also anxious."

Dr. Michael and Martha nodded while Dr. Laura continued to hold me in her steady gaze. "Would you also say you feel..." A beat. "Hope?"

Emotion rose inside me. "Yes. I would say I feel hope."

"See this truck stop?" I was jarred back to the present by Martha, pointing out an Interstate 80 landmark. "It's known for human trafficking, children and young girls."

"What? Where do you hear this stuff? Did Whitey tell you that?" The place did look a little seedy, but come on, this was Iowa!

"Maybe. But I've heard it from other people, too."

I chuckled and shook my head. Oh, Martha. Dear, funny, fear mongering Martha. I laid my head back on the car headrest, still so very tired. The fatigue and weakness had become painfully apparent upon leaving the hospital. I refused the wheelchair ride out, opting to walk to the pharmacy. Thankfully Martha stopped at the snack shop to get a couple of Diet Pepsis, and deposited me to rest on a bench outside. I made it through waiting in line for my prescriptions but badly needed another rest after that. Sitting outside the hospital entrance while Martha got the car, I let the fresh air wash over me.

The fatigue made me testy when we were in Walgreens, picking up vitamins and shampoo. I think nervousness and impatience were also making me testy. I just wanted to get started. *For Christ's sake Martha, I don't care which multi-vitamin! Just pick one!* When we finally got out of there, the mist had turned to rain and I sagged onto the passenger seat. It was noon so we discussed lunch and our timeline. It took an hour to get there and we had to be there by two. Eating was still dicey for me—I had an appetite but I filled up quickly. We decided on Panera because finicky Martha liked it, it was nearby, and I knew they had soup. I got a bowl of soup but it was too much, a cup would've been a better choice. Martha, a finicky *and* slow eater, got a turkey sandwich. A *big* turkey sandwich. I tried not to keep looking at my watch. We got out of there by one, still on schedule.

"Davenport exit signs," Martha announced. Davenport was right next to Bettendorf, two of the four of the Quad Cities. "We get off at I-74."

It was weird but I felt kind of excited, like I always did when getting close to a road trip destination. Treatment, part deux, here I come.

"Here's our exit," said Martha, pulling onto the off-ramp. "What are we looking for next?"

"Kimberly Road," I replied. "You made good time. We're a little early."

A few minutes later, we saw the sign for our next exit. Martha merged onto the ramp. "Take a left," I directed her. "Then we look for 14th Street."

Driving east, the town became increasingly residential, nice older houses, each one different with varying degrees of upkeep. I leaned forward in my seat. We were close.

"Where is it?" I asked urgently. "It's gotta be coming up."

"I know," agreed Martha, also straining forward.

And then, there it was, on the crest of a hill, blonde brick walls and towers, a big sign on the sloping lawn: The Abbey Recovery and Treatment Center. Martha stopped the car in the driveway, and we looked at each other, then back at the Abbey—a golden dome gleamed atop the monastery.

"A golden dome," I murmured. "I can't believe it." Our dad had graduated from Notre Dame, the golden domes of *all* golden domes to anyone with an allegiance to the university. We had grown up watching Notre Dame football. We had grown up watching our dad throw fits during Notre Dame football. We had gotten out of school to go to Notre Dame football games with our parents. We adored Notre Dame.

"It's a sign," Martha said.

I looked over at her, then back up at the dome. "It is, isn't it?"

We stared a moment longer, then Martha continued up the driveway. She turned to me. "Are you ready?"

I looked at the entrance, the golden dome, then her. "Yep. I'm ready."

Martha dragged in the big suitcase while I carried the duffel bag and a bag full of books. We walked under a portico through heavy wooden double doors into a foyer with three carpeted steps leading down to a short marble tiled hallway. It was hushed, like a church, the clattering of the suitcase wheels startling on the marble floor. The hallway led to what looked like a lobby of an upscale hotel, which The Abbey once used to be, furnished with a vintage sofa and velvet wing chairs. We set the bags down and walked up to the check-in desk. Martha and I looked at the bell on the counter, then at each other. I nodded. She rang it, the ding so sharp that we both jumped, then tittered. I glanced at a flyer lying on the counter, seeing an item that caused my stomach to lurch: *Visiting hours Sunday 12-5.* I slid the flyer toward Martha, pointing at the visiting hours. She frowned. Just then, a slender woman appeared on the other side of the counter and smiled softly at us.

"Hi, I'm Jules. Can I help you?"

The kind voice accompanied a kind and pretty face. I guessed her to be about our age, very healthy looking. Her light brown hair was cut in a short bob, the kind you shook into place when it was wet. Her smooth, lightly freckled face was free of make-up, her gaze intelligent. I wondered if she was the woman I had talked to on the phone. I liked her immediately.

"I'm Lisa. I have an appointment at two. This is my sister Martha."

We exchanged pleasantries. Martha and I commented on the beauty of the monastery, me telling Jules about what Patty said, how it reminded her of the school in "The Trouble With Angels." It was like I was starting a vacation. Except that I wasn't. My eyes wandered down to the flyer with the visiting hours. I had to ask.

"So visiting hours are only on Sundays?"

The kind gaze held mine. "Yes. Only on Sundays. We'll talk about that during your assessment."

So that was that. Jules told us to take a seat until they were ready for us, so Martha and I chose a sofa at the back of the lobby. Tall windows stretched up almost to the ceiling. I wondered if my room would have any windows. Through the nearest one, I saw a sliver of the golden dome. A man and woman entered from the opposite end of the lobby, taking seats in the wing chairs near us. Was he an inmate? Was she? They both looked young, She was short with short, dark hair and dark-framed glasses. He was tall and good-looking with thick brown hair, the kind of hair that looked attractive even when unkempt. I knew that Martha was watching them too, trying to figure out the dynamic. My curiosity about people had served me well during my journalism days. It made me a good interviewer. With Martha, it had turned her into an adept eavesdropper and internet stalker. I had read somewhere that Woody Allen got dialogue from eavesdropping in restaurants and coffee shops; I've used this tidbit to defend my eavesdropping. From what I gathered, the man was the patient and the woman worked here. He was talking about his marriage being over and how his wife really meant it this time. She listened sympathetically. I couldn't quite catch what he said next. He really needed to speak up.

A young, clean-cut guy entered the lobby. I couldn't see him that well since I wasn't wearing my glasses, but I could see that he turned and smiled at us before scampering up the stairs. A patient, I guessed.

Jules returned with a questionnaire for Martha. Good, Martha had something to keep her busy. I followed Jules through a white wooden door next to the check-in counter into a room that looked like a doctor's office. I sat in the chair next to the desk where Jules took a seat and the tedious assessment process began. I answered the same questions that I had answered all last week. When finished, I took a bathroom break and checked on Martha. She was still on the first page of the questionnaire. *Geezus, Martha. Dinner is at 4:30.* I returned to the office where a doctor had replaced Jules. His questions were more about the physical symptoms and he talked about addiction and how it manifests itself. Then the $64,000 question.

"Are you an alcoholic?"

"Yes," I answered without hesitation. No hedging. I was beyond hedging. I will hedge no more! And I realized I meant it. I wasn't just spouting what I thought they wanted to hear. I really meant it. I was an alcoholic.

Another break. Martha was plugging away at the questionnaire. I gave her a synopsis of the intake and she asked annoying detail-seeking questions, and I got exasperated and told her I didn't recall all the details. Jules walked toward us.

"We're going to meet with Karen the director now," she said. "Your sister can come too."

We returned to the doctor's office. Karen wasn't there yet so Jules talked about the daily routine. The day started early with an AA internal meeting at 8 followed by the daily community meeting at 9. What about breakfast? Martha asked. Breakfast was not served but there were breakfast bars, English muffins, and fruit in the dining room. Just then, the director walked in. She was tall with dark brown hair cut into a bob. Her eyes were also dark brown, warm and steady, another gaze holder. I liked how she was dressed, a knee-length skirt, tights and flats, one of my go-to looks when I had cared about my appearance. She talked about The Abbey's mission, to heal physically, mentally, and spiritually. I bristled inwardly at the mention of spirituality but remained silent. I waited for a pause to ask about my main concern. "Visiting hours are only on Sunday?"

The brown eyes turned to me, slightly hardening as she readied to tell me something she knew I wasn't going to like hearing. "It's not just visiting hours on Sunday," she explained calmly, in a voice that was girlish yet strong. "We call it Family Day. It starts at noon with an Al-Anon meeting for family members, then there is a two-hour session led by a counselor for families and residents. After that, there is free time to spend with your family." She and Jules exchanged a look. "But since you got here on a Monday, your family won't be able to participate the first Sunday because you have to be here a full seven days before that happens."

It was Martha and mine's turn to exchange a look. "That's almost two weeks!"

"It is," Karen said. "It's the unfortunate timing of your coming in on a Monday. We believe in immersing you completely into the program for the first full week."

"But I'm only one day off," I pointed out.

"It's a full seven days," she countered evenly. "Tomorrow is your first full day."

"What about phone calls?" Martha asked.

"Because of the full immersion, you'll be able to make phone calls next Tuesday."

I was silent, feeling cornered and trapped, much like my first rehab experience. I believe Karen sensed it. "We want you to be fully focused on getting better. No outside distractions from family members the first week."

Martha also sensed it. "That makes sense, Lisa."

I shot her a quick glare. I wasn't excited anymore. Or hopeful. I felt trapped and abandoned. Here I was, about to be cut off from the world. The dark thought returned. *I wouldn't be here if my plan had worked.*

Martha was crying. "You need to be somewhere safe," she sobbed. "And this is that place. I've told you. I want to grow old with you."

What could I possibly say after that dramatic plea? But I knew Martha wasn't being calculating, that her concern was genuine. I teared up but remained calm. I was distancing myself from my sister. I had to. I was on my own with these strangers. I got quiet while gathering my inner resources. It was time for Martha to go and for me to start this venture.

Martha, Jules and I walked out to the lobby. My luggage was gone; Jules told us it had been taken up to my room. My room. At least I had my own room. Martha wasn't done with the questionnaire—*Geezus, Martha*—so Jules took me on a tour. We went through double doors at the far end of the lobby and into a huge room with a couple of not-so-gently used faux leather couches and mismatched chairs arranged in a semi-circle and a large flat screen TV. *We get to watch TV!* A friendly face looked up at us from one of the chairs, a round moon face with brown eyes, closely cropped brown hair and a goatee. Jules introduced me to Sean, who smiled warmly and welcomed me. We walked through rectangles of light cast by the waning late afternoon sun through tall windows. The red and gold pattern of the carpeting was bold and splashy. A circle of chairs had been set up behind the TV area with three round tables, unsurprisingly reminiscent of those found in a hotel banquet room.

"This is where we hold group sessions and meditation, and there's games, puzzles and movies over there on the shelves," said Jules, pointing. Books too,

I noted. After the tables, the carpeting ended at a section of hardwood floor, most likely used for dancing at weddings. This was where yoga took place, Jules explained, and I made the appropriate interested sounds, even though I didn't care. After crossing the wood floor, we walked through a set of propped-open double doors into a small foyer. On the right was the kitchen, from which meal preparation noises emanated, and to the left was the dining room with two more round tables and a bar on one end, set up with coffee and healthy snacks. Behind the bar were mini fridges filled with soda, milk, and juices. Jules pointed out a bulletin board where the daily schedule was posted along with the weekly chores list. They weren't kidding about being busy all day. The schedule started at eight in the morning and continued until eight at night. Chores included changing tablecloths, taking out the garbage, and rolling silverware, much lighter than the chores at my first rehab stint, where we had to mop the floors and wash dishes. The bulletin board hung next to a door that opened onto a large expanse of lawn and an old-fashioned swimming pool, now covered. The pool looked like something out of old Hollywood. We returned to the lobby and Martha, but she had one page left on the questionnaire, so we went up to see my room. It was two flights up and I was breathing hard by the time we got there. And what a room it was. It was huge! A king size bed in a corner room with, three tall windows. *I'm gonna spend a lot of time here.* The furniture was clearly left over from the hotel days—a television hutch without a television, matching nightstands on each side of the bed, a desk. Next to the desk, a door opened into a small closet. Then the bathroom. *My own bathroom!* It looked like a hotel bathroom, but in a nice hotel, not a Super 8. Good lighting and bigger than the bathroom in my apartment. I was careful not to look at myself in the mirror. I was itching to unpack my bags but Jules kept us moving. We walked through a small sitting area at the top of the stairs and down a hall with more tall windows, overlooking a parking lot with a basketball hoop. It was chilly in the hallway. We entered another long, large room, a smaller banquet room than the one downstairs, a set of huge wooden doors at one end. This space was furnished with long tables, arranged in a square and covered by white tablecloths. There were books on the tables at some of the seats.

"You'll be spending a lot of time up here," Jules said. "The community meetings and group sessions are held here."

We skirted the wall behind one of the tables to the doors, which were heavy and intricately carved. Jules pushed open one of the doors and I was immediately slammed by my Catholic past. Slammed, and then comforted. It was so fucking familiar: the chapel, dim and hushed, untouched by renovations, reminded me of our church growing up before it was modernized. Gilded paint, countless statues, a carving of the Last Supper on the front of the altar. It still moved me. I felt my throat tightening with emotion. The chapel can be used at any time, said Jules, who then gestured to a door next to the altar that led to a meeting and meditation room.

Back in the lobby, Martha was *still* working on the questionnaire.

"I'll leave you to say your good-byes, but dinner is in 20 minutes," Jules told us.

I sat down next to my sister on the couch. "How much more do you have left?"

"I'm on the last question," she said, somewhat defensively. "Hold on. I lost my train of thought."

I rolled my eyes and shook my head. *Keep that train moving, Martha, keep it moving.* She looked like she was finished, then started flipping back to previous pages.

"No you don't," I said, grabbing the clipboard.

"But I just have to check—" she sputtered.

"It's not graded for style and content, for God's sake."

She looked pleadingly at the clipboard. It was time for her to go. It was good it was happening this way, with me irritated, pushing her out the door. We hugged, did our European brush kiss on each cheek—our little inside joke—then a final hard hug.

"I believe in you," she murmured in my ear.

Martha walked out but I did not watch. I walked dry-eyed to Jules, who was talking to the good-looking guy who earlier had been sitting in a wing chair. His name was Brent and he was good looking up-close too. We left him behind in the lobby and walked through the TV room. My sentence at The Abbey had begun.

Chapter Ten

C hatter and clinking cutlery grew in volume as Jules and I approached the dining room. We stopped at the edge of the room.

"Everyone, this is Lisa," Jules announced. "Please welcome her to The Abbey."

There was a flurry of greetings and some gesturing toward an empty seat at the table next to the bar. I picked at the salad, uncomfortable being the new kid on the block and eating in front of others, my own personal hang-up. A plate of chicken stir fry was set down before me. *Wow! They bring the food to you.* It looked delicious but I was already getting full, so I set the salad aside and started on the main dish.

"So, what was your poison?" asked the guy sitting next to me. He introduced himself as Chris.

"Vodka. I was a vodka girl."

There were nods around the table, occupied mostly by guys. Chris was jovial and appeared to be well-liked. The other woman at the table was talking about a recent event, an incident involving her and another resident. She was younger than me, in her 30s I guessed, in full make-up, a little heavy on the eyeliner. I tried to follow her story but Chris was talking to me. "Where are you from?"

"Iowa City. But I grew up in Fort Dodge."

"I live in Fort Dodge! Well, and Des Moines. I'm an attorney and I work in both places."

We discussed Fort Dodge, where he lived, where he hung out, people he knew. He knew a couple of people I was familiar with but didn't know personally. He was easy to talk to and before I knew it, the meal was over. I carried my plates to the tubs for dirty dishes, set on carts outside the kitchen door. I regretfully scraped the uneaten food into the garbage before setting the plates and silverware in a tub. *No dish washing!* I dropped the cloth napkin (*Cloth napkins!*) into a laundry bag. Several people greeted and welcomed me as they dropped off their dirty dishes. I followed them to the TV room where others were already settled into the couches and chairs. What now? I wanted to go to my room to unpack and lay down, but instead I introduced myself to the men on the couch—one was the guy I saw going up the stairs while we waited in the lobby—and in the chairs, who were closer to my age, one with an unusual name that I knew I was going to mess up. Marvin, Derwin, something like that. I sat in a vacant chair next to Derwin. The eye liner woman, whose name was Kelli, was standing over me.

"You took my chair," she said, pointing to the pack of cigarettes on the chair arm. I honestly had not noticed the cigarettes, apologizing as I started to get up.

"Don't get up," Derwood said. "She's new," he said to Kelli. "She didn't notice."

"You can stay," she said, an edge in her voice, obviously irritated. Oh, dear. I felt unease, recalling the careful navigation of personalities during my first rehab, which had often been unpleasant. Kelli sat on the adjacent loveseat with the only other female. Chris plopped down on the floor in the middle of the group, surprisingly flexible for his size.

"So what are we doing on my last night?" he asked the room.

"It's my last night too!" said Kelli.

Someone asked Kelli about seeing a certain someone after she got out, and she admitted that she didn't know what she would do. From what I had gathered at dinner, this person had "outed" her about being at The Abbey. I felt like an outsider not knowing the full story. The conversation shifted to Chris, who quietly said he had damage to repair with his wife. *And I have damage to repair with Kelli after stealing her chair.* Committing a social faux pas in my first few hours here was not cool, but it didn't make me anxious. I wasn't here to make friends. I was here to get better. I had my own room, the chores were lighter, and the group was smaller. Sure, I wish I knew more about the guy who outed Kelli. Hell yes, I wanted Chris to go into more detail about his marriage. Shoot, I wanted to know more about the good-looking guy in the lobby. But for now, I was content to sit back in my stolen chair, listening and observing. About half of the residents were close to my age. Clint, the clean-cut guy, and another young guy sat on the couch facing the television. *That must be where the popular kids sit.* The other young guy had a football and tossed it back and forth between his hands. Two of the men my age sat in chairs next to each other, having a private conversation. They were both tall and looked like college-educated professionals. As he tried to engage me in chit chat, Derwood reminded me of the older guys in Fort Dodge rehab, redneck good ole boys.

I got up to check out the bookcase, perusing the titles and pulling out mysteries, some of which I had already read. I bypassed the literary classics, preferring a relaxing, contemporary read. I pulled out a trade paperback, favored over a hardcover or pocket-size paperback format. I recognized the author, Anita Shreve, whose bestseller *The Pilot's Wife* I had liked very much. This one was about a widower and his daughter who find an abandoned baby in the woods and about their relationship in the aftermath. I tucked it under my arm and went to make my getaway but Derwood caught me before I made it to the door. "Hey, you leaving us?"

"Yeah. I want to unpack and get settled."

He spotted the book under my arm. "You a reader?"

"Yep. Always have been."

"Not me. Racing magazines maybe, Playboy. But not books."

"Not everybody is," I said, turning toward the door. "Well, good night."

I heard a couple of good nights as I walked out of the room. I've often wanted to walk out of a room, then stop and lurk outside to eavesdrop in case something was said about me. What has stopped me? Fear of what I'd hear. Or they might say nothing at all, completely disinterested. That might be even worse.

I walked slowly up the stairs. There wasn't anyone around, so I stopped at the top to catch my breath, then continued down the hall to my room. Inside the door, I felt around for the light switch and the wall lamp next to the bed illuminated. I turned on the desk lamp and walked to the window overlooking the parking lot. Another window overlooked the portico that covered the entrance and the third overlooked the driveway entrance through the bare branches of a shrub. I pulled a cord and the heavy fabric closed shut. I opened the big suitcase on the floor at the foot of the bed, but I was too tired to unpack it all. I hung the tunics and pants in the closet and placed a few tops in a drawer of the hutch.

I pulled out the pajamas Martha had gotten for me, holding them to my face, smiling softly as tears stung my eyes. It wasn't a matching set, Martha had explained, but they still went together. The top was a nice soft cotton, the pants a warm and cozy flannel. I changed into them, luxuriating in their soft comfort after the annoying hospital garb. I sat on the edge of the bed and stretched out my legs before me. My ankles were still swollen. I was dehydrated and undernourished. My palms and fingertips were still peeling. I got the lotion from Kitty from the duffel bag. Martha had taken the metal basket with her when she went to pack, but not before I had plucked out the really good stuff—the lotion, the snacks, the earrings. The lotion felt really nice and smelled good, fresh not flowery. I pulled back the covers, excited to crawl into the king-sized bed. What an improvement from that narrow, uncomfortable hospital bed. But first I went to pee in my luxurious bathroom. The vanity was next to the toilet so I could use it to push myself up. I had really wreaked havoc on myself. Swollen ankles, peeling palms, too weak to get up from the toilet. I walked over to the big bed, savored the moment, then crawled in and stretched out my arms and legs. I propped myself up to read. As I started, the wind rattled the windows and a flicker of light flashed between the partially open drapes. Thunder and lightning in March? I waited for another round. I loved thunderstorms. I set the book aside, pulled the covers up to my chin, and waited. I was rewarded with another round of lightning and thunder. It was weird, with all my fears, with all my anxieties, thunderstorms were not one of them. One of my favorite memories with my dad was the time a tornado went through Fort Dodge when I was a junior in high school. My dad and I kept looking out the front picture window, hoping to see something exciting, much to the hysterical dismay of Martha. She screamed at us to stay away from the windows and that we needed to go down to the basement. When she and Mom descended to the basement, Dad and I ventured outside. We didn't see a funnel cloud or hear the train sound but the sky was a jaundiced yellow, filled with flying debris. Branches, pieces of two by fours and insulation flew over us as we gazed up at the sickly, golden sky. We had looked at each other, then back up at the sky, awestruck into silence yet unafraid. Later we learned the twister had struck just a few blocks away at the public high school. Dad and I had exchanged a conspiratorial smile, ignoring Martha as she scolded us.

The Bettendorf sirens wailed. I opted to snuggle deeper into the covers. The time between lightning flashes and rumbles decreased; the storm was upon us. The sirens wailed again. I heard footsteps, a door slamming, then voices.

After the third siren, there was a light knock on my door. "Lisa, are you awake?"

"Yeah." I scrambled out of bed and opened the door. It was the other female resident who wasn't Kelli.

"We're going down to the kitchen," she said. "There's no basement so I guess that's where we go."

"Ok. Just let me get my slippers."

I followed her down the hall to the sitting area as some of the guys came down the stairs from the third floor. They looked grouchy. We joined their procession down the stairs to the TV room, where a petite, dark-haired girl—and I mean girl!—was giving instructions. She stood before the group, calm and confident, then led us back to the kitchen.

"We aren't going to the basement?" someone asked.

"No. We're going to the pantry. There's no good way to get to the basement."

There was some joking as we passed through the kitchen, mainly about nuns buried in the basement and nun ghosts roaming the halls.

"Are we going into the cooler?"

"Do they have a panic room here? We might need one."

"Are you taking us to the dungeon where nuns tortured people?"

"There's a cooler in the pantry," said the unflappable young staffer, opening a heavy metal door. She flicked a switch, illuminating a dimly lit, brick-walled walkway lined with wooden homemade shelves. The walkway opened up to a small square space, also lined with shelves.

"Sorry. There's no chairs. You're gonna have to make do."

Most of the guys headed to the open space while Kelli and the other female hopped up on a built-in table along the walkway. There would be no hopping for me. I stood there, quiet and tired. Brent, the good-looking guy from the lobby, straggled in. The guys started playing euchre and jovial Chris asked if I wanted to join them. I quietly demurred. The staffer, whose name was Sam, re-entered with Sean. Sam reported that we were still under a tornado warning, so we weren't leaving anytime soon. I shifted my weight against the table, the only way to get more comfortable, and yearned for my king-sized bed. Brent bantered charmingly with the girls, occasionally raking his hand through that gorgeous hair, while Sean smilingly stood by, a balding onlooker. *Dude, you don't stand a chance against that hair.* Led by jovial Chris, the cardplayers seemed to be having a good time.

"What a way to spend your first night," Sean said to me.

"I love thunderstorms but...."

"How long do we have to stay in here?" bellowed one of the cardplayers.

"We're still under a tornado warning so we have to stay put," replied Sam. I was impressed.

I looked around the cramped pantry. I was going to spend a month with these people. At least I had a nice big room to go to for refuge. In Fort Dodge rehab, I had a single bed in a double room of a converted nurses' dormitory. I hadn't had a roommate, but our rooms were locked through the evening because of a brouhaha that had occurred right before I got there. The brouhaha had involved sneaking in booze and sexual activity on the men's floor. There was nowhere to go for solitude during free time, which had sucked.

Sam said she was going to check the weather radar again and consult with Karen. She returned shortly, informing us the storm had passed and that we could move to the TV room because Karen still wanted us all together. I chose the side couch under the windows, across from the chair I had stolen from Kelli, who was already sitting in that exact chair. Someone turned on the television, clicking through the channels until they got to the weather channel. The satellite radar showed a red blob over the Quad Cities but on its way out, more red blob in Illinois than Iowa.

"It's on its way out."

"Can we go back to our rooms?"

"It's 11 o'clock. I think we should start an hour later tomorrow. Sleep is important."

I agreed with the commentators but kept silent. Sam said she was going to check with Karen again and walked out, then returned to release us. We streamed toward the lobby and up the stairs, me straggling behind. I opened the door to my room. I kicked off my Aladdin slippers and crawled under the covers and turned off the bedside lamp, relishing the soft darkness and the

distant, low rumbling of the departing storm. I slept better than I had in a long while.

I awoke early and unpacked some more, first neatly arranging some shirts in a drawer, then underwear and socks. I found it soothing. I was not a neat freak by any means, but I liked orderliness. And I liked ample storage, being able to put things away out of sight, knowing where they were when I needed them. Satisfied with the drawers, I sat three pairs of shoes in a row next to the hutch.

I decided to take a full shower, hair washing and all. The water pressure was glorious compared to the shitty pressure in my apartment. I had a lot of hair, or at least I used to. It had gotten thinner the last few months, clumps of hair collecting in the bathtub drain after a shower and in my comb after untangling my wet hair. Another result of my sickness, I suspected. I hoped I wasn't going bald.

I pulled on leggings and a tunic and shoved my poor, swollen feet into a pair of flats. I walked down the hall to the meeting room, where I'd seen a schedule posted. Women's meeting at 7:30 in the sacristy. I looked toward the wooden doors that led to the chapel. The sacristy was the room where priests got ready before Mass, the door that Jules had showed me yesterday. I returned to my room and finished getting ready. It was a little bit before 7.

Back in my room, the phone jangled, startling me. An unfamiliar voice reminded me of the 7:30 meeting, confirming the location. I checked myself in the bathroom mirror—still no makeup—then opened the drapes onto another gray day, but a little less bleak, with patches of blue showing between white, billowy clouds. I made my bed, lying down on it afterward, already wiped out from all the activity. Reluctantly I got up and left my room, walking a second time down the hall to the meeting room, this time to the chapel doors, hesitating before opening the heavy door to enter the hushed dimness. I let the chapel wash over me, my parents and paternal grandmother flickering through my mind. My grandmother had been devoutly religious, but quietly so, not in your face, preachy or evangelical. She went to Mass every day, getting there early to pray a full rosary before Mass. She embodied humility and kindness.

The chapel door opened, and in walked an attractive, fresh-faced young woman who introduced herself as Jamie, a counselor. She tried several keys before finding the one that opened the door. We walked through a small room into a larger room furnished with mismatched chairs. It was bright in there, with windows on two sides. Jamie adjusted the blinds and told me I could sit anywhere, taking a chair that seemed like the counselor chair, her back to a window. I sat down, one chair between us.

"How was your first night?" she asked. "Kind of exciting."

"It was. I didn't expect to spend it in the pantry."

Even in this unforgiving light, her skin was flawless.

"How do you feel about being here?" she opened. My eyes shifted to the window and a riveting view of a bridge spanning the Mississippi River, cars traveling in both directions. I wasn't quite ready to return her gaze.

"I have no choice. I have to be here. But this time, it's my choice." I looked at her. "I've been in treatment before."

The door creaked open and Kelli and the other woman, Katie, entered. Kelli, in full make-up again, sat across from me while Katie curled up in a comfy chair in front of the window. Kelli chattered incessantly about it being her last day. She was nervous and excited. She was worried about hearing from some guy. Jamie asked if she had changed her phone number and she breathlessly replied that that was one of the many things she had to do when she got out. Once I realized this meeting was going to be all about Kelli, I settled back and listened politely. The guy she was worried about was her dealer, and also her boyfriend. She was returning to work at her mother's restaurant, from which she had regularly stolen. She would be working to repair that relationship and her relationship with her husband and daughter. I was intrigued by her half laugh, lilting upward at the end of each sentence, even if the subject was serious.

"I'm afraid of what I'll do if I hear from my dealer," tee, hee, hee, hee? "I don't know if my husband can ever forgive me," tee, hee, tee, hee?

Jamie deftly steered the discussion to Katie, but the subject was still Kelli. She asked her how she felt about Kelli leaving, shifting to Katie without completely cutting out Kelli. Bravo, Jamie. In this all-revealing light, I realized how beautiful Katie was, and not without a twinge of comparative envy. She and I were going to be the only female residents after Kelli's departure. Her dark brown hair was long and luxurious, pulled back in a loose ponytail. Unlike Kelli, her makeup was subtle and minimal, smoky long-lashed eyes behind hip, rectangular eyeglass frames. Her demeanor and catlike posture transmitted aloofness, wariness. I did not foresee us becoming confidants. But I liked her.

"I'm gonna miss her," she answered in her low voice. "But I'm happy for her." She looked at me with those smoky eyes. "At least we have another female." High praise, indeed. But I knew what she meant. I smiled at her.

"Yeah, those guys are slobs," tee, hee, heh, heh? "And they're so immature," eh, heh, heh? "I'm glad you came when you did," eh, heh. "You picked the right place. It did wonders for me," heh, heh, tee, hee?

Meeting over, Jamie held me back to inform me we would be having a one-on-one either today or tomorrow. I returned to my room and finished unpacking, then wandered downstairs where there were a couple of guys watching TV. They said good morning and a couple of others in the dining room also greeted me. I wasn't ready to start conversations. When meeting new people, I started slow, cautiously, feeling my way around. This was the phase when people would say to me, "You're so quiet," in a tone that was just short of an insult, a tone that made me bristle. *I am quiet at first. So what?* Making small talk was exhausting.

I made my way slowly up the stairs and entered the big room where a couple of people were already seated. I chose a seat opposite of the head table as others drifted in. Sensing a presence, I turned and saw one of the older, tall guys standing behind me.

"You're in my seat," he said curtly.

I scrambled out of the chair, apologizing. *Another stolen chair!* And I hadn't even been there a full day yet.

"Those are my books," he added, pointing to some books on the table that I honestly hadn't noticed, just like the cigarettes. *I'm sick. Ok? I'm not real alert. I get it. This is your seat.* I moved a couple of chairs down, next to the football guy who this morning was wearing a baseball cap on backwards, not my favorite look. But he smelled good so that made up for it.

"This one's not taken," he said.

I sat down and the tables slowly filled. Sean next to the head table, good-looking Brent next to him. I heard Kelli before I saw her, walking in with Katie. They took seats around the corner from football guy.

"So you're leaving us today," he said to Kelli.

"Yes. But I'll be back for group," she replied.

Once again, we heard about Kelli's worrisome dealer and going back to work at her mom's restaurant. Jovial Chris sat down next to her, also excited about getting out. Karen entered, smiling serenely and taking her place at the center of the head table. She looked around, her gaze stopping at me, smiling softly, then moving on to Chris and Kelli.

"We have a lot of business this morning, so we better get started," she announced.

The meeting started with a reading from "Daily Reflections," but instead of reading from the corresponding day, they mixed it up, rotating through each month. Kelli volunteered to read. Her laughing tic mysteriously disappeared.

The next order of business was the drug schedule, the residents choosing either morning or evening for their daily dose, a clipboard passed around for everyone to indicate their choice. I decided to pick morning, getting it over with right away. Next came the good-byes, starting at one corner of the tables and moving around the perimeter. A common theme for Chris was his fun-loving nature and young-at-heartedness. For Kelli, it was her strength and how far she'd come. From the various comments, it sounded like she was quite a mess when she arrived. When it came to me, I echoed what others had said, adding that I wished I could have had more time with them. Then I felt Karen's eyes on me. *Uh oh.*

"We have a new member among us," she said. "Lisa, would you tell us a little about yourself and what brought you here?"

I started off strong, then quickly faltered, getting through "just the facts"— from Fort Dodge, living in Iowa City, been in treatment before—but I crumbled when I got to current events. I sobbed as I recounted trying to drink myself to death, being found on the kitchen floor and ending up in the hospital for a week. I recovered somewhat when I expressed my sincere hope to get better but ended on a quavering note. A Kleenex box appeared at my elbow.

"We're glad that you're here, Lisa," Karen said, "to help you get better. And now that Kelli's leaving, there's another female here for you, Katie," she added.

"That's great," Katie said. "We can watch something besides sports. All they want to watch is basketball."

"I like basketball," I said timidly.

As some of the guys cheered their approval, I looked at Katie, shrugging apologetically. Liking sports was a boon for attracting men, at least for the type of man I was attracted to. And I genuinely liked sports, especially football.

It was not a ploy. It impressed guys when you recognized a holding penalty or called for a tight end pass on second and goal. Drinking and watching football had been one of my favorite pastimes, especially in sports bars. I had met my second husband at the Big 10 Pub. I had met my first husband while bartending on a Badger football Saturday at another sports bar. Sports, bars, meeting men. For me, they had always been inextricably intertwined.

Chapter Eleven

E motionally exhausted from the community meeting, I went to my room until "Group," as it was called, which convened in the same room. I noticed two books on the desk in my room, having completely overlooked them before. One was a hardback version of the *Big Book*, the classic blue cover concealed with a jacket. The other was a trade paperback edition of "Daily Reflections." They must have placed them here when they brought up my luggage. I went to the bathroom, using the vanity to boost myself up from the toilet, then scrutinized myself in the mirror. I was puffy and wan from crying, and those gray roots were rearing their ugly little heads. I shrugged. *Oh well. I'm not here to meet boys.* I grabbed the books, carrying them like I was going to class, and walked back to the conference room. Only the jock guy was there, as I thought of him now instead of as the clean-cut guy. He had reacted when I said I liked basketball and I had overheard him saying he played football. I scanned the tables, looking for books, this time noting the seats with books in front of them. I spotted one with no books in front of the windows. Others started drifting in, the tall guy with the mustache, the older guy with the weird name, Marvin, Darvin. I still wasn't sure. Mustache guy walked behind me and took a seat at the end near the head table next to jock guy. Mervin sat right across from me as Sean, the moon-faced guy, sat down in the same spot as earlier, kitty-corner from me. Someone sat down next to me to my right, a smoker, the distinct smell reaching my nostrils. From introductions earlier, I remembered this was the guy from a small town near Guttenberg, north of here. But I couldn't remember his name. About my height, slight of build, balding with a wispy, graying mustache. I remembered him from last night, sitting apart from the others, a fellow quiet one. I was glad I chose this spot.

"Hi, I'm Dave," he said as I turned towards him.

The girls entered, taking seats across from Dave and me, Kelli explaining that she wasn't leaving until the afternoon while Chris was packing, getting ready to leave around noon. Someone I didn't recognize sat down at the head table, front and center. Had to be a counselor. He was youngish and wholesomely handsome, with light brown hair and a matching beard. He looked nice but I also got a sense you didn't mess with him. The older guy whose seat I had stolen meandered in and sat in his spot around the corner from Dave. Brent casually strolled in, aloof, sitting down next to Sean.

"So we have some people leaving and we have a newcomer," the counselor said, his eyes settling on me. "I'm Andrew, one of the counselors here."

"I'm Lisa." I paused, unsure if I was supposed to add the "I'm an alcoholic" part. I forged ahead. "And I'm an alcoholic. But I guess you already knew that...I mean, since I'm here and everything." A few chuckles eased my nerves.

"Welcome," replied Andrew, smiling at me.

The discussion revolved around the Twelve Steps, the necessity to check off each one, and how at The Abbey, they concentrated on the first three. Step One, we admitted we were powerless over alcohol, that our lives had become unmanageable. *Check.* I think not going into work and trying to drink myself to death qualified me for the unmanageable part. And yes, I am powerless over booze. I can't drink anymore.

Step Two, we believe that a Power greater than ourselves could restore us to sanity. A half check. To restore me to sanity, I had turned myself over to the U of I hospital staff, my sisters, and now The Abbey. But that wasn't the Power they were talking about. Andrew assured us this Higher Power could be anything, but they really wanted it to be God, a religious God. They could spin it however they wanted but I knew what they wanted. They wanted me to pray to God. My religious resistance twitched but I was too sick and tired to get worked up. At least for today. I put Step Two on hold.

Step Three was more of a directive: "Made a decision to turn our will and our lives over to the care of God, *as we understood Him.*" That part in italics was supposed to give you some leeway but then there was the word "Him" with a capital "H." What was up with that? I knew what they wanted. Unlike last time in treatment, I decided to keep my skepticism to myself. For now. I really did want to get better. I didn't have to overhaul the program.

It was time for lunch. I chose a seat, salad waiting, at the other table, populated by the older crowd—mustache man, guy whose seat I stole, Delvin or Marvin. I really needed to learn his name. Since they had heard my backstory, I decided to find out about them. But mustache man beat me to it. His name was also Dave, an attorney from Cedar Rapids, a beer, wine, and gin drinker. *I bet he's a Republican.* Dave had gone to law school at the University of Iowa so we discussed hangouts. Deadwood? I asked. No. Copper Dollar? No. Magoo's? No. George's? he asked. Yes! Best burgers! I exclaimed. He agreed, best burgers, classic dive bar ambiance. Maybe he was okay.

Next up was Dennis, the guy whose seat I stole, a doctor from Des Moines, wine and opiates. He spoke thoughtfully, a psych doctor who had easy access to pharmaceuticals. Clearly very intelligent, his manner reminded me of an ex-boyfriend who was older, a state legislator. It was with him that my daily drinking had begun.

Then there was Delvin, who was really Darvin, a tough-talking local, proudly rough around the edges, addicted to everything, booze, cocaine, hookers. What a crew! Sean and small-town Dave joined us as they brought out the entrée, chicken enchiladas, so the conversation switched to food. It looked and smelled so good but I knew I wasn't going to be able to eat it all. I pushed my unfinished salad aside and started on the enchiladas. Best burger talk veered to best pizza in their respective hometowns. I hated wasting food, especially really good food, but I couldn't eat anymore.

"You okay?" Mustache Dave asked.

"I'm fine. I just don't have an appetite yet."

"It'll come back," Dr. Dennis assured me.

After dumping my dirty dishes, I walked out to the TV room and again chose a seat on the couch under the windows. Football guy was on the couch facing the TV, ball in one hand, clicker in the other. Unsurprisingly, he was clicking away, channel after channel, fleeting glimpses of house flipping, bad movies and sports appearing, then disappearing on the screen. He settled on CNN, Trump's face large on the screen. I groaned.

"I voted for him," football guy said.

"So did I," added Katie, who was curled up across from me with her ever-present sketch book.

I felt myself bristling but I tamped it down. *You're here to get better, Lisa, not change the world.* "Well, at least you voted," I said evenly.

Lawyer Dave strolled up and stretched out in what I considered the prime chair–faux leather with a matching ottoman. Maybe he'd say who he voted for.

"Aww, turn to something else," he said.

Football guy obediently switched to ESPN, a safe choice, eliciting a frown from Katie, who continued her sketching.

"Meditation starts in ten minutes, Kyle," said Dave, addressing Football Guy. *Kyle. So that's his name. I will be steering clear of him.*

"Meditation turns you into a Democrat," I thought I heard Kyle say.

"Meditation turns you into a Democrat?" I repeated back to them.

"What?" Kyle gawked at me. He and Dave exchanged a look and chuckled.

"He said meditation turns you into a demon," Dave smirked. "But I like that. Meditation turns you into a Democrat."

I grinned sheepishly. I did that a lot, mishearing something and repeating it back incorrectly.

It was time for group. This one would be held right behind us, Kyle said, in the circle of chairs. I got up and moved to the circle, which gradually filled up. A slender, bald man joined the circle, nicely dressed in khakis and a blue button-down shirt. Another counselor, I guessed. He took a chair at the head of the circle and waited patiently for the stragglers. There was an air of post-lunch drowsiness, languid murmurs accompanied by barely stifled yawns. I felt it myself.

"How's everyone today?" the counselor asked, looking around the circle. Behind his glasses, I noted, he had nice eyes, dark blue rimmed by dark lashes. Thankfully, someone made a comment, his eyes moving away from me.

"I need a nap," Kyle said, stretching.

"I ate too much," said Lawyer Dave, rubbing his belly. There was a murmur of assent as I stifled a yawn. I felt a soft tap on my shoulder and turned to see counselor Jamie standing over me.

"Do you want to have a one-on-one?" she asked.

I didn't think I could say no, so I nodded and quietly left the circle. We walked up the stairs and she asked me about the morning. I felt weak going up the stairs. Usually I stopped at the top to rest when alone but now I pushed through, keeping my answers short. I wasn't sure where she was taking me, but when we walked through the chapel doors, I guessed it was the sacristy. Jamie once again fumbled with the keys then opened the door, then both of us chose the same chairs as earlier.

We started off with a synopsis of what had brought me here, a story that was becoming almost mechanical. We then moved onto my family history and upbringing, which had also become somewhat rote. Jamie asked when I started drinking and how I drank in those early years. I told her I started when I was fourteen, drinking beer before a dance the summer leading into my freshman year of high school, then not really drinking again until my junior year. Just beer on weekends, I said. A memory popped up of sneaking drinks while waiting for my friends to pick me up. My parents out for the evening, Martha up in her room, the dark kitchen, pulling out a bottle from the cupboard above the refrigerator, usually of peppermint schnapps, and surreptitiously taking a swig. If the wait was long enough, I'd take a second swig. Even then, I told Jamie, I was getting a head start on a night of drinking.

"Did I have the makings of an alcoholic back then?" I asked.

Jamie nodded ruefully. "I'm afraid so. It's a progressive disease."

I continued with the college years, which I thought were pretty typical for a college student. Sure, I drank to get drunk but who didn't? My shift from beer to vodka-lemonades started after college. Then I moved to Wisconsin, the perfect state to cultivate a drinking habit. My drinking tapered off, I told Jamie, when I got married and returned to school, finally getting a degree in journalism, but it was a constant thread throughout my 30s and 40s. About ten years ago, the drinking escalated when living with a fellow alcoholic.

Jamie stopped me there. "You were married and you lived with someone. Tell me about your relationship history."

I'd rather talk about my drinking history. "Well, I've been married twice. And divorced twice." I stopped to think. I really didn't want to start with how I lost my virginity to a gas station attendant who I met at a party. So I started where it really began, my first real relationship for me, one in which I felt a connection, one in which I had good sex for the first time, one in which I got my heart broke. It wasn't a "certified" relationship by any means. It was a three-year long hook-up. We didn't go on dates, he didn't meet my family—although he did meet Paula—he didn't come over to my place to watch TV. We ran into each other around Iowa City during my college years, having met him on my first Ragbrai. Kitty had been with me when we first met and she once described it as "....when Lisa met her match." Of course, I always wanted more than just hooking up. But I pretended I was cool with it.

"I guess my first real relationship was this three-year long hook-up with a guy I really cared about." I paused, feeling an emotional surge percolating. I didn't want to cry. "It was Brian, the guy who found me on my kitchen floor." And with that, I burst into tears.

"What is it?" Jamie asked. "Are you still in love with him?"

That shored up the floodgates, stopping me in mid-sob. *Was I?* I loved him, for sure. But not the "in love" way. I truly had made peace with everything. I adored his wife, he had a great marriage, one that I admittedly admired and envied. They were perfect for each other. I said as much to Jamie.

"But he found me! I feel awful about putting him through that, getting him involved!" The floodgates reopened.

"But just think if he hadn't," Jamie murmured.

The flood of tears gradually subsided. What a strange, bumpy circuitous route my relationship with Brian had taken. "I think I'm glad it was him."

I continued with my relationship history. After moving to Wisconsin, I met my first husband while bartending. He was a nice guy, funny, kind of a pushover, and we married because I wanted to be married. All my high school friends were getting married and this was a "certified" relationship. It ended after I met a hunky, charismatic Italian from Boston, also on Ragbrai. It would have ended eventually. After a short-lived long-distance relationship with the Italian came an ill-fated affair with an older married man, also handsome and charismatic. An affair sounds glamorous and romantic—martinis, secretive candlelit dinners, checking in to hotels. It wasn't. It was sordid and messy, a huge stressor. And it ended like I think most affairs with a married guy end—he stays with the wife. The next major one was my second marriage to another charismatic man who aggressively pursued me after I had broken it off. He wooed me back, then surprised me with a marriage proposal in front of friends at the University of Wisconsin spring football game. Finally, my last relationship with yet another charming, charismatic man who had swept me off my feet before becoming critical and mean. He disapproved of my drinking, even though he was a drinker, which led me to sneak it.

"Do you see the pattern here?" she asked. I shook my head, drawing a blank. "These men are like your father, charming, strong personalities."

How mundane. But I didn't think I was seeking a father figure and I said so to Jamie.

She agreed. "Not a father figure. But you're attracted to men *like* your father."

I pondered that. Although I had feared him, I admired his easy, joking way. Conking people on the head with the collection basket during mass. Teasing my friends when he answered the phone, telling them there was no one here by the name of Lisa. Chasing and tickling my religious grandmother until she giggled helplessly. I loved that side of him. Jamie was right.

"Why don't we end there," Jamie said. "We've covered a lot."

Exhausted, I left the sacristy, my mind whirling. I rejoined group as unobtrusively as possible. I half-listened. The topic was how alcohol affects men and women differently.

"What does Lisa think?" said a voice. I tracked its source, Dr. Dennis from Des Moines. "You're sitting there wide-eyed, staring. I want to hear what Lisa thinks."

I blinked a couple of times, taken aback. "I'm sorry. I don't really know what you're talking about and I'm kind of emotionally drained from my one-on-one."

There were some murmurs of sympathy from the circle and Dennis softened his tone.

"I just wanted to hear what you had to say," he said. "You seem like an intelligent person."

"Sure, sure," I replied. "But not today." I sat quietly for the rest of the session.

Chapter Twelve

Following group, we had half an hour before leaving for an outside AA meeting, so I went up to my room for a little alone time. I didn't feel like making nice in the TV room. After my brief respite, I got up and grabbed a gray zip-up wool cardigan given to me by the politician. For whatever reason, it brought me comfort. Down in the TV room, we gathered until summoned by the staffer who had been counseling Brent in the lobby. Brent hadn't been at group this afternoon and he wasn't here now. We filed through the lobby to the parking lot, where the big white van awaited us. I stood in line while the guys piled in. When it was my turn, I grabbed the door frame to boost myself up—and fell backwards, banging my shin on the floorboard, caught from behind by an unseen gentleman. How embarrassing! I couldn't even hop into a van, I was that weak. Sean reached out his hand. His grip, along with a couple of hops, got me in.

"I can't believe I can't even get into a van," I said to him.

"Hey, don't worry about it," he assured me. "When I first got here, I was weak as a kitten."

His words eased the embarrassment. The van filled and the door slid shut. Small town Dave, sitting shotgun, turned and asked if I was okay. I nodded and smiled. We were off, out of the parking lot into the streets of Bettendorf through a residential neighborhood, down a hill, past a church into another parking lot of a single-story cinder block building that looked like a community center. It was a community center. I hopped out carefully so as not to end up on the asphalt, and Sean gave me a hand. I followed the others down a dim hallway to a fluorescent-lit room furnished with three long tables and metal folding chairs. Plastic coffee pots dotted the white tabletops. A desk, set on a dais at the end of the middle table, was occupied by a beefy, bald man who looked like a bouncer. I expected him to growl at us to see our Abbey IDs. I sat at the front of the righthand table with our group, except for Sean and Dr. Dennis who took seats across the room under the Twelve Steps and Twelve Traditions banners. I scanned the room, populated mostly by older white men with a sprinkling of younger males. Most of the women filled the middle table, all ages represented. *Even at an AA meeting the boys sit with the boys and the girls sit with the girls.* A couple of the middle-aged guys were attractive—tall, balding with goatee facial hair. I checked for wedding bands—one did, one didn't, the one without probably had a girlfriend. I frowned. *Why do I do this? Why am I scanning the room for an attractive available guy?* I had already checked off the men at The Abbey, coming up empty because they were either married or I had no interest. *But why do I do it at all?* It was ingrained in me to look, to hope for a possibility. I hated it.

The bouncer gaveled the meeting to order, then read a passage from the blue book. Upon finishing the short passage, he gestured to the person at the end of Sean and Dennis' table to start the discussion. And the clichés began. "I love that reading." "I pray every morning to not take a drink." "Coming to these rooms keeps me sober." I paid closer attention when Sean and Dr. Dennis spoke. Sean was drinking the AA Kool-Aid while Dr. Dennis spoke about addiction as a disease that attacked both the mind and body. He spoke slowly and deliberately, again reminding me of my ex, the politician. The declarations wound around the room, up and down the tables, a few drunks passing. They were now at the far end of our table. Shoot! There were ten minutes left and it was going to get to us. Unease stirred. When it got to me, I passed. Trump voter Kyle and Clint the jock were both surprisingly thoughtful. *Hmmm. Who are these guys? Am I going to have to reevaluate them? Was my first impression wrong?* I hate it when that happens.

Meeting over, we hustled out to the van, a new worry added to my repertoire—can I get into the van? Durvin set out a step stool, Small Town Dave assuring me from the front seat that he needed to use it too. It really made a difference. I gushed my thanks—*How nice of them!*—and stepped up, plopping down in the front row.

"Who are we missing?" a voice behind me asked.

"Big Dave. He was talking to someone. He's always talking to someone after."

"Sean's still in there too. He was talking to someone."

"That's good that they're talking to someone," said staffer Teresa, our driver. "It's part of the fellowship."

"Not before dinner. No fellowship before dinner." I was pretty sure that was Kyle, who apparently was hungry. They all were. I heard impatient grumbling behind me. The alcoholics were restless. Sean emerged, hopped in the van and sat down next to me.

"Dave's still talking to someone," he reported, triggering groans from the back of the van. I smiled in the dark. These guys were funny.

The community center door opened, illuminating Dave, still talking to someone. He pointed to the van, shook the guy's hand and jogged over, seemingly oblivious to the hunger and impatience awaiting him. *Was he oblivious?* He slid open the van door and casually jumped in. "You waiting for me?" he asked, his obvious question met with loud groans.

"Come on! We're hungry!"

"Who were you talking to this time?"

"A couple of guys," Dave replied. "It's part of the fellowship, part of the cure."

"Not before dinner, it's not!"

The good-natured banter continued for the rest of the ride back. We beelined to the dining room where our salads awaited us, looking scrumptious. I chose a seat at the older guys table.

"Anybody need something to drink?" asked Big Dave as I was starting to think of him.

"Could you grab me a water?" asked Dr. Dennis.

"And a milk?" I added.

Dave delivered our beverages. I was liking him more and more. Did I have to reevaluate him too? The salad was so good, but I had to save room for the entrée. And here it was, a large chicken breast, juicy and golden, with roasted red potatoes and grilled vegetables. It looked and smelled so delicious, but I knew I couldn't eat it all. I just hated wasting food. A staffer, whom I did not recognize, led in a big guy, guiding him to the other table.

"Everyone, we have a newcomer," the staffer said. "This is Pat."

A chorus of greetings welcomed Pat, who looked dazed and out of it. *Did I look like that?* Unsteady on his feet, Pat was bloodied on the bridge of his nose and the side of his face. Either a fight or a fall, I surmised.

"He looks rough," Big Dave observed.

"Yeah, real rough," Derwood agreed.

"We all do when we come in," added Dr. Dennis. Conversation turned to tonight's activity, which was meditation.

"I'll pass," Big Dave said.

"It's not that bad," Little Dave said to me.

"It's lame," chimed in Kyle from the other table.

Sitting next to me, Katie silently picked out the red peppers in her salad, then the red peppers from her grilled vegetables. I think she missed her sidekick. I got up, scraped the uneaten food into the garbage, then walked through the TV room, where Clint was slouched on the couch, listening to cable TV music channels. Love songs. Maybe he was missing someone. On the way upstairs I passed a descending Brent carrying a book. He barely acknowledged me. *He really does come and go as he pleases. Good looking people always get away with shit.*

I entered my room, which was awash in blue from the parking lot lights. I walked to the windows to close the curtains, pausing to look out. There's the white van I couldn't get into. *There's the lights of the homes we drove by on our way to the meeting.* I wondered how many troubled souls were out there, drinking alone, feeling lost. I pulled the cord and lay down on my king-size bed in my little sanctuary. What I would have given to stay up here and read. I sighed and got up, trudging downstairs.

In the TV room, an older man was setting up for meditation, placing candles and bells on the floor at the edge of the circle of chairs where Sean and Pat, the new dazed guy, already sat. Clint, Kyle and Delvin were watching some cop reality show until the yogi, or whatever you call a meditation instructor, softly requested they turn off the television. After some grumbling, Kyle and Darvin left the room, the former tossing and catching his ever-present football. Clint, however, joined us, lying down on the floor, his feet propped up on a chair. He looked so comfortable but if I tried that, I'd need help getting up. Little Dave joined us, but his tall counterpart was nowhere to be seen. The yogi's name was Bill, a recovering alcoholic who had started meditation twenty years ago.

He settled easily into the lotus position on the floor and explained that there would be three intervals of ten minutes, the bell signaling the end of each segment. We started, Bill murmuring to concentrate on our breathing and to clear our minds.

"Should we be chanting or saying some word over and over?" This from Pat, the new guy.

"No," Bill softly replied. "We want to quiet our minds and just focus on our breathing."

"Should I have my eyes open or shut?" Again Pat.

"Whatever you're comfortable with," Bill evenly advised him.

Oh, Lord, Pat was gonna be one of *those* guys. The rest of the first set passed quietly, the silence broken only by a couple of murmured reminders from Bill to concentrate on our breathing. The segment ended with a gentle chime.

"Does it make a difference sitting Indian style?" Pat asked. "I just can't sit that way anymore."

"I'm able to because of years of yoga," Bill replied. "It's all about feeling comfortable so you're not thinking about how you're sitting."

The second set began, and I tried to focus on my breathing, but I never reached that state of complete mind clearing. I concentrated on each nuance of breathing—filling my lungs with air and holding it there, picturing the air in my lungs, then slowly releasing that air through my nose and mouth. I got close, but then I started thinking about not thinking, and about how much longer we had to go. Honestly, I just wanted it to be over.

After, I scurried out to the lobby and up the stairs to my room. I changed into my pajamas and crawled under the covers, stretching out over the great expanse of empty mattress, relishing its vastness. I set the radio alarm clock to 5:20 a.m., having chosen the morning shift for getting my meds, which were only dispensed until 6 a.m. They ran a tight ship at The Abbey. I doubled up the pillows for reading and opened the book. Starting a book took complete concentration. It was like meeting someone for the first time, tentative, careful, hopeful, some expectations but not too many, aware it may not go well. Those first pages were crucial in setting the pace of the relationship. Would it be a gradual, unhurried unfolding? Or an immediate attraction? This book was somewhere in between. Its graceful prose made me want to spend time with these characters, with these words. It was a successful introduction. I hated being disappointed whether it was a book, a movie, a person. Disappointment made me want to drink. I nestled in with my book until I got drowsy, then turned off the light. Before I fell asleep, the door slowly opened, a dark head silhouetted against the hall light. I shut my eyes until I heard the door quietly close. Bed check. Unlike at my first rehab, I was comforted by the check rather than annoyed.

I awoke in the morning before the alarm, still not sleeping deeply. It was 5:10. The halls were so quiet. Halfway down the stairs, I heard voices. I dutifully sat on one of the chairs outside the office; muffled voices came through the door. It opened, warm light spilling out onto the hallway floor. Derwood emerged.

"Good morning," he said.

"Good morning."

"Hey, you got a customer out here!" he called back into the office.

I entered, joining a tall, slender, dark-blonde staffer who introduced herself as Jane. She was about my age. She opened a file cabinet drawer and lifted out a plastic container filled with pill bottles. I'd sat in this same chair during my assessment, but hadn't noticed the filing cabinet nor the examining table. While Jane continued to rustle through the containers, I squinted at the one on the examining table, trying to read the name on the post-it note attached to it. Without my glasses, I couldn't do it. Jane returned that container to the top drawer.

"Not there," she confirmed, opening the middle drawer.

She finally found mine and set it on the examining table. There was a lot of shit in there, anti-depressant, vitamins, antihistamine. Jane set my daily dose on the desk, the assortment of pills contained in a mini plastic cup like the ones used for ketchup at fast food restaurants. She handed me a mini bottle of water and I began swallowing the pills, one at a time with a pause between each. I got up to leave but Jane stopped me, gesturing toward a three-ring binder on the examining table. My name was at the top of the page, along with a medication name and the dates of my stay. I signed next to today's date, then turned the page to the next pill, doing the same for each medication. Then there was one more thing.

"We need a urine sample," said Jane, handing me a small wide-mouthed plastic jar with a screw-off cap.

"What?" I asked, incredulous. "Why?"

"It's policy. I'm sure it will be clean. We do it for everyone when they first come in."

I was annoyed. "I don't have to go right now."

"Take it with you and bring it back after you go."

I tried to tamp down my irritation, but the feeling of being imprisoned returned. Out in the lobby, I checked the daily schedule. Bettendorf meeting at 7:30. It wasn't even six o'clock yet and I was hungry. I strolled through the TV room, casually holding the pee cup in my hand, not really expecting to run into anyone. I was mistaken. There were Melvin and Little Dave, watching Fox news. I curled my fingers around the cup and smiled at them.

"There's coffee ready," Darvin said. I continued to the dining room where it was dim and quiet, smelling of freshly brewed coffee. I was normally a coffee drinker, but my beat-up body just wasn't ready for it. I plucked a breakfast bar from the basket on the counter, then pulled a Diet Pepsi from one of the refrigerators. Upon return through the TV room, where Derwood and Little Dave were still watching Fox news, I held the breakfast bar and pee cup in one hand, the Diet Pepsi in the other, scurrying quickly past them. Once back in my room, I sprawled out on the bed for a while, then showered and dressed—leggings and tunic—lamenting again my swollen feet and ankles. I scrutinized myself in the mirror, then decided to try mascara again. Even with wet hair, my gray roots taunted me. I turned away from the mirror.

There were fewer people at the Bettendorf meeting, though some familiar from the night before. We sat in our usual spots. Big Dave sat apart from us. He was such a schmoozer. Across from me, Katie pulled out her notebook and started sketching. I was surprised to hear some insightful comments. Meetings in Fort Dodge had consisted of the same guys going up to the podium, spouting the same clichés and stories meeting after meeting, not a lot of insight. At my turn to share, I passed again, not trusting myself to speak without crying.

Back at The Abbey, we gathered upstairs for the community meeting. Everyone sat in the same place as yesterday. Karen entered and took her place, front and center, surveying the room as the rest straggled in. Our eyes met and she smiled softly. Little Dave took his seat next to me, smelling of cigarette smoke. The odor was unpleasant, and maybe I was more sensitive to it because I was still unwell. I was too new and Little Dave was too nice for me to say anything about it.

"Good morning," said Karen, silencing the group. Sean volunteered for the daily reading, then it was time to introduce the new guy. Pat was dazed and a bit incoherent as he described what brought him here. He was from Des Moines, just went through a nasty divorce, had been sober for ten years and had tried to kill himself. He joked about looking beat up, which wasn't from a fight. Drinking at home, he had fallen. Sounded familiar.

Later on, we learned more about Pat, how he hated AA, hated the Catholic church, and hated his wife. Andrew, the morning group counselor, pointed out how dangerous resentments are, drinking at someone, consumed by the hate, the importance of letting go.

"I'll let the cunt go," Pat muttered, "right over a cliff."

A nervous tittering followed.

"Looks like we have some work to do on resentments, Pat," said Andrew, unflappable. More tittering, this time less subdued.

"I guess I do," said Pat grinning. He could laugh at himself, a good sign. Any unease in the room dissolved.

Lunch was delicious again, and again I was unable to finish it. Dr. Dennis and Pat talked about Des Moines stuff, discovering shared experiences. After Dr. Dennis left, Big Dave turned to me.

"His only son died of an overdose."

"Oh no! How awful!" I exclaimed.

"I've got two sons. I can't even imagine it."

Learning someone's backstory was so important. In my mind, Dr. Dennis had shifted from a guy who put me on the spot to a father who had lost a son. He had shifted from a blustery intellectual to a man in unspeakable pain. After that, I was more tolerant when he went off on a medical tangent in his slow, deliberate way. I now bristled when the younger set rolled their eyes at him. Yes, he rambled and used big medical terms, but that was his way of contributing. He never talked about his son but did often mention how easy it was to get pharmaceuticals.

That afternoon in group, we were joined by another new resident, also from Cedar Rapids. Upon introduction, Jesse told us his drug of choice was booze and his drinking had gotten to the point where he was drinking in his vehicle during his lunch hour at work. His complexion ruddy, Jesse had the closely cropped hair of a balding man and what we called growing up, a lazy eye. I placed him in his 30s, a fast talker with a whiff of a gay vibe.

After Jesse's introduction, Mark, the counselor with the nice eyes, turned to me. "What about you, Lisa. What's your story?"

"But Jesse was telling his, he was talking...." I stammered, taken aback.

"Jesse, do you have anything more to add?" Mark asked.

"No, I'm done."

"Your turn," said Mark, grinning mischievously. This counselor was soft-spoken yet keen. The kindness of his eyes belied their sharpness. I had overheard Katie talking about him before meeting him. "He's the bald one," she said, shuddering. I thought Katie's expectations must have been very high, like super model high. I had seen a photo of her buff, hunky husband, whom she described as critical and controlling. Over the years, my expectations for men had been whittled down to fairly attractive and kind with a sense of humor. The group was waiting for me.

"It's pretty typical," I said. "I started in high school and continued through my adult years. And it got out of control to where I ended up in the hospital." There, neat and concise.

"Did your parents drink?" Mark asked.

"Yes. Socially, like when they went out to eat with their friends or get together to play cards." A beat. "My dad was abusive, not to me, but to my mom. We were all afraid of him." I had exhaustively gone over this so many times I now had a Cliff Notes version.

Mark chose a new line of questioning. "Have you ever been married?"

"Yes. Twice. I met them both in bars." Several people nodded.

"Do you think your dad's abuse led to your drinking?"

I shrugged. "I don't know. I don't think so. Maybe. But my four sisters didn't become alcoholics. Just me."

"Some people feel things more deeply than others."

I wasn't sure I agreed with that. My sisters were all very passionate, headstrong women.

"Do you have kids?" Katie asked.

"No."

Big Dave followed up. "Did you want kids?"

"No." I paused a moment before elaborating. "I never felt the tug. But during my second marriage, I almost caved." What I left unsaid was that I couldn't imagine not drinking for nine months. But that was only part of it. I've never really liked kids. I don't gush over babies and I don't find the antics of young children adorable. I think if you want to have kids, you're acutely aware of it and if you don't, you're reluctant to talk about it. I never felt like there was something wrong with me, but I knew there was a lot of judgment.

"That's okay," said Big Dave, the equivalent to a pat on the head.

"It's changed, but I know there's still a stigma about not wanting to have kids."

"Oh, there is," Big Dave agreed.

"And about being single, especially for a woman," I added, met by nods of agreement around the circle. "Being alone and lonely was definitely a factor in my drinking. Especially near the end."

Mark looked satisfied and Pat picked up the thread, addressing the loneliness after his divorce. The rest of the hour passed quickly.

After group, Jesse and I watched yoga but declined to participate. We watched like an old couple watching the dancers at a wedding. The yoga instructor and another trim, healthy-looking woman unfurled rubber mats; the latter was Jo, another counselor. Pat lumbered up, wearing jeans, and stood at the edge of the dance floor. "Are you joining us?" the instructor asked Pat.

"I am," Pat said. "At least I'm going to try."

Pat unfurled his mat while the two women stretched out on theirs, two graceful swans in spandex and a gentle giant in denim. It was soon apparent that Jo was experienced, easily moving into and holding the beginner level poses, Pat grunting and bumbling through each one, laughing when he couldn't quite stretch a certain way. He apologized profusely when he passed gas, and the yogi assured him that happened all the time. I admired his enthusiasm and lack of self-consciousness, plodding and sweating without complaint through the entire session, his face alarmingly red. Although the yogi said they were beginner poses, I knew with my weakened condition that I would be challenged.

"What do you think?" Jesse asked.

"I think it's harder than it looks." But I wanted to try. Jo and the yogi helped up a panting and grinning Pat.

"Next time I'm not wearing jeans," he gasped.

"I think that's a good idea," the yogi said, grinning and glowing.

Later that evening during the van ride to the AA meeting, Pat rehashed his yoga session. "It's harder than it looks. Double dog down...."

"Double doggy style down?" Derwood joked.

"Yeah, double doggy style down," Pat chuckled, then caught himself. "Sorry, ladies."

"I don't care," Katie replied.

"I'm not easily offended," I added.

"You heard it guys," Darvin exclaimed. "Lisa's not easily offended."

"And one of the ladies doing it is a counselor," Pat continued. "Jill, Jane, Jan..."

"Jo," I interjected.

"Oh God, Jo!" Big Dave groaned.

"Oh, no, Jo!" piped in Kyle.

"What's wrong with Jo?" Pat asked. "She was nice."

"We got in trouble with her in art therapy," Big Dave explained. "It wasn't pretty."

"What happened?" Pat asked.

"She yelled at Dave," Kyle said.

"Not just me!" Dave exclaimed. "She yelled at everybody."

I turned to Katie, sitting next to me.

"What happened?"

"They were messing around and pissed her off," replied Katie, boiling it down in her straight-up, no nonsense way. I did not ask her to elaborate. During dinner, it came up again.

"Is it art therapy tonight?" Big Dave asked.

"Moosic thapy," said Derwood with his mouth full.

"Good. I like music therapy. She's nice."

"What did you do to Jo in art therapy?" I asked.

"What did we do, Kyle?" replied Big Dave, over his shoulder to the other table.

"Nuthin'," Kyle answered, mouth also full. He swallowed. "We were just talking and joking around, and she yelled at us. She's a bitch."

"I didn't realize she was a counselor," explained Big Dave to us newcomers at the table. "I thought she was someone who just came in for art therapy. Like the meditation guy."

"And the music girl," Derwood added.

"So, it was like she was the substitute teacher," I said, "and you took advantage of her."

"That's exactly what it was like," Big Dave agreed, grinning at me. "Are you a Catholic girl, Lisa?"

"I was *raised* Catholic," I clarified. "Twelve years of Catholic school."

"St. Edmond's?" he asked. "Did you go to St. Edmond's?"

"Yes! You know St. Ed's?"

"Sure. We played against you guys."

"What school?"

"Cedar Rapids Xavier."

"Oh," I nodded. "I don't really remember playing against Xavier. Carroll Kuemper, yes. Des Moines Dowling, yes. Sioux City Heelan. But not Xavier."

"We're gonna start going to Mass Saturday nights, aren't we Derwood?" Dave said to Darvin. I smiled. The nickname was starting to stick. To me. "Do you wanna go with us?"

"No," I answered flatly.

"Ah'll goo," said Pat through a mouthful of food.

"Alright!" Big Dave exclaimed. "We got another one!"

"You said you hate the Catholic Church!" I said, calling out Pat.

"I do," he said, still chewing. "But I'll take whatever help I can get."

We all laughed. But Dave wasn't done with me.

"Saturday, Lisa. We're going Saturday."

"That's nice, Dave. I'm not going."

Music therapy devolved into laughter therapy, which really is the best therapy of all, so I guess it morphed. It wouldn't have happened if Angela, the music therapist, hadn't been such a good sport. She was bright and cheerful and very pretty. She sparkled. She was also fat. I hated myself for noting it, but Angela seemed like someone who was comfortable with her size. She was upbeat and positive. I longed to not be so judgmental.

Music therapy featured hand bells—hollowed, square cylinders made of heavy metal with a clapper inside. Angela divided us into tonal groups of two and three. The Daves and Delvin made up one group; Pat, Kyle and Clint made another, Jessie and I made the third, and Sean and Dr. Dennis were absent. Katie declined to participate, and instead curled up in a blanket on the couch next to us, sketching away. Everyone got one bell except for me—I got two. As soon as the instruments were in our hands, a cacophony commenced.

"Oh my God! Stop!" Katie cried from the couch, and the clanging diminished.

Angela explained that each individual had a different note. I had a D and a G.

"I have an A for athlete," announced Kyle.

"You're not an athlete," Clint joked. "Just because you walk around here with a football..." Kyle good-naturedly punched Clint in the arm, and Clint returned the punch.

"More like A for asshole," chimed in Big Dave, and Kyle gave him the finger.

"I got a C for..." Derwood caught my eye.

I looked at him quizzically. "Cat?"

"Yeah, cat."

Delvin and I grinned at each other.

Angela patiently instructed us to keep our bells silent until she pointed to a particular group, at which point that group should shake their bells twice in quick succession. She demonstrated, shaking her bell with two measured strokes of her arm. This naturally led to a second round of noisy chaos.

"Oh my God," cried Katie.

"Come on Katie," said Big Dave, twisting around in his chair, shaking his bell at her. "Don't you want to join us?"

"Nooooooooo," she wailed.

We were finally ready to make some music. Angela put us through some practice rounds. The guys were really concentrating. Something warm and soothing swirled inside me, like a balm. We were ready for a song, Angela declared, and the group leaned forward in anticipation. The hesitant notes of "Old McDonald" began, Angela directing and pointing like an orchestra conductor. At first, it was a hodgepodge of clangs and dings, then gradually the hodgepodge turned into a recognizable tune.

"That was pretty good," said Big Dave, grinning.

"It really sounded like a song!" I exclaimed.

"Let's do another one!" Kyle said.

Beaming proudly, we eagerly waited for Angela's cue. Even Little Dave looked excited. This time, the clangs and dings transformed into a recognizable tune much sooner.

"That was pretty good," said Katie grudgingly from the couch.

"I think I'm getting the hang of these dongs!" Pat exclaimed.

Sheepish looks passed around the hushed circle. Then the giggling started.

"You're hanging on to your dong?" Kyle started.

"You just now got the hang of your dong?" Big Dave added.

"Don't let go of your dong, Pat!" Derwood piled on.

Even Little Dave contributed. "My dong's doing pretty good!" he said, giggling.

"You guys and your dongs!" I added.

"Oh my God," Jesse murmured.

Somehow, we managed to get through another song.

"My dong's getting better!" Kyle exclaimed.

"My dong's better than your dong!" Big Dave countered.

"My dong's bigger than your dong!" chimed in Pat, making the inevitable size comparison.

"They're all the same size!" I couldn't help pointing out, laughing harder than I had in a very long time. I had a feeling the same could be said of the others. Little Dave rocked and howled. Clint wiped tears from his eyes. Delvin was speechless. Katie peered over the back of the couch, shoulders shaking. To Angela's credit, she allowed the laughter and silliness to flow. It was, after all, music *therapy*. A staffer stuck her head into the room.

"What is going on in here?" she asked.

"We're playing with our dongs!" Pat declared.

And with that, music therapy ended, the group convulsing with fresh peals of laughter.

That evening, I hung out in the TV room until almost ten o'clock, our designated bedtime, watching bad television with the others. The stirring inside me from music therapy remained, comforting me. Later, as I laid in my king-size bed, listening to the muffled, distant voices, the soft thuds of doors closing, a smile crept its way onto my face.

Chapter Thirteen

The next morning at the community meeting, I met a new counselor. He was called Eff Jeff because he was fast and loose with the f-word. He sat at the head table next to Karen with a mischievous grin on his face. He was cute. I squinted at his left hand to see if there was a ring. There wasn't. With his healthy head of salt and pepper hair and handsome laugh lines, I guessed him to be about my age, maybe a little older. But definitely young at heart.

"How was your first night?" Karen asked Jesse. "Lisa had a thunderstorm her first night."

"There wasn't a storm," Jesse answered carefully, "but it was interesting."

We all started giggling.

"Music therapy was great!" said Big Dave.

Little Dave and I shared a glance and a giggle.

"What the fuck happened at music therapy?" Eff Jeff asked.

"We were playing with our dongs," explained Little Dave matter-of-factly.

"You were playing with what?" asked Karen, befuddled.

"Dongs," Eff Jeff repeated. "He said *dongs*." Somehow, repeating it made it funnier.

Karen looked around the room at these laughing, crying drunks and addicts. "I don't think I want to know."

"I do," piped in Eff Jeff.

"Of course, you do," murmured Karen, unsuccessfully fighting a smile.

"We had these hand bells," broke in Big Dave, using his lawyerly voice. "And we actually got quite good at it...until someone called them dongs."

"It was Pat," I clarified.

"And we were off," concluded Clint. He had an infectious giggle. I liked it when someone laughed with their whole body.

Eff Jeff joined our laughter while Karen smiled demurely. She knew when to rein it in. "Alright, let's get to the daily meditation. What month are we on?"

We quieted and opened our books, but the happy spell lingered throughout the meeting like cigarette smoke, only pleasant and sweet.

Led by Eff Jeff, the topic at morning group was triggers. Stress, loneliness, depression, boredom. Or an oldie but goodie: "I just like to get fucked up," Derwood said.

Though she appeared disinterested, Katie really did pay attention, even though she was constantly scribbling. Her infrequent comments were always thoughtful. "Fear," she said without missing a pen stroke. Nods and murmurs of assent followed.

"That's a fucking huge one," Eff Jeff agreed.

"Fear of failure," Kyle said.

"Fear of being alone," Pat added.

"Fear of living," Delvin added.

The discussion turned to how we drank. Alone? In the morning? At work?

"Adderall all day, every day," Kyle said. "And I used the intense kind so I could get high faster."

"How did you end up here?" Eff Jeff asked. "Did you OD?"

"Yeah. I thought I was having a heart attack. I ended up in the emergency room."

"Adderall," said Big Dave, shaking his head. "I don't get it."

I nodded in assent. I didn't get the allure of opiates either. I'd tried Vicodin once and it did nothing for me, but I had also been drinking.

"Now that I think of it," Kyle continued, "there's some Adderall in my couch. I spilled a bottle and it went behind the cushions."

"Dude, you gotta get those out of there before you go home," Eff Jeff warned. "Even if you have to rip that couch apart, you gotta get those out of there."

Kyle nodded. "Yeah, just knowing they're there, not good."

Pat lived with his teenage son and drank nightly until he passed out on his living room couch. He'd been sober for ten years but had started drinking again after his wife left him and "hooked up with that AA fucker." He tried to kill himself around Christmas. With suicide, I always wanted to know the method. A celebrity's suicide is eventually made public but when it was an acquaintance, the only way to find out was to ask. Apparently in rehab, this wasn't considered indelicate.

"How'd you do it?" Darvin asked.

"Pills and vodka," Pat replied.

"Hawkeye vodka?" Big Dave asked. "Was it Hawkeye vodka?" Ah, Hawkeye vodka, the favored brand of working-class Iowans.

"Usually that's what I drank," Pat answered. "But I upgraded to Phillips for this." The drinkers in the room nodded knowingly.

"I upgraded last time, too," I chimed in.

"Tito's?" Big Dave asked.

"No. Smirnoff."

It was strange, talking so casually about suicide, yet not strange. An outsider would probably find this discussion appalling. With this group, it was comfortable and ordinary.

Eff Jeff turned to me. "How did you drink, Lisa?"

"I was a social drinker. I drank *with* people. But I did my real drinking at home," I explained. "I'd meet people at George's, have a couple of beers. But I couldn't wait to get home to my real drinking."

"How did you feel on your drive home from George's?" Eff Jeff asked. He opened up the question to the group. "What do you think she was feeling on that drive home?"

"Impatient," Kyle offered.

"Excited," Katie added. "Anticipation."

Once again, Katie nailed it. I hadn't thought about it before, but on that drive home from George's, or from work, I couldn't wait to start drinking. Something else occurred to me. "And sometimes anxious. Anxious that I wouldn't have enough to get me through the night."

Several heads nodded. Eff Jeff explained the intertwining of the psychological with the physiological, deferring to Dr. Dennis for the technical explanation. Dennis detailed how the neurological impulses contributed to the cravings. As he methodically continued, I bristled at the eyerolls and seat shifting, hoping he was oblivious. I had been spending time with him and had really grown to like him. He was really smart, but not arrogant. We'd been sitting next to each other in the TV room between group sessions and in the evening, talking about old movies, trips we'd taken, and our favorite authors. Sure, he spoke slowly, deliberately, using big words. But that was his contribution to the group. He never spoke about losing his son. And I didn't ask.

At lunch, Eff Jeff circled the two tables, joking around while eyeballing our plates. "You don't like the salad? Sure, I'll take that." "You're only gonna eat half your sandwich? I can take that off your hands." He scampered off with a full plate and returned with an empty one, filling it with more unwanted scraps. At least all that food wasn't going to waste. "Does he do that all the time?" I asked our table.

"Yep," Darvin replied, still chewing. "He takes it home."

"It's good food," garbled Pat, mouth full. "Why waste it?"

"He probably doesn't get paid that much," Big Dave added. I looked at the untouched half of my Reuben, then got Eff Jeff's attention, pointing to my plate. "I'm not gonna be able to eat it."

"I'll be right over," he grinned.

We covered a lot of territory that afternoon. Dennis got real. Clint opened up. Pat reopened up. It started with Eff Jeff, who warmed up the group like a comic warming up an audience before the main show. He told us about the depths of his addiction and where it had led him—multiple rehab stints, hospitals, jail—and painted a colorful, lively picture of very dark events. Eff Jeff had been a drug dealer. Pills, powder, pot, he did it and he sold it. He had transported drugs up from Florida and been jailed in Dade County and Cook County.

He got serious. "This disease kills, if you didn't already realize that," he said, somberly. "I'm one of the lucky ones. My friend Tammy is not so lucky. She's dying from this fucking thing." The room quieted as Eff Jeff told us about Tammy. Now bedridden and helpless, she had been in and out of treatment, in and out of AA, but she just couldn't kick it and had decided to stop trying.

Hospice wouldn't take care of her because they didn't recognize her condition as a disease. So, Eff Jeff was taking care of her, making her as comfortable as possible. And he did that by giving her vodka. Her body so wracked and weak, she was unable to lift a glass to her lips. If they didn't give her small doses of vodka, he explained, her emaciated body would be tortured.

"This disease kills," he stated flatly, his voice trembling.

A swell of emotion filled me as I thought of myself passed out on the kitchen floor, a glass of vodka inches away from my outstretched hand. My eyes filled with tears, and my lips trembled. I covered my mouth.

"It killed my son," stated Dennis, breaking the hushed silence. "I found him in his room right before Christmas. He'd been sober for seven months. Needless to say, that led to my tailspin."

In the same deliberate, unhurried tone he used when giving a scientific explanation, Dennis described the culmination of that tailspin. He'd been working from home because it had become increasingly difficult to be at work and not use. I nodded—that's why I had stopped going to work. I had become so physically dependent, I couldn't make it through the day without a drink. Dennis described how he was in his office in the basement drinking red wine, rationalizing that drinking wine wasn't really drinking. After going upstairs to the kitchen for a refill, he stumbled coming back down, tumbling to the bottom, the glass of wine flying out of his hand and spraying the wall. It looked like a crime scene, he said. His wife came home to find him hysterically and drunkenly scrubbing the wall. They called The Abbey shortly thereafter. The room was quiet, but then an unexpected source broke the silence.

"I was so fucked up at the end, I was picking at my face until it bled," said Clint, who had never spoken specifically about himself. "I'd been up for two days doing coke. I'd lost everything, my job, my house, my fiancé. I took a picture of myself with my bloody face and sent it to my sister. That's how I ended up here."

"Rock fucking bottom," Eff Jeff commented. "We've all been there."

"Mine usually land me in jail," Derwood said. "I've had so many."

"How many times have you been in rehab?" Big Dave asked.

Darvin's brow furrowed as he mentally checked them off. "This is number nine. It gets worse every time you go back out there. Next time, I won't make it."

That evening, art therapy with Jo took place without incident, perhaps because Big Dave wasn't there. With alt rock tunes playing softly, we drew pictures of how we wanted our lives to look after we left The Abbey. Good-looking Brent graced us with one of his cameo appearances. He seemed to get along better with the female counselors. Women, including myself, are just as susceptible to a pretty face as men are. Brent caught me staring at him—he probably catches people staring at him all the time—so I quickly looked down at my drawing, which was of the outside of my apartment, flowers growing, a birdfeeder hanging, the backside of me in shorts and tennis shoes heading out for a run. I wanted to be healthy again. I wanted to enjoy simple things again like birds and flowers. Was it possible?

After art therapy, Big Dave appeared in the TV room. He asked how art therapy went, a sneer in his voice.

"It was okay," Kyle said. "We didn't get yelled at."

Kyle could draw. When we had shared our sketches with the group, I was quite impressed with his. He had whipped it up effortlessly, a cosmic landscape of swirling colors and bright lights, yet with darkness lurking. It reminded me of an album cover from the 70s. Katie's was impressive, too, but that was expected; hers was a colored pencil sketch of her and her young son walking on a beach. In the TV room, Kyle paced nervously. "Hey, where's my ball?" he asked. "I thought I left it on the couch."

Big Dave and Derwood exchanged a sly look, and a knot of disquiet pinged in my gut. I watched with growing unease as Kyle scoured the room. I caught Big Dave's eye and shook my head at him.

"I found it!" announced Kyle, triumphantly lifting the ball over his head, then tossing it up and down with one hand. It had been hidden behind the curtain on the windowsill. Dave and Derwood exchanged another glance, which Kyle caught, too. He left the room, tossing his football. My disquiet dissolved.

The next morning, I shuffled down for my daily meds, then returned to my room with a breakfast bar and a Diet Pepsi. I was developing a morning routine. After getting dressed, I opened the curtains, starting with the window overlooking the shrub, the sky clear and brilliantly blue. And there she was in the shrub, a female cardinal, hopping from branch to branch. Tears filled my eyes. Years ago, Paula had told me about a legend where cardinals represent loved ones who are deceased. And now, here was my Mom, female cardinal Phyllis. I stood motionless, watching her tilt her head from side to side, hopping to another branch before flying off. I stood there a moment, still crying before moving to the next window. I pulled the cord, opening the curtain, and there she was again, on the edge of the portico. I held my breath, hearing a faint chirp from her bright red beak through the glass. And then, there he was, my Dad, joining my mother, flying in and landing next to her. Cardinal Augie hopped to the edge of a puddle, dipping his red beak for a drink. They tilted their heads at each other, their own private communique, then flew off. I remained at the window, stunned, wishing I could share this with my sisters.

I carried the cardinal visit around with me all day, a golden nugget to hold close, warming my soul. I was unwilling to share it with the group because a) I'd cry, b) I didn't know if they had ever heard of the cardinal legend, and c) I just didn't want to. Sharing it might dispel the magic.

That afternoon in group, Jo pulled me out. I reluctantly got up from my chair—Pat was going off again about his ex-wife leaving him for some AA guru—but I had no choice. We walked up the stairs to the sacristy. Jo took the counselor seat, her back to the windows, and I sat facing her. When she asked, I rehashed the Cliff Notes version of my drinking history, and then Jo asked what had brought me here. My eyes drifted to the window overlooking the bridge spanning the mighty Mississippi.

"I tried to drink myself to death," I said matter-of-factly.

"And how do you feel now, being here?" she asked.

My eyes drifted back to the bridge, drawn to that structure's engineering magnificence, a Midwestern Golden Gate. "It's different this time. Rehab, I mean. Last time wasn't my choice. This time was. I mean my sisters would've made me go anyway, but this time *I* knew I had to go."

"What else is different this time?"

Again, my eyes strayed to the bridge, to the ever-streaming line of cars crossing it. They returned to meet Jo's steady gaze. "I'm open to it this time. I have to be. Even the Higher Power thing. That was a big hindrance the first time."

"It's a big roadblock for a lot of people."

"Things have been happening," I murmured, thinking about the cardinals.

"What kind of things?"

"Like right when we drove up and saw that golden dome." I went on to explain Martha's and my reaction to seeing it when we first arrived. "And then this morning...Have you ever heard about cardinals representing loved ones who have died?"

Jo had not, but I forged ahead anyway. The tears resurfaced and flowed as I spoke.

"They found me. My mom and dad found me."

"Your Higher Power is speaking to you," Jo said softly. "And you're listening."

Back in group, Pat was *still* railing about his ex-wife and the AA guru, now about how they lived down the street from him and he sometimes saw the guy in his bathrobe taking out the garbage. Big Dave took the words right out of my mouth. "Why don't you move?" he asked. "And what was going on in your marriage before all this happened?"

Before Pat could respond, Jules walked in with a tall, young man. And I mean young. He looked like a sickly teenager, pale and fragile. His name was Dan and he silently took his seat as we welcomed him.

"Welcome Dan," said Counselor Mark. "What brings you to us, and from where?"

"Iowa City. Heroin overdose," he responded flatly.

I looked quickly at Dennis, who was staring intently at the newcomer.

He looked so tired, with dark, purplish circles under his eyes, stark against his delicate, pale complexion, his lips full and rosy. I made a snap judgment: he was a pretty, spoiled college boy who dabbled in drugs out of boredom and to spite his parents. I wondered how old he was.

After group, some of us stayed in the TV area, where I quickly snagged the comfy chair with the ottoman. Dan lay down on the couch across from me, Big Dave took a chair next to him, and Kyle sat on the main couch, clicking through channels until finally settling on ESPN, where the football draft was being discussed. Derwood sat down next to me in the second most comfy chair. I scooted closer so we could share the ottoman.

"What happened to you, man?" Kyle asked, remote in one hand, football in the other. "You OD'ed?"

"Yeah, I was with a friend in his car shooting up and I started to seize,"

Dan replied calmly. "He called 911 and took off. They got to me just in time."

"Some friend," Dave muttered.

"He was scared," Dan said in the same flat tone. "I get it."

"Did they give you Narcan?" Kyle asked, tossing the football from hand to hand.

"Yeah. It was my third time."

"You've OD'ed three times?" exclaimed Dave.

"It happens a lot," Kyle said.

"What happens a lot?" asked Clint, intercepting the ball from Kyle.

"ODing multiple times on heroin," replied Kyle, grabbing the football back.

"Happens all the time," Clint said. Then to Dan, "Is that what happened to you, dude?" Dan nodded. "Glad you're here, man, glad you're here. Hey Dave, you want a chew?"

"Yeah." Dave visibly perked up. "I thought you were out."

"Close. I think I got enough to get us through tomorrow."

Dave pinched some tobacco from the tin Clint offered him and stuck it in the side of his mouth, Clint then doing the same. *How sweet, chewing tobacco together.* I had never understood the allure of chewing tobacco. Smoking it, yes. Chewing it, no. Once Kitty and I had tried Skoal Bandits, those cute little tobacco pouches, and we had both ended up puking. Nope, I didn't get it.

"That reminds me," said Dave, adjusting the wad in his cheek. "My wife is getting some stuff from Walgreens. Do you need anything, Lisa?"

"Cigarettes for me!" Derwood interjected. "Carton of Marlboro Lights."

"Yeah, I know, and Copenhagen chew for Clint. Karen's gonna love picking up this shit. Do you need anything girly, Lisa?"

"Let me think about it." My gray roots were really bugging me, but I wasn't quite comfortable enough with Big Dave to request hair color.

After dinner, I returned to the dining room for a bottle of water, and found Delvin, Kyle, and Dennis still sitting in there and laughing hard. Dennis was laughing so hard he was crying and pounding the table. "What is going on?" I asked, feeling like I'd walked in on people smoking pot. Dennis waved helplessly at me, unable to speak, crying and pounding.

"I just told a joke," giggled Kyle. "A fart joke." He giggled again. "Do you want to hear it?"

"I'll pass," I said.

"Yeah, you'll pass gas," said Derwood.

I grinned. I loved sophomoric humor but not fart jokes, and these guys talked about farting a lot. Perhaps I wasn't accustomed to it because I hadn't had any brothers. I preferred sex jokes, like the dongs. I smiled and shook my head as I walked away, my heart warmed by Dennis's laughter. It was the first time I'd ever heard it.

"Are you sure you don't want to hear it?" Darvin called to my retreating back.

"I'm sure," I called back from the hallway, grinning all the way back to my seat in the TV room.

Kyle was on a roll that night. While Big Dave dozed during a lame action movie, Kyle covered him with folded "No smoking" placards he had picked up from around The Abbey. He carefully placed them, taking whispered suggestions from his complicit audience. "Put one on his chest." "His crotch. Ya gotta put one on his crotch." Kyle "crowned" his achievement by placing the final placard on top of Dave's head. He stirred but it did not fall. We watched with bated breath a few moments, but he didn't move, so our attention returned to the lame movie. Apprehension nibbled at me. *What if Dave gets pissed?* I could see him and Kyle getting into it. It was the same apprehension I had carried around in my youth, anticipating one of my dad's sudden tirades. I was starting to like these guys and I didn't want anybody to fight. Dave moved again, the placards on his right shoulder and arm tumbling to the floor.

"I think he's waking up," said Clint, giggling.

Dave's eyes opened, then he stretched, the placards on his left shoulder and arm fluttering to the ground, followed by the one on his head. The ones on his legs and torso remained in place. "What the fuck?" he said, picking up one from his stomach and reading it. He brushed off the rest and stood up. I scrutinized him, looking for anger as he placed his hands on his hips and scanned the room. He was amused.

"Who did this? Kyle? Did you do this? This looks like your handiwork."

Kyle fought a smirk and failed. "No man. I came in here and they were there."

"Yeah, me too. I walked in and they were there," said Derwood unconvincingly.

Dave looked at me, probably figuring I was most likely to cave. I shrugged and kept a straight face. He stooped and picked up one of the placards, thoughtfully looking at it. "I'll get whoever did this. Remember. Payback is a bitch."

After he stoically left the room, we broke into giggles, much like grade schoolers after the teacher leaves the classroom.

"You know he's gonna getcha," Derwood said.

"Yeah, I know," Kyle grinned.

The next morning, I inspected my graying roots, and decided to ask Big Dave to order me some root touch-up.

Dr. Dennis was leaving today, and a celebratory air permeated the community meeting. Counselor Andrew joined Karen at the head table and the round of goodbyes began, starting with Kyle, meaning I would be second-to-last. Shit! I'd rather go early since I still cried when I spoke. Katie and Darvin set the tone, affectionately teasing Dennis for his long-windedness.

"You drove me nuts," Katie said to a grinning and nodding Dennis. "You'd start talking and I'd think 'Here he goes again.' But you finally got it and you'd cut yourself off."

"I didn't understand what you were saying half the time," Derwood said. "But when I did, I learned from you."

Andrew began with congrats and well wishes for staying sober then suddenly switched gears, his voice somber. "I know this is a deadly disease and we can't save everyone," he said, his voice starting to tremble, "but I wish I could've done more for your son."

Dennis' son was at The Abbey? And Andrew was his counselor?

"I know you did everything you could," Dennis said. "I've always known that. This disease kills. That's all there is to it."

Andrew looked down at the table, tears spilling from his eyes. A hush hovered over the room until Karen nodded at Big Dave to continue. Dave joked about Dennis being an egghead, but I was still emotionally shaken. Clint was next, then Jesse. Then me.

"I've really enjoyed your comments and learned from them," I said, dry-eyed, voice steady. "But then again, I've only been here a week." I heard a sprinkling of chuckles and pressed on. "I also enjoyed your company and I will miss that." My eyes filled with tears and my mouth trembled. Time to wrap it up. "I wish you the best."

"My wife and I occasionally come to Iowa City and we like to eat at that sushi place, Formosa," he said to me. "You wrote your number down in my book?" I nodded tearfully, unable to speak. "Maybe we can get together sometime."

Afterward, Dennis gestured me over to introduce his wife, who wasn't anything like I had pictured. Short and petite, she barely brushed his shoulder, her dark hair cut in a sleek chin-length bob. From the way he described their interactions, I had envisioned a matronly figure, tall and stern.

"Lisa, this is my wife, Anne." We shook hands, her grip light, her eyes kind. "Lisa lives in Iowa City."

"Oh," she brightened. "We love Iowa City. We get over there fairly often."

"That's what Dennis said," I replied.

Dennis and I looked at each other. This was my first Abbey good-bye. We moved toward each other for a nice, tight hug.

"Take care of yourself," I said, still in the hug.

"You too. Get better," he said into my hair.

I left the lobby and walked to the dining room, needing to be alone. I gazed out the window at the Sunset Boulevard swimming pool. I hate the sight of people leaving, of seeing them walk away.

That evening at dinner, Big Dave revved up his campaign to go to Mass, having discovered Dan was Catholic. "Come on, Lisa," he cajoled. "Pat's coming. Dan would be if he felt better. It's good for your sobriety."

"No, Dave. I'm not going to Mass." Although my Catholic roots had been stirring, mass at a strange church was not part of the awakening. I let Dave blather on a little more, then reiterated my stance.

"No, Dave. I'm not going."

Poor Dan, he was pale and lethargic, lying on the couch at every opportunity. He said his heart was racing, which was part of the withdrawal, and it exhausted him. Three overdoses by the age of twenty-four! His poor heart. His poor body. I worried about him.

Even the night before family day, jockeying for phone time was still fraught. The phone was located on a desk in the TV room, only a few feet away from the couch and chairs—not very private. The phone was turned on for a couple of hours in the morning and in the evening, with a sign-up sheet on the desk for 15-minute slots. Without fail, Kyle exceeded his allotted time bickering with his wife, while Sean talked to his mom to check in on his "fur babies." Clint eagerly awaited his phone time to talk to his fiancé, his voice changing to a soft, baby-talk tone. Katie spoke so softly, I never knew who she was talking to. Big Dave's calls were practical and perfunctory, talking to his wife about work, their sons, or the shopping list for Walgreens.

"No, not a pack of cigarettes, a carton," he corrected, feet up on the desk like he was talking to his secretary in the office. "Copenhagen tobacco, four tins for Clint, those are up by the cigarettes. Hair color for Lisa." He squinted at the list in his hand. "Clairol Root Touch-Up, black."

Little Dave made his phone calls in the morning, and Derwood called throughout the day to deal with insurance coverage, which always made him surly. A lot of stuff made Delvin surly—Johnny law, female counselors, anything on TV that wasn't Nascar, Kyle's football, and politics. Once he stormed out of group when politics came up. I was glad but surprised that he was going to Mass with Dave and was joining them for an evening rosary up in the chapel, an activity started by Pat and also pushed by Dave.

In addition to leading the rosary brigade, Pat wrote letters to his sons, to his siblings, to himself. During TV time in the evenings, he sat at a table scribbling away on a legal pad, occasionally shouting out spelling inquiries. His Walgreens order for Big Dave's wife was stamps. He noticed that I was getting mail, cards from my sisters, my high school friends, and my cousin Peggy, who had spearheaded my first rehab and civil commitment.

"Lisa, you got mail again," he informed me at lunch.

"Well, aren't we popular," quipped Big Dave.

"I just get legal notices," grumbled Derwood.

"Wish I got mail," garbled Pat, mouth full, but still managing to sound forlorn.

"Oh, it's just my sisters," I said. But these enveloped expressions of outreach warmed my heart and adorned my room. I savored them during quiet moments, sometimes rereading a card from my growing collection displayed on top of the hutch.

I hoped Pat got some mail.

Chapter Fourteen

At the morning community meeting, Kyle reported that he had found crackers in his bed, under the covers, still in the packet. He set the crushed packets of crackers on the table before him. All heads swiveled to Big Dave, who was expressionless except for a twitch of his mustache.

"Those darn nun ghosts," he said. We all chuckled, including Kyle.

Before family members started arriving, I retreated to my room to read. Family day started with family members gathering downstairs at noon in the main room for an Al-Anon meeting while we met upstairs with Abbey alumni for a pre-family day huddle. At twenty minutes to noon, I walked down to the dining room to grab a Diet Pepsi, coming across unfamiliar faces milling around in the lobby. Karen was talking to a couple of guys who came to internal AA meetings; Sean and a woman, who I surmised was his mom, chatted with Little Dave and Darvin; Big Dave stood next to Counselor Mark, glancing repeatedly toward the end of the lobby, obviously waiting for his wife. I returned upstairs to the community room where a circle of chairs had been set up at the opposite end of the tables. Already seated there were Jesse, Pat and a couple more guys who turned out to be Abbey alumni. Lobby people began drifting in along with Clint and a pale, wobbly Dan.

Counselor Mark joined the circle, waiting quietly for us to settle into silence. After introductions, Mark explained that after the Al-Anon meeting, we would join family members downstairs for a large group session, for which we needed a discussion topic.

"Any suggestions?" His blue eyes roved around the circle.

We exchanged glances.

"Trust," growled Kyle sitting grumpily with his arms folded across his chest.

"Trust is a good one," Mark agreed. "It's a big issue between addicts and their family members. Anything else?"

"Isn't that enough?" Big Dave asked wryly.

"Yes, I suppose it is," Mark agreed again, moving on to instructions for those of us without family there today. Our job was to set up the chairs downstairs. After the huddle, I walked down to the big room, where I found people lingering. I felt someone come up beside me. "Are we gonna have to kick them out?" Jesse asked, reflecting my thoughts.

"I don't know. But they're not moving."

"Come on, let's grab some chairs," said Derwood, coming up behind us.

"But they're still in them," I said.

"They'll move." Jesse and I followed him.

Darvin was right. As soon as we started dragging over chairs, the chatting family members dispersed. Mark had estimated that we needed thirty-five seats, which was going to make a pretty big circle. We dragged and shuffled chairs, expanding the circle. I stood back and counted. And counted again. I kept forgetting which chair I started with. "Thirty-six, thirty-seven, something like that," I said. "We have enough."

After grabbing another Diet Pepsi from the dining room, I returned to find many of the chairs filled, limiting my seat choice. I chose one facing the darkened flatscreen television and lobby door. Seated across from me were Sean and his mom who, like her son, had a kind, friendly moon face. They were cute together, chatting amiably about his two dogs that she was pet sitting while he was here. Sean missed them terribly, I overheard him say. I wished I had a fur baby to miss. Kyle walked in with one of the alumni, a hip, beatnik-looking guy, who had piqued my interest at the huddle meeting. He was impossibly cool, slender, languid, impeccably groomed from his razor-thin goatee to his red Doc Martens. And his voice matched his overall coolness, deep, rich, unhurried. They sat down next to Sean and his mom, filling up the last of the seats. Big Dave and his wife sat across from me, and I discreetly studied Dave's wife, who was very attractive—tall, thin and blonde, classy from head to toe, from her sleek, shoulder-length, expensively cut hair to her polished, black riding boots. She was leggy, accentuated by her tucked-in skinny jeans. I guessed she didn't take any shit from Dave.

Mark took his seat at one end of the circle, which was really a lop-sided oval, and scanned the gathered faces. "Welcome to The Abbey. Let's go around and introduce ourselves." This round of introductions revealed the beatnik guy's name was Cody, but I continued to think of him as the Beatnik Guy. Counselor Mark announced the topic of trust, which was met with uneasy silence and shifting in chairs. Beatnik Guy broke the ice, telling the group about the broken trust with his wife. She had repeatedly tested him with bottles of wine in the refrigerator and quizzes on his whereabouts.

"I get the quizzing because I lied all the time about where I was," Cody said. "But the wine in the fridge? That's just mean. She doesn't drink that much. It's like she can't handle me sober and she's trying to sabotage me." Legs crossed, voice smooth, Cody shared this like he was at a sophisticated dinner party.

"That's co-dependency, a whole 'nuther subject," Mark chimed in.

"What's co-dependency?" a family member asked.

"It's like an addiction," Mark replied, "to taking care of others at the expense of taking care of yourself. It happens a lot with an addict's spouse or partner."

The discussion then turned to living with an addict, the uncertainty, the stress, the disappointment. The father of Jon, an Abbey outpatient client who sometimes attended our group sessions, disclosed that hearing other addicts' stories helped him better understand his son's affliction. "You guys are sick!" he exclaimed, soft chuckles drifting around the circle. "Once I got that it's a disease, it changed everything. Jon can't help himself. He can't just get a little high, he has to get completely fucked up, pardon my French."

Something quivered inside. I wished my sisters were here to hear this. I raised a finger to signal my intent to speak, but Kyle beat me to it.

"Yeah, it's not like I just took Adderall," he said. "I had to take the strongest, fastest-acting kind. And when it started to wear off, I'd take more."

Mark had noticed my raised finger and nodded at me. "I never wanted to have just a couple. What was the point? That wasn't enough for a decent buzz. I drank to get drunk. I wish my sisters were here so they could hear all of this. They get it about it being a disease. But I still don't think they really *get* it."

Jon's dad was nodding vigorously. "I've learned more from listening to you guys than anything else. Even more than Al-Anon," he added, almost apologetically.

"That's why I encourage family members to go to an AA meeting," Mark said. "And there's one at 5:30 that you all can go to."

The second hour passed quickly with Jon's dad and Cody contributing the most. I had hoped Big Dave's wife would say something, but she sat silently at his side. Afterward Dave beckoned me over. Karen was just as pretty up close, a classic beauty. She pulled out the box of root touch-up from a Walgreens bag and handed it to me, which I gratefully and unselfconsciously accepted. She smiled knowingly. I liked her instantly.

At dinner, everyone was subdued, and I surmised it was the post-family day effect, emotionally satisfying to be with your loved ones, then BAM! They're gone. I'd find out next Sunday when the sisters came. I went up to my room early to read, wanting to finish my book.

Next morning after drug dispensation, I touched up my roots. What a difference! There was enough colorant to apply to the underlying grays too. My eyebrows needed some cleaning up, but they had seized my tweezers and razor. That would have to wait until I reclaimed my tweezers.

At morning group, Kyle and Katie had a tiff, resulting in his leaving the room in a huff. I didn't hear what had precipitated it, but I did hear Katie's dig about "that stupid ball you carry around all day."

"Is he okay?" counselor Andrew asked.

"Who cares," Katie muttered, angrily sketching in her notebook.

"Maybe he had to fart," said oblivious Pat, adding to the awkwardness in the room.

"What?" Big Dave asked.

"That's what I do when I have to fart," Pat explained. "It's a courtesy fart. I get up and leave the room, then come back when I'm done."

Derwood shook his head and chuckled. "Pat, you're not right."

"I don't think that was it, Pat," added Big Dave. "He's not coming back."

Unflappable as always, Andrew steered us back to the discussion of Step One, admitting our powerlessness over alcohol, a step I had wholeheartedly accepted. I think swigging vodka straight out of the bottle at six in the morning and continuing throughout the day was clear evidence of my powerlessness. It had started with weekend and occasional weekday social drinking, then daily drinking, then drinking whenever I was awake. Drinking had eventually consumed me.

The tension between Katie and Kyle continued through lunch; usually talkative Kyle was sullen and terse. It affected us all, and made our conversations careful and subdued. The mood was listless in the TV room after lunch, where Katie curled up on the floor draped in a fleece blanket. She was one of those people who is always cold. Kyle thumped down in his chair, arms crossed over his chest. Counselor Mark sat down next to him, scanning the circle, sensing something. His nice eyes rested a moment on Katie, who was arranging the blanket around herself.

"So, what's going on today?" he asked.

Met by shifting in chairs and the exchange of careful glances, Mark launched the discussion. "Katie, what's going on with you? Have you found a place to stay?"

Katie had been at The Abbey for almost two months, one month longer than the typical term. Like good-looking, come-and-go-as-he-pleased Brent, Katie's marriage had fallen apart so she was not returning home. Via long-earing, I had heard her say she couldn't go back to her grandmother's. There she had left behind a trail of disappointment and stashed vodka bottles in her wake. What an awful feeling, having nowhere to go. I checked off my apartment on a mental list of things to be grateful for.

Katie pulled the blanket tighter around herself and shrugged. "I'm still here."

"How's that going?" Mark pursued. "Finding a place."

"I can't go back to my husband," she intoned. "I can't go back to my grandma's. I might be able to go to my aunt's." A beat. "I feel like a piece of shit."

"It will work out," Mark assured her.

"Will it? What about my son? I don't even have a place for my son to visit me! I hate this! I feel worthless. I am worthless!" She dissolved into tears, which was unnerving since she rarely showed emotion. I ached to comfort her but didn't feel comfortable doing so. Big Dave and I exchanged helpless looks.

"You are anything but worthless," said Kyle earnestly, leaning toward her. "You're smart and beautiful and you're always saying shit that sticks with me." She looked up at him through her tears. "Yeah, I can be a dick, but I'm listening."

Kyle went up a few notches in my esteem. Warm affection for both Katie and Kyle spread within me, spurring me to speak. "You're beautiful and talented, Katie!" I gushed. "Your drawings are amazing! And Kyle's right. The stuff you say in group is so spot on."

"I always listen whenever you say something," Big Dave chimed in.

"I do too," added Clint.

"Thanks, you guys," sniffled Katie, wiping her tears.

"And you're hot!" said Pat, met by a chorus of groans and cries of "Oh, Pat!"

"What?" he asked. Mark sat quietly, and I caught Katie smiling slightly through her tears. I ached for her but was happy she had opened up. We all had our demons.

The topic at the Bettendorf evening meeting, once again, was having a higher power. I was softening to the concept, but the rebel in me would not fully surrender. I'd experienced glimmers but was still far from full acceptance. I didn't want my higher power to be God, nature wasn't enough, and my deceased loved ones didn't feel right either. Although atheism and agnosticism used to appeal to me, they now seemed dry and airless, like outer space, cold and scientific without emotion and heart. But Christianity, which was the predominant higher power of choice in this room and rooms everywhere, was never going to be it. Was I being deliberately contrarian? Possibly. Was it because I grew up Catholic? Most certainly. It just didn't make sense to me and never had, putting all your cards on this one figure who existed in fairly recent world history. I did believe Jesus Christ was a remarkable individual who came along when a beacon of hope and compassionate leadership was desperately needed, much like Buddha, Gandhi, Abraham Lincoln, and Martin Luther King, Jr. But the son of God? I just couldn't buy it. And the hypocrisy and blood thirstiness of Christians throughout history didn't help.

The comments wound around the tables, some describing dramatic, ah-ha moments, others subtle, gradual awakenings. A couple of attendees shared their continuous struggle to get there. Then it got to Clint, who usually passed or spoke briefly. He was seated next to Big Dave at the end of the middle table, rather than in our regular Abbey seats. I always got a little nervous when one of us shared since learning, through eavesdropping, that there was animosity from some meeting regulars toward Abbeyites, that we were looked upon as outsiders, interlopers. Even AA could be cliquey, as I had discovered in Fort Dodge. Clint started off admitting he struggled with this part of AA, but something had been happening, he said, a shift, a change.

"I'm finding it within the walls of The Abbey," he said, "through discussion and the people. I'm finding my Higher Power in the fellowship there. And here too," he added, a sudden afterthought.

Wow. I didn't know about the rest of the room but that really hit me. Was that happening to me too? A spiritual transfusion? These dark, lurking emotions were spilling out of me every day, crying out the toxic ones and replenishing with healthy ones. Was that part of a spiritual awakening, a step toward a higher power? The rest of the meeting passed in a blur; I passed when it was my turn.

Dinner that night was a self-serve buffet—pork roast, mashed potatoes, green beans. I stood in line behind Clint, his comments still with me. *Should I say something to him?* I felt shy around him, I think because I was attracted to him. I stared at his broad shoulders and timidly reached out and tapped one of them.

"Clint?" Nothing. He didn't turn around. "Clint?" a little louder. He turned around, his face expressionless. I forged ahead. "I really liked what you said tonight." Still no expression. "At the meeting." Still nothing. "About fellowship and your higher power." His face softened into a smile. "Thanks," he said. Then with a slight tilt of his head, "Thanks." I wasn't sure if it was proper AA etiquette to compliment a share, but I was glad I had. Later that evening in the TV room, we smiled at each other, that single outreach shifting our relationship. Something trembled inside, something familiar but not exactly welcome.

The next morning, I noticed when Clint entered the room and took his seat down the table from me. During group, I was more aware when he shared, and he shared a lot. He talked about how much his addiction had cost him—his job, his home, his fiancé, his status. He admitted he liked to impress people. With the car he drove, with the neighborhood he lived in. Clint said he liked money and had been good at making it until his addiction took over. He was starting to realize that money hadn't made him happy. He had felt empty inside and filled the void with cocaine, ending up in front of a mirror picking at his face until it bled.

Now it was Pat's turn. He had obtained it all, too—a wife, two sons, a house, a good job, ten years of sobriety. But then his wife and AA fucked him over. Even though he did all the right things—chairing meetings, sponsoring—it still came crashing down. Big Dave interrupted this f-word laced diatribe, reiterating something he had mentioned a couple of days before. "There must've been something going on in your marriage before she hooked up with that AA guy."

"Yeah, it didn't just happen," Delvin added.

"I had some anger issues," Pat admitted. "I was kind of a dry drunk."

I had heard that term before and never really understood it, so I asked. Andrew explained it was when someone stops drinking but doesn't do anything else, such as AA or rehab, so they end up being negative and embittered.

"But you were in AA," said Big Dave.

"Yeah," Pat considered that. "I guess I'm just angry. I've been angry since I was a kid. I was always getting into trouble. Stealing, fighting. That's probably why my mom gave me Quaaludes."

This new Pat morsel was met with startled gasps and alarmed looks. I never knew if Pat was kidding or not. I wasn't the only one.

"Come on!" challenged Derwood. "Your mom gave you ludes?"

"Yeah. She was an alcoholic and she gave me drugs. I was drinking and drugging when I was ten."

Pat described his younger years, filled with delinquency and inebriation. He spoke without self-pity or bravado, just the facts with a tinge of self-deprecation. Once again, he monopolized the group session, which had become a trend, but this tale of woe was so sordid, so woeful, he deserved it. His dry drunk anger manifested itself once in the car, he said, when a guy who had been tailgating them flipped off his wife at a stoplight. From the passenger seat, Pat had screamed obscenities at the guy who had screamed back insults at his wife, including the c-word. Pat had gotten so angry, he punched the windshield, cracking it and bloodying his knuckles. His young son had been in the backseat. We sat in stunned silence.

"You cracked the windshield?" Kyle asked, almost in admiration.

"Yeah, I'll never forget how my wife looked at me. It wasn't good."

I was excited. Finally, my first phone call. Who to call? Paula? Martha? What time should I call? The evening slots between 8 and 9 filled up fast, so I had written down my time early that morning. I chose 7:45, after Sean who always called his mom and before Kyle who always went over his ten minutes talking to his wife. Phone time could get tense. If you weren't there for your designated time, look out! You were hunted down in the halls of The Abbey like a truant middle schooler. I was nervous about my first call—not about the call itself, but making the call, the mechanics of it, using a phone card. Herein lies a lot of my nervousness: figuring out how things work, like creating an Excel spreadsheet or driving an unfamiliar car or turning on an unfamiliar shower. My lifelong strategy to get out of challenging tasks was to act so helpless and hapless in front of a competent person that they are compelled to take over. Like when ironing my dress before my sister Cindy's wedding, clumsily thumping and jerking the iron across the dress, repeatedly getting it caught in the fabric, thereby creating new wrinkles. Paula had stood there awaiting her turn, watching me thumping and sighing, her impatience growing. Impatient and appalled, she had pushed me out of the way and finished the job. Manipulative? Yes. But would it work with these guys? Rather than helplessly pressing and punching buttons on the phone, wasting my scheduled phone time, I took the direct approach. Right before phone time, I asked Sean for help. He took one look at my phone card and shook his head.

"What?" I asked.

"You have the Walgreen's card. They don't work very well."

"Really? What's wrong with them?"

"I don't know but you get a busy signal or a message saying your call didn't go through. Here, you can use mine. It has a ton of minutes left on it. I was gonna leave it here when I left."

"Are you sure? I can give you some money for it."

He brushed my offer aside, patiently showing me how to use the card, which numbers to press and when.

The phone turned on, Kate and Big Dave went first, the former curling up in the chair wrapped in her fleece blanket, the latter leaning back, feet up on the desk like he was at the office. Again, Katie spoke too softly for me to long-ear and again Dave gave his wife instructions. Sean was up, taking over the chair from Dave. My anticipation grew and my impatient mind raced. *Your fur babies are fine, Sean, not much change from yesterday. Your house is fine, it's not going anywhere, it wasn't broken into. Your mom is fine, no different from yesterday.* I remained seated until he hung up. Sean stayed at the desk while I sat down in the chair.

"Do you want me to dial for you?" he asked kindly.

"No, I think I got it. Dial 9 to get out, then the calling card numbers, then wait until they ask for the number I'm calling."

"Exactly. I'll be right over here if you need help."

I took a moment before picking up the receiver, then pressed the buttons carefully, conscious of the guys behind me and the lack of privacy. I was a loud phone talker. I heard a click, then ringing, the call going through. Another click, then Martha's voice, and my self-consciousness was gone. I gushed. I told her I was doing great, still weak but getting stronger. I quickly described my daily routine, rushing through the details. She peppered me with questions. How was my room? Was the food as good as everyone said? I was forced to interrupt her, my time running out. It went by so fast! I had to tell her about the cardinals. I lowered my voice and got through it without crying, my voice trembling near the end. There was a moment of silence at the other end of the line.

"Oh Lisa, that is such a big sign," she said. "They know where you are, and they know what you're going through."

I nodded. "I know."

We signed off, a prolonged good-bye. "Bye, #4. See you soon." I reluctantly hung up, then sat a moment in the afterglow. I spun around in the comfortable desk chair to find Dan peering at me from the main couch where he was sprawled. He sprawled a lot. Dan often lobbied for watching DVDs in lieu of regular group because it afforded him an opportunity to sprawl. I was surprised to see him looking at me.

"What's that number four business?" he asked.

"You were eavesdropping on my call?" I replied, pretending offense.

"It was hard not to," he grinned. "So, what's the number four thing?"

"I have four sisters. I'm the youngest so I'm #5, Martha's second to the youngest so she's #4. Capiche?"

"Huh. Four sisters. That's cool."

We smiled at each other before he turned back to the TV. My heart warmed a little more, my first interaction with Dan other than asking him how he felt. Like with Clint, a single interaction had altered our relationship.

Chapter Fifteen

A meetings were kind of a pain. Perhaps because of when they took place—first thing in the morning, right before dinner, late Friday evening—the prospect of the meeting was worse than the actual event. There were good moments at each meeting, but there were also the mundane, the clichés, the gushing over a mediocre reading. Kyle, Big Dave and I joked about how once, just once, we'd like to hear someone say, "I hate that reading!" "I don't like that reading at all!"

One memorable quote came from Marty, a guy about my age: "I don't have to get fucked up on a nice day. I can enjoy a nice day without getting fucked up." And from one of the few Black guys at the meetings. "First time I walked in here, I thought it was a bunch of old white guys sitting around, drinking bad coffee. Now I know it's a lot more." At the morning meeting, there was ever-cheerful Chuck who replied, "Hi So and So!" to each alcoholic louder and more enthusiastically than anyone else. Some found him annoying. I found him endearing. Upbeat, serene Bonnie was always smiling with a warm glow, making it all the more startling when she talked about the dark side of her addiction. There was another crier, still drinking, who sat with her boyfriend up by the moderator. Each of us had someone whom we found annoying. On the ride back, we rehashed the highlights. This was how I learned that the drinking crier was a former Abbeyite who had gotten kicked out.

"She drank perfume and hand sanitizer!" Kyle exclaimed. "She tried to get drunk on hand sanitizer!"

"She what?" I turned around in my seat.

"Yeah, she's a mess," said Katie, sitting beside me.

"The one who beat up the cops?" Big Dave asked.

"I'm not buying that bullshit," chimed in Derwood. "She loves to make up the drama."

"She drank hand sanitizer?" I couldn't let that go. Perfume I could kind of see, but hand sanitizer?

"Yeah, there's no way she attacked those cops," Kyle agreed. "She'd still be in jail."

Big Dave and I looked at each other. "Hand sanitizer?" he said to me.

"How would you keep it down?"

"Would you get a buzz from it?"

Kyle and Big Dave had developed feuds, all of which were invented by their testosterone-fueled imaginations, in my humble feminine opinion. Kyle's was Shifty Eyes, the self-proclaimed MMA fighter, whose doughy physique belied that claim. He glared at Kyle from across the room, according to Kyle, and made faces at him while he shared. I refrained from suggesting that perhaps he was glaring at our group because of the Abbey resentment. Instead I mischievously pricked Kyle's animosity.

"I caught him staring at you," I said.

"That MMA wannabe mother fucker," he sputtered. "Was it while I was talking?"

"It was the entire time," I intoned ominously, before a grin broke through. Kyle laughed and waved me off. I had noticed Shifty Eyes looking our way, but between the glare off of his eyeglasses and me not wearing mine, I couldn't tell what he was looking at. I didn't feel as strongly as Kyle, but I did find him annoying and sniveling.

Big Dave's feud started when he thought a guy wearing a Michigan sweatshirt criticized his share. "Did you hear what that Michigan guy said, that going to church wasn't enough, that you had to do a lot more to stay sober?" Dave's share had been about going to Saturday mass and praying the rosary every night. I hadn't interpreted it as a criticism and I was pretty good at recognizing digs.

"I thought he was saying that it didn't work for him, going to church," I had suggested. I knew Dave wouldn't budge.

"No, he looked right at me when he said it. I know what he meant."

I shook my head and hummed The Kinks "Paranoia will destroy ya...." to myself. Oh, these guys. They did keep it interesting.

Eff Jeff's friend died so he was not his usual jovial, profane self. Seeing someone who is normally vivacious be quiet and subdued is unsettling. Morning group consisted of worksheets about triggers. The information was worthwhile but I much preferred unstructured, free-for-all discussions. I watched Eff Jeff surreptitiously while filling out the worksheet, my heart aching at the sorrow etched on his face. I fought back tears. At lunch, he didn't make his usual appearance in the dining room looking for food scraps.

"I'm not gonna be able to finish this," said Jesse about his turkey club sandwich. "I wish Jeff would come out."

"I know," I said. "He was so quiet."

"It really sucks to see a guy like that in pain," Pat added. A beat. "But I'd be happy to take that off your hands, Jesse."

"Geezus, Pat," Delvin said. "You want the rest of my salad? My veggies?"

"Nope. Just the sandwich," smiled Pat, reaching over to Jesse's plate.

That afternoon we watched a video for which Eff Jeff managed to muster up some enthusiasm. Taking place in Utah among massive red rock formations with a folk music soundtrack, a tall, dark, handsome doctor, dressed in Columbia hiking gear, drew parallels between the crevasses and fissures of the rocks with the lobes and synapses of the brain. Before leaving the TV room, Eff Jeff told us it was his favorite video on addiction. It was much better than some of the cheesy or cringe worthy videos we had viewed, very watchable and relatable. Even tough critic Derwood gave it a thumbs up.

I prepared to give a strong thumbs down to the DVD chosen by Kyle, John Wick. First off, it starred Keanu Reeves, red flag number one. Secondly, it was an action movie. But the guys were excited and tried to sell it to me. "He's an ex-hitman and his wife dies of cancer and they pull him back in," Kyle summarized.

"'Just when I thought I was out, they pull me back in,'" Big Dave quoted, waiting for a response.

"Godfather 3, Michael Corleone," I said.

"Yes!" he exclaimed. "Good job, Lisa."

"But what about the dog scene?" Clint asked. "I don't know. It'll remind me of my dog."

"There's a dog scene?" I asked, alarmed.

"It's actually a puppy," Kyle said, grinning mischievously.

"A puppy?" I cried.

"They don't show it. It's off camera," clarified Brent. Where the hell had he come from?

"What are you guys talking about?" shouted Pat from the far end of the room.

"John Wick!" Big Dave shouted back. "Have you ever seen it?"

"Oh, yeah. That's a good one. Wait, I'm almost done with this letter. Don't start it yet."

The guys successfully coaxed me to stay. Thankfully, the puppy scene was at the beginning so once that was over, we could settle into mocking Keanu's acting and his frequent escapes from death. It reminded me of a similarly bad movie, Cobra, starring Sylvester Stallone, which I had seen years ago with Paula and her husband Mike, who is known for his dry quips. After yet another outlandish, death-defying scene, Mike had commented, "You know, I have a better chance of dying during this scene than he does." Although I was tempted to steal his line, I just sat back and let the inanity flow over me. The plot was glaringly predictable, the dialogue painfully stilted, but just like watching Cobra with Paula and Mike, the shared experience and audience interaction warranted a thumbs up. These guys!

We got another new resident that week, Matt, a whiskey-drinking engineer from Moline, Illinois, originally from South Dakota. He was ruggedly handsome, dark eyes and hair, a nicely kept full beard, in his late 30s or early 40s. He was younger than me but older than Kyle and Clint. He filled Dr. Dennis' spot in the upstairs community room. There was a lot of turnover that week, with two new guys coming in and Sean and Little Dave leaving. I was dreading Dave's departure but not Sean's. I mean, he was a nice enough guy, he was the first one I met and talked to. But once I had started getting to know the other guys, he kind of faded into the background. Much later, after he was gone, Kyle told me he was a perv, that I only saw Sean's polite, nice guy persona. Leave it to Kyle to pass along the underbelly of anything, whether it's the evil effects of meditation or a government conspiracy to withhold a cure for cancer (which I actually kind of believed, too).

The dongs had really opened up Little Dave. Eff Jeff referred several times in group to the dongs incident and how it unleashed pure joy in Dave, how it broke through and shined light on his darkness. It was revealed in group that this sweet, gentle, small-town guy had witnessed unspeakable horror in his volunteer job as an EMT. He was a comforting presence at upstairs group and at outside AA meetings, handing me a Kleenex box whenever I cried, refilling my coffee. The big reveal occurred during an upstairs group led by Andrew, who asked Little Dave if he could share his story. I glanced quickly at him, he gave a slight nod. My stomach churned. The discussion had been about making certain changes to stay sober, from minor ones, such as a different driving route to avoid going past a certain liquor store or tavern, to major ones, such as ending a relationship, or in Dave's case, leaving a job. Little Dave had been drinking away the scenes of carnage and gore that he came upon as an EMT, never speaking of them not even to his wife. He just drank and drank and drank in his chair at home. Never a mean drunk or a violent drunk, Andrew told the hushed room, Dave drank himself into a self-destructive isolation, alone with his demons.

"Like PTSD," Derwood murmured.

"Exactly," Andrew said. "Dave loves helping people, serving the public. But the ugliness of the job was eating away at him. And eating away at his marriage. He can't do it anymore."

I looked at him, but he did not meet my eye.

"No, I can't do it anymore," Dave said. "Not if I want to stop drinking. Not if I want to stay married."

The phrase "quiet desperation" popped into my head. I wasn't sure who coined it, but that's what had brought Little Dave to The Abbey, to this chair beside me, to this moment in time. I blinked back tears.

Chapter Sixteen

isters Day was here! I was practically giddy. So much had happened! So many people for them to meet! I chose one of my favorite tunics and carefully applied my make-up. The giddiness dimmed somewhat, remembering that Little Dave was leaving today. Our round of goodbyes to him and Sean had taken place at the community meeting yesterday morning, with me last again! Bolstered by the prospect of the sisters visit, I had felt confident I could get through my farewell to Little Dave without tears, but as soon as I had turned to him, my emotions surged.

"I'm going to miss you," I got out before the tears flowed. "I'm going to miss you sitting here next to me. You've been a comfort to me. I wish you all the best. You can do this." We hugged. It was an awkward one but a good one, with me sobbing into his shoulder.

I ventured downstairs for a Diet Pepsi and a breakfast bar. Upon my return trip through the TV room, I came across Derwood and Dan. "Your sisters coming today?" Dan inquired.

"Yes," I replied.

"Which numbers are coming?" he asked.

"Number three and number four."

Derwood was confused. "What the hell are you talking about?"

"The order we were born. I have five sisters and I'm the youngest so I'm number five. Second to the youngest is number four..."

"Oh, okay. I get it," Darvin said.

I was hesitant to ask Derwood if he had family coming as I was unsure of his situation. He didn't talk about it. I knew Dan's family wasn't coming because it was too soon. Derwood saved me from asking.

"My ex-wife's coming," he said. "I know it sounds weird but we get along better now than when we were married."

"I don't think it's weird at all," I replied. "I think it's great she supports you."

"I think it's weird," grinned Dan from the couch.

"Oh, what do you know. You're just a kid," Delvin growled.

"Better than being a dirty old man," Dan joked back.

Oh, Dan. It was so comforting to see him feeling better and opening up. I stayed and watched Pawn Stars with Dan and Derwood, my ears tuned to voices in the lobby. The sisters said they would be here by 11:30, and with Paula driving, they most likely would be. It was 11:15. Dan and Darvin wandered off, leaving me alone with my anxious vigil. An older couple entered my line of vision through the doorway, then left. Not them. I relaxed but remained perched on the edge of my chair. New voices. I straightened up like a meerkat in the grasslands of Africa, hearing heavy taps like the heels on a boot. These voices were robust, animated. I sprung from my chair to the door. There they were, talking to Karen. I watched a moment before approaching, appreciating them, admiring them. Paula looked chic and beautiful, a scarf perfectly arranged around her neck, her skin glowing. Martha, also expertly scarfed, channeled sporty chic, from her fleece vest to her hiking shoes. My heart swelled.

"Hi!" I greeted them.

"Lisa! You look great!" Paula exclaimed. We hugged tightly. God, it felt so good to hold her, to smell her. We pulled away and looked at each other, the tears in her eyes mirroring mine. I turned to Martha.

"You really do look great," she said somberly before we hugged.

"Do you want to see my room? Do you want a tour?" I was giddy.

"Oh yes," Karen said, "give them a tour. Enjoy your day together." She smiled softly.

I escorted them upstairs, pointing out the little sitting room at the top of the stairs, then teasing them with a moment of suspense before I opened the door to my room. "Voila!" They both gasped.

"This is really nice, Lisa," Paula said.

"The bed is huge!" Martha commented.

"I know," I grinned and nodded.

"Is this the bush?" asked Paula who had moved over to a window.

"Yes," I murmured, my eyes filling with tears. Martha moved over next to her and looked out at the shrub. I walked over to the second window. "And she flew over here to the portico," I said, reenacting the cardinal visit. "But I didn't realize it until I opened the curtain." They moved over next to me.

"And Dad joined her," Martha murmured.

"Yes. Dad joined her." I sighed. We stood there, shoulder to shoulder looking out the window, three sisters thinking of their deceased parents, wishing they could see them again. A moment later, the tour continued.

"Nice bathroom," Martha said. "Good lighting."

"How's the shower? The water pressure?" Paula quizzed, remembering how I hated the weak water pressure at my apartment.

"It's great. I love it."

Out in the hallway, I pointed at Katie's door across from mine. "The other woman's room."

We moved through the sitting area and down the hall to the big meeting room. "This is where we meet in the morning and for most groups," I told them, walking to my spot at the tables. "This is where I sit." I led them into the chapel and gestured to the door on the left of the altar. "That's where we have one-on-ones. One of the counselors calls it the Molestation Room."

Paula chuckled while Martha frowned. "Which counselor?" Martha asked. "That's not very professional."

"Eff Jeff. I'll tell you about him later." I glanced at my watch. It was 11:45. "We better go downstairs."

In the TV room, I showed them the desk where we make phone calls. "You really *don't* have any privacy," Paula noted. We crossed the wooden dance floor. "Here's where we do yoga." I had tried it that week, but wasn't really thrilled with it. I had struggled with most of the poses because of my weakness and I was too self-conscious. My favorite part had been at the end when we had laid on our backs and placed our feet high up on the wall, allowing the blood to flow to our heads. That I could do without struggling. I wasn't sure if I was going to try it again.

"And here's the dining room. Do you guys want something to drink?" As I fetched their beverages, they looked out at the walled-in backyard. And the smokers out on the steps.

"Are you smoking?" Paula asked.

Paula knew about my part-time smoking. She didn't know that I didn't feel like smoking when I wasn't feeling well. Or drinking coffee. Funny, I could always drink vodka, sick or well. Drinking had never been unappealing.

I shook my head. "Nope. Don't feel like it."

As we looked at the weekly schedule hanging on the wall, Karen walked in.

"It's that time," she said. "Al-Anon meeting down here and you're upstairs, Lisa."

She opened the backdoor, repeating the announcement to the smokers as we departed. The circle of chairs was filling up in the main room. "See you in an hour," I said, reluctant to leave them.

Upstairs, we gathered for the pre-family briefing. I was pleased to see Impossibly Cool Cory but disappointed that Dan was missing. Attendance was required whether you had family coming or not, but both Katie and Brent had been absent before, so I guess there were exceptions. Jo was the counselor/moderator and the topic was forgiveness. I wondered if the sisters would forgive me for all I'd put them through. Since I had family here, I didn't have to help with chair set-up. Nervousness nibbled at my insides. Upon entering the TV room, I found the sisters talking to a blonde woman who walked away as I approached.

"Who was that?" I asked.

"Susan something," Martha replied. "She's from Des Moines."

"Des Moines? Is she here for Pat?"

"Yes. Pat's her brother," Paula said.

"She's really pretty."

Flanked by my sisters, I felt proud and loved. During the discussion, it became apparent that Pat and his sister were close, much like my sisters and me, affectionately bantering, finishing each other's sentences. Her cheekbones were exquisite, her skin glowing, her shimmering blonde hair untouched by any Clairol product. Or she had a really good colorist, but I didn't think so. She reminded me of an Olympic skier, beautiful and athletic. She talked about cleaning up Pat's place, throwing out some of his stuff. "She threw out the couch where I always passed out!" cried Pat. She had been through this alcoholic rodeo before with Pat. And with her ex-husband. But there was a big bone of contention between them—she was still friends with his ex-wife. I winced and exchanged a pained look with Big Dave.

"After what she did to him?" burst out Dave. I whispered to Paula about the ex-wife situation, causing her to gasp. Martha leaned in, wanting to hear but I mouthed to her, "Later."

"She's the mother of his children!" Susan countered. "I really like her!"

"He's your brother!" Dave fired back.

I couldn't remain silent although I did feel a little out of line. "But if it bothers him—" I started.

"That's messed up," Kyle added.

How many times had we heard Pat rant about his wife, calling her the c-word? I didn't blame him, but I think he needed to defuse that anger. His sister maintaining a relationship with his ex-wife could feed that anger. I loved how we were jumping to his defense. Big Dave and Kyle were usually silent during these family day discussions, but not today.

Near the end, Martha talked about her husband, who had stopped drinking twenty years ago, acknowledging a better understanding of alcoholism now. Back then, she said, if he wouldn't have stopped, she would've kicked him to the curb. "He could've drank himself to death for all I cared."

I recoiled. Jo noticed my reaction. "Lisa, you reacted to that. Why did that make you cringe?"

I was taken aback by Martha's comment, so severe after all these years. "That's harsh, Martha. I'm a little surprised you feel that way after all this time. I'm glad you didn't feel that way about me."

"It was different," she said, her voice flat and stern. "It was affecting my children. It was affecting my family."

"You wouldn't have tried to get him help?" Paula asked.

"No. He would've been on his own."

"That was twenty years ago," I said. "Alcoholism was treated differently back then."

"Yeah. I doubt Dennis would've gone to treatment," Paula added.

"And he never went to AA," I said.

"Nope. Never," Martha finished.

Shortly thereafter, it was time to introduce the sisters. We chatted amiably with Big Dave and his wife Karen, revealing that we had two more sisters. "Your poor father!" Dave exclaimed. Like we hadn't heard *that* before. Karen was an engineer—impressive!—having graduated from Iowa State.

"Smart, pretty *and* tall," Paula commented after they walked away, poking fun at herself for her height envy.

"I bet she doesn't take any guff from him," Martha said. Paula and I agreed, laughing at Martha's use of the word "guff," a word our father had used.

Clint sauntered into the TV room and plopped down on the couch. We had been talking more that past week, mostly about football. I had been dazzling him with my vast football knowledge. In high school, he had been the quarterback and in college he had played defense at Loras in Dubuque. Loras! Three of my sisters, including these two, had graduated from Clarke College in Dubuque, Loras' sister school. That's how I introduced him.

"Clint went to Loras. He played football there." To him. "These guys went to Clarke. Did you know any Clarke girls?"

"I dated a girl from Clarke," Clint grinned.

We chatted for a while, Paula mentioning that March Madness started this week. For many years, she had hosted a NCAA basketball tournament pool, me faithfully mailing my bracket to her every year. The selection show was in an hour.

"You guys should fill out brackets," Paula suggested. "Don't you think that would be fun?"

Clint and I looked at each other. "We *should* fill out brackets," I said.

"It would be fun," he agreed.

"Would they let you do it?" Martha fretted. "It is gambling." We ignored her.

Paula pulled out a Ziploc bag filled with her sinfully tasty M & M peanut butter cookies. She unzipped it and offered the bag to Clint. "Do you want a cookie?" she asked.

"You gotta try them, Clint," I urged. "They are *so* good."

Clint was a utilitarian eater. Although he sat at the other table, I had noticed that he ate quickly, no dawdling, no chitchat, efficiently cleaning his plate then off to the TV room, mooning over love songs on a music channel. I had also noticed that he had a sweet tooth; the chef baked decadent red velvet cupcakes, and Clint had asked politely then enthusiastically taken a second. He later walked into the TV room eating a third, which he said appeared at his door.

"Did you eat it?" asked usual suspect Kyle. "Maybe somebody put something in it."

"I did eat it. It was delicious," Clint had smirked. He also snuck downstairs in the wee hours of the night for furtive bowls of sweet cereal. Oh yes, Clint was going to like the cookies.

"Oh my God," Clint moaned after one bite. "These are so good."

Paula beamed. These were her culinary masterpiece. Her husband blamed them for his heart attack. "Have another one," said the cookie pusher.

Clint grabbed two and sprung up from the couch. "It was really nice meeting you." He smiled warmly at the sisters. "I'll let you guys visit."

Half an hour later, it was time for the sisters to leave. We walked out to the lobby, where we found Little Dave and his wife talking to director Karen. Dave's wife was smiling, younger than I had expected even though her long hair was gray. Her face was kind. She was taking her husband home. Her sober husband. I hoped he made it out there. I believed he would.

"This is Dave," I said to the sisters. "He sat next to me at group upstairs. And at AA meetings." We smiled at each other. "He's going home today."

Then it was final good-bye time. Little Dave moved toward me for a hug.

"You take care of yourself," I murmured. "Remember the dongs." I felt him chuckle.

"Keep getting better," he murmured back.

Turning to my sisters, I felt reinforced, shored up for this goodbye. Saying good-bye to Little Dave, a forever good-bye, had eased the hardship of this farewell. But it did not erase it completely. Paula's eyes sparkled with tears and mine burned with unshed ones. The goodbyes were emotional, but not sad.

At dinner that night, I was one of the subdued—the post-family day blues—but the melancholy was counterbalanced by the reaction to the sisters. They were a hit!

"Karen really liked your sisters," Big Dave said.

"So did my sister," echoed Pat.

"Yeah, they're pretty cool," added Jesse.

I left the Ziploc bag of cookies on the counter in the dining room, but not before securing a few for myself. I retired to my room early, the melancholy lingering. It had been a good day.

Chapter Seventeen

T he next morning, I started my campaign for a basketball tournament pool. Clint, Kyle, Matt, and Dave were onboard (sadly, we didn't have to distinguish between the Daves anymore), Derwood was against it, and Pat was confused by it. I approached Karen, who referred me to Andrew, who apparently was a sports guy.

"Oh, yeah, he's a baseball guy," Kyle said. "Played in high school. Basketball too I think."

"Yeah, he was a jock," Clint added.

Knowing this about Andrew softened his stern persona. I caught him during the morning break. "Hi Andrew. I asked Karen and she said to ask you about it, but we'd like to have a pool for the basketball tournament, fill out some brackets." I rushed through my spiel, a little nervous.

"That's a great idea," he said, smiling. "No money, but sure, you can fill out brackets. I'll print some out. I think I'll fill one out too."

I was excited. It was going to be so fun watching the games. Iowa, Wisconsin, Iowa State, and Notre Dame were all in the tourney. I reported at lunch that the tournament pool was on, that Andrew was printing brackets.

"So how does it work?" Darvin asked.

"It starts with sixty-four teams and you pick winners in each round, then it goes down to the Sweet Sixteen, the Elite Eight, then the Final Four," Big Dave explained.

"I've heard of the Final Four," Derwood said.

"It's fun," I pitched. "It's fun to watch the games and follow your picks."

"I might do one," grumbled Derwood.

"Good." I was proud, like I had scored a personal victory getting Darvin involved.

That evening, Kyle persuaded us to watch a zombie movie. Big Dave and I vehemently resisted. "Oh, Kyle, I hate zombie and vampire movies," I exclaimed. "If it's not Night of the Living Dead, I don't wanna see it," Dave huffed. Kyle had Clint and Dan on his side, the young whippersnappers versus the old fuddy duddies.

"I don't normally like zombie movies either," Clint said. "But this one's got more to it."

So, we watched 28 Weeks Later, which turned out to be better than your typical horror flick. It was engrossing (and gross) and plausible rather than completely absurd, meaning it would stick with me.

"Thanks Kyle," I said. "Now I'm gonna have nightmares."

"Yeah. Me too," agreed Dave. "I'm gonna have to take a soak in my hot tub."

"Do you really have a hot tub in your room?" I asked for the umpteenth time.

"Yes. I requested it. It's the only one, a corner room," he replied, straight-faced. "I wouldn't have come here otherwise."

Again no one disputed it. The Abbey had once been an upscale hotel, I reasoned. And I did have a king-size bed in my room. And Big Dave was arrogant enough to demand one, so it was possible. Or was I once again falling prey to pranksters who sensed my wide-eyed gullibility? It wouldn't be the first time.

In my king-sized bed to push out disturbing images from the movie, my mind turned to Clint, the way we smiled at each other during group; the way he had looked during downstairs group in his usual pose, chair tilted back against a post, saying to me, "You're the coolest chick I've ever met," then correcting "chick" to "girl," then to "woman." I had halted him at "woman," not wanting to hear another synonym. "I get it. That's really nice to say. Thank you." I had been warmed by the compliment. Too warmed. I had been conscious of his hand brushing my hair and shoulder as he walked behind me in upstairs group on the way to his chair. *Stop it Lisa. Don't get caught up in a girlish crush. Concentrate on your recovery.* So I switched to thinking about Dan, who was opening up as he felt better. We had started calling him *Ben* after Pat forgot his name during group.

"Who's Ben?" Derwood had asked.

"Him," replied Pat, pointing at Dan.

"That's Dan, you idiot," Derwood corrected, not unkindly.

"Oh," Pat shrugged. "My memory's as bad as my spelling."

"I don't mind," Dan grinned.

The pool got rolling. Andrew printed off the blank bracket sheets, and Clint devised a point system—two points for each winner in the first round, four points for each one in the second round and so on and so forth. We secretly decided to make it more interesting, a dollar a person. Andrew didn't need to know. The previously disdainful Derwood now peppered us with questions as he filled out his brackets. "Is Iowa any good this year?" "What about Iowa State. Are they any good?" "Duke. Duke's always good, right?" We scoffed when he picked a #16 seed to go all the way to the Final Four. "I gotta go with St. Mary's, a good Catholic school. Yep, I'm going with St. Mary's."

That Tuesday morning while getting ready before the internal AA meeting, I turned on the clock radio. It was the first time I'd had the urge to do so. I fiddled with the dial, looking for classic rock. My finger paused on the dial, my ear poised to discern the song. I sat down on the edge of the bed, the dawn of recognition spreading a smile across my face. I turned up the volume on Gloria Gaynor singing "I Will Survive." I got up and started dancing, body twirling, arms raised to the ceiling, softly singing along. I hadn't felt like dancing in eons. I couldn't wait to talk about it at the meeting. But the meeting moderator was staunch-Catholic, retired-cop Kevin Murphy. Talk about checking all the Irish boxes. I wasn't sure if he'd appreciate my "I Will Survive" share.

As the shares wound around the circle, I chomped at the bit, eager to speak, which was a big no-no. I should be listening, not planning what I was going to say. Kyle was next and he was bursting with eagerness. Something had happened to him, too.

"It's like we're reborn," he said, leaning forward, eyes shining. "We are lucky to have this happen to us. Think of all the people who go through life not having this happen to them. They go through life wanting material things, wanting to be better than everybody else. They never get this rebirth."

Kevin was nodding vigorously. "It's a gift," he said. "It takes a while to get there, to see it that way, but it's a gift. Our alcoholism is a gift."

Wow! I was blown away. A gift! I had never thought of it that way. Would I ever reach that point, seeing rehab as a gift? I don't know. Pretty soon it was my turn.

"Kyle, that is powerful stuff," I started, "and all I got is Gloria Gaynor." I described how I hadn't yet turned on the radio in my room, how I hadn't felt like turning on the radio, until this morning. And the song I found was "I Will Survive."

"That's the kind of shit I'm talking about!" Kyle exclaimed. "That's the kind of shit that's happening!"

After the meeting, I rushed up to Kyle. "Kyle, what happened? Where did that come from?"

"I don't know. I felt..." he paused, grappling for the right words, "like a force going through me. I was shaking."

"Wow. I loved it. I loved what you said."

"I love that you heard 'I Will Survive.'"

We grinned at each other. What the hell was happening?

I was queen for a day. Katie had finally found a place to live; she was moving in with her aunt who lived in a small town outside of Clinton. I was going to miss her steady, wise presence, ever-sketching, ever-bundled up in a fleece blanket. Every day, the staff assured me there would be another female and every time, I assured them back that I didn't mind. And I truly didn't. I enjoyed the male camaraderie and, admittedly, the male attention. Although I was buddies with these guys, they made me feel attractive. I was completely comfortable baring my soul before them. But my reign for a day came to an end.

She arrived at dinnertime, attractive, tiny, thin, younger than me. I was immediately threatened. She was pretty in a put-together way, makeup carefully applied, dark, shoulder-length hair straightened. I'm sure guys would describe her as hot. She was chesty for being so petite and I tried to withhold catty judgment, but the thought had already popped into my head: *Were they real?* I hated cleavage on myself. Guys were so preoccupied with breasts anyway, why in the world would you want to draw additional attention to them? I wasn't sure where this self-consciousness came from. Perhaps from my Mom. She instilled a sense of modesty, setting that example with her own clothing choices and the outfits she allowed us to wear. From swimming suits to summer frocks, the Avelleyra girls had not dressed provocatively. Even in my 20s, newly liberated from living at home, you'd think I would've thrown cleavage caution to the wind. Not so. Once on Ragbrai, when we were still wearing swimsuits and tube tops when we biked, my friend Teresa pointed out that she could see a nipple when I leaned over the handlebars. The crossover one-piece swimsuit I was wearing as a top covered me otherwise, but on a bike, you could see my boob. Neither of us had a safety pin or tape on us. And in those days, we didn't carry extra clothing on our bikes. We pedaled our bikes through the stopover town, seeking a solution, me frantically tugging at my top for coverage, my bike weaving.

"You're gonna wipe out if you keep doing that," Teresa had warned. The town had been so small our options were severely limited, not a hardware nor convenience store in sight. But resourceful Teresa prevailed, ordering us to wait at an auto body shop where she disappeared inside. Upon return, she proudly wielded a heavy-duty stapler, and altered my deep V-neck to a more modest V-neck. It was during those fledgling years of Ragbrai that we accidentally stumbled upon day drinking. The bike ride across Iowa wasn't just a party in the overnight towns. It was a party all day! There was drinking in every town!

I squelched my insecurities about the new girl, instead channeling the goodwill and camaraderie that I had been experiencing, warmly welcoming her and asking questions. She was from Des Moines, which made Pat perk up, or should I say perk up even more. Pat often professed his love for women, how they look, feel and smell, which sometimes made me squirm. I noticed his eyes gravitating to her chest while he chewed. Mona told us she had been hospitalized, she was a vodka drinker, and her grandfather had just died. I fought to stop comparisons and listened sympathetically.

The next day, another new resident arrived, shuffling in during downstairs afternoon group, wearing sweats and a ball cap pulled low over his eyes. He slouched in his chair, arms crossed. I took an instant dislike to him. So much for goodwill and camaraderie. He mumbled that his name was Jim and was from Mason City, which was up by my hometown.

Later that week, counselor Mark had us illustrate our lifelines on over-sized sheets of paper, drawing with markers and colored pencils. I sat at one of the round tables in the TV room, pondering how I was going to tackle this exercise, fighting my annoyance with it. And Mark wanted some of us to present theirs to the group. Not me! I'd grown comfortable with these guys, but not with making a presentation in front of them. I would fully cooperate on paper—honest, open and willing. *I bet Dave hates this,* I thought, watching him. This was a form of art therapy. I looked over at Derwood, sitting at the table next to mine. He rolled his eyes and I grinned back. I decided to trace my life and drinking geographically, drawing outlines of Iowa and Wisconsin, the latter distorted and elongated because I didn't leave enough room. I drew stars and arrows to designate cities and my moves back and forth, writing down milestones near each city. Next to Madison: *Got divorced. Drinking increased, eventually to daily.*

I paused to check on everyone else's progress. They all looked engrossed, heads down, markers moving. I predicted that Kyle's would be really artistic, Pat's would be a crazy hodgepodge of images, and Dave's simple and matter of fact.

"How are we all doing?" Mark asked. "Are we ready to present?"

Everyone was pretty much done. "Let's go with what you have and share some of them," Mark directed. We gathered in a half circle over by Mark, who stood in front of the white erase board. "Who's going first?" he asked.

After some chair shifting and furtive glances, Kyle stood up. "I'll go."

He clipped his illustrations to the white board, standing next to it, using a marker as a pointer. His sketches were excellent, no surprise, and I wished I had my glasses to see the detail better. Kyle presented us highlights of his life, starting with high school when he was a jock, golf being his showcase sport. A football injury had dashed plans for a golf scholarship and that's when he started using, first for the pain, then because he was depressed about the injury. This was illustrated by a guy swinging a golf club, next to a guy grabbing his knee, screaming in pain. Kyle also turned to drugs when he was betrayed by a girlfriend who cheated on him; a halved, bleeding heart surrounded by pills represented his pain. The betrayal led to a stretch of time during which he was unable to commit to any relationship, hence the drawing of a heart surrounded by a wall.

Just then, counselor Andrew entered the TV room and, to my surprise, walked over to me. A one-on-one with Andrew? I was instantly nervous. I followed him up the stairs to a small room, furnished with a couple of comfortable chairs. This was my second session here; the first was with Jamie, and would stick with me forever. I had been lamenting that I cried all the time, particularly when I spoke in group or at AA meetings. "I hate it. I feel so weak. I start out okay but by the time I'm almost done, I'm crying," I said, my voice trembling, my eyes filling with tears. "See?" I had pointed to my eyes and we chuckled.

"It's not weakness, Lisa," Jamie had said. "It's your emotions spilling out. You are feeling so much, you can't hold it in, so it comes out in the form of tears. When you talk about what you're feeling, that emotion rises to the forefront then spills out with tears."

I had chewed on that a bit. And now I sat in the same chair across from Andrew, hoping that this one on one would be matter of fact, no "spilling." It started out that way, him asking me how I was doing, sleep-wise, eating-wise, anxiety-wise. Then it shifted.

"What do you plan to do after you leave The Abbey?" he asked.

I'd been trying *not* to think about going back to work, then coming home from work and being alone in my apartment. Whenever I allowed any of those thoughts to creep in, I immediately felt gnawing in my stomach. I shifted in my chair and hedged. "I'm trying not to think about it. I get nervous if I think about it."

"That's normal, being nervous about returning to the real world outside of here. But what do you *want* when you leave here?"

I shifted in my chair again. What was he getting at? What did he want from me? It didn't matter what he wanted. I knew my answer, as simplistic as it may sound. I met his unblinking gaze.

"Peace of mind."

"Okay. That's good. But what do you want to *do*?"

"I want to stay sober."

Andrew leaned forward, his eyes never leaving mine, boring into me, apparently not satisfied with my answer. "What do you want to do? Did you ever ask yourself that before?"

"No...I guess not...well, not lately."

"So, what do you want to *do*?"

"I don't know," I murmured. His gaze was intense, but I willed myself to return it. I forced myself to sit still.

"What is it you really want to do?"

"You mean more than not drinking?"

"What do you want to *do*?" he repeated.

We stared at each other and suddenly my bewilderment cleared. "I want to write," I stated, the tension and squirminess draining away. What was this feeling? Hope? Determination? I wasn't sure. Andrew sat back in his chair, a satisfied grin spreading across his face. I couldn't help but smile back.

"I want to write again. I want to write about this."

"What has stopped you from writing?"

I pondered that. It was not a pleasant realization. "Laziness, lack of motivation." A beat. "Drinking." I told him about how I had started jotting down notes and quotes from group, from AA meetings, from sitting around in the TV room. I told him I had a journalism degree, having worked in newspapers for six years, most of the enjoyment coming from writing columns and interviewing for stories, eventually soured by the cutthroat nature of it. I told him about my last newspaper interview with Senator George McGovern, who had been in Madison for the opening ceremony of a recovery center named after his alcoholic daughter. She had frozen to death in a snowbank near a bar I had frequented. I told him how candid and sincere the Senator had been, how we had both teared up.

"Teresa McGovern," he said, nodding and smiling softly. "I read his book about her."

Soon after, Andrew let me go and I returned, lighter of heart, to the lifeline presentations which were just wrapping up. Derwood and Kyle walked toward me, both shaking their heads.

"You missed it," Darvin said.

"What? What did I miss?"

"Pat," Kyle replied. "He was up the rest of the time after you left."

"The whole time?" I asked.

"The whole time," Kyle intoned.

"Wow, you missed it," chimed in Dave who had just walked up. "Did you tell her?"

Over Dave's shoulder, I spotted Pat approaching. "Shhhh, he's coming."

"Sorry about that, guys," Pat apologized. "Once I got started, it just came pouring out."

"Don't worry about it man, you needed to talk about it," said Kyle, patting Pat on the back. Out of Pat's line of sight, he mouthed to me, "OH MY GOD."

"Yeah, you gotta let out that shit," assured Delvin.

"Don't worry about it, man," said Dave, also patting him.

As Pat walked away, Dave stayed behind with me. "What happened?" I asked, dying to know.

"It was bad, really bad. He took up the rest of the time. But he needed to."

"Bad how? Worse than his wife messing around on him?" Dave nodded. "Sex abuse? Was he abused?" Dave nodded again. "We'll talk later," he said.

Later in the TV room, Dave and Derwood filled me in, the sexual abuse by family friends, his mother's drunken neglect of him, his acting out.

"Poor Pat. No wonder he got in trouble and used so young," I said. "His demons started early."

"Yeah, it explains all the anger. That's for sure," Dave said.

"I really feel bad for the guy," Darvin added.

The discussions were rich and wide-ranging that week. I don't know if it was because we were all more comfortable with each other, or because some were near the end of their stay. Whatever it was, there was a lot to absorb, and I was jotting down quotes more and more. Clint talked about his dream of coaching football, which he'd forgotten in his pursuit of making money. After he lost it all, his friends disappeared too. I ached for him.

"You should do it, Clint," I said. "You should coach. You'd be great with young kids. And now you have more to offer."

Dave still stubbornly resisted the first step, refusing to admit he was powerless over alcohol. But at least he admitted he couldn't admit it. He knew he had to quit drinking. But forever? I believed that it would be hard for Dave to admit he was powerless over anything, he was that type of guy. He easily offered advice to others, but didn't share his own issues. "Pat, you gotta let go of that anger. You're not going to be able to stay sober with that anger." "Dan, you gotta stop hanging out with that heroin crowd. You gotta find different friends."

Eff Jeff used a device where he'd interrupt a share and direct the speaker to use the pronoun *I* rather than *you*. He used it a lot with Dave. For example, when Dave addressed Pat, Eff Jeff interrupted him saying, "*I* gotta let go of that anger..." When he addressed Dan, Eff Jeff interrupted with "*I* gotta stop hanging out with..." It clearly irritated Dave.

"But I don't hang out with heroin users," Dave bristled.

"But what about those golf buddies you hang out with?" Eff Jeff countered. "They're big drinkers, right?"

That silenced Dave.

Once, Kyle shared an anecdote. "My wife was using you statements and I said to her 'You're using you statements when you should be saying I instead.' She told me to shut the fuck up."

Dave admitted he was embarrassed by all of it. "I'm embarrassed about saying mean shit to my kids, mean shit to my wife. I regret that."

"That's what amends are for," Eff Jeff replied. "Which attorney would you want to hire? The alcoholic working the program or a self-righteous prick? Is there also some guilt and shame thrown in there?"

Dave nodded.

"Guilt is normal," Eff Jeff continued. "Guilt is a kick in the head. 'I did a shitty thing, but I can make up for it.' But shame is like a kick in the face. Shame is 'I'm a shitty person.' Shame can consume you."

I mulled that over. Was I embarrassed? Did I feel guilt and shame? Maybe I felt some embarrassment about work and how I stopped going. But now I mainly felt trepidation about going back. I felt bad for putting my sisters and Brian through it all. That was guilt. But shame? I didn't think so. I had come to believe that I had to get this sick to finally get better. My first time in rehab, I hadn't even been close to how sick I was this time. That first time, I had gone on a week-long bender, but since I was living with my mom, I held it partially in check. What was worse that time was *how* I ended up in rehab, the intervention, the cops taking me away, the civil commitment to in-patient treatment. I'd always kind of been a fatalist and now I truly believed it had to happen this way for me to stay sober. Acceptance was pushing any guilt aside and making room for hope.

Dan was feeling neither acceptance nor hope. Physically he was better. He didn't sprawl on the couches as much, he roughhoused with Clint and Kyle, usually over Kyle's beloved football, and he was crushing on Sam, the staffer. It was cute. He'd perk up when she entered a room. When she drove the van to

AA meetings, Dan rode shotgun. I think the older guys felt paternally toward him, and for everyone else he was our teacher's pet. He definitely brought out the softer side of Dave. Dan had been successfully recruited for Saturday evening Mass and occasional evening rosaries, an accomplishment that Dave used in his continuing campaign to lure me. "Dan really enjoyed going to Mass, Lisa. Didn't you Dan?" I'd look at Dan, who would then enthusiastically nod, then grin impishly at me as soon as Dave looked away. "Dan even got a rosary blessed by Father Thomas." Again, the enthusiastic nod, followed by the impish grin. He was like the little brother I never had. I couldn't wait for the sisters to meet him. At Dave's final art therapy session, the assignment was making postcards for our loved ones and he and Dan huddled and giggled over their creations. I chose the collage route, cutting and pasting words and images from magazines. Dave and Dan chose the glitter route, hence the giggling. Dan's turned out quite nice but I never saw Dave's. I guess he didn't want to leave any evidence that he had used glitter. But there was glitter everywhere, on their clothes, in their hair, on their faces. Dave's mustache sparkled. For the rest of my time there, glitter made unexpected appearances, at meals, at group, in the TV room. Seeing those two enjoy art therapy together warmed my heart.

Then there was Cary Grant. According to Abbey lore, Cary Grant had stayed at The Abbey back when it was a hotel while on tour for a one-man show. Apparently, he had stayed in room 305, Dan's room. And Dave's sister had had tickets to that one-man show in Des Moines. Unfortunately, Cary had died the night before the performance.

"He died in Dan's room?" Kyle exclaimed.

"No. He died in Des Moines, you knucklehead," Dave replied.

"Did she get her money back?" Derwood asked.

"I don't know," said Dave exasperated.

"Who's Cary Grant?" asked oblivious Dan, the youngest among us.

"He's someone I'd want in my room, if you know what I mean," I said, resulting in hoots and hollers from the guys.

"Really," said Dan, interest piqued.

"He's like the Brad Pitt of your generation," said Pat.

"No, he's more like George Clooney," interjected Eff Jeff, the counselor at the time. "He was suave, sophisticated."

"There's really no one comparable today," Dave said.

"And he was really funny, Dan," I said.

"He was a good actor," Darvin mused. "No one like him today."

"We'll find you a picture of him," Eff Jeff said. Later at lunch, Eff Jeff came out with his phone and showed Dan, as promised, a photo of Cary Grant.

Most of the time when Dan shared, he expressed trepidation, fear of life after treatment, life without heroin. "Now that I'm feeling better, I'm having cravings," he admitted. "I don't know if that will go away. I'm afraid of the obsession of using, even the rush of getting it."

"How many times have you overdosed?" Eff Jeff asked.

"Three."

"I'm sorry to be so blunt, but if you use again, you're gonna die," Eff Jeff said. "With booze it's gradual, but with smack, it's quick. You've had three second chances. There's not going to be a fourth."

We sat in hushed silence. Hearing it said aloud, it sounded so simple— don't use or die. For alcoholics, it took effort over time to drink oneself to death. Even drinking straight out of the bottle took time to get to that desired destination of oblivion. For heroin addicts, that oblivion was a crapshoot every time they used. I had never tried heroin—the needles and tying that snapping rubber arm band thing freaked me out—but from everything I'd heard and read about it, the initial high was immediate and intense. And short-lived. Once used, the craving for that next high was locked in. A heroin user's addiction started and continued behind closed doors whereas an alcoholic's addiction started and continued out in public, at bars, at parties, at sporting events. An alcoholic's demise was gradual. A heroin addict's demise was abrupt, unexpected, an ever-lurking possibility with each plunge of the needle, each snort up the nose.

"I know," Dan said softly. "I know."

And we always had Pat to contribute. His narrative had shifted from anger over his broken marriage to tales of his wild and troubled youth. At one point, his family had been so frustrated with him, they sent him one summer to live with his Uncle Dick and Aunt Dix—"Yes, those were their names," Pat said— who lived in a wooded area of Maine. He had lived in a shed on their property and his uncle would come and visit, bringing a bottle of whiskey to share with his young nephew. The visit did not end well. "I burnt down their house. It was an accident!" he replied to our cries of dismay. "But I did burn it down."

He and Jesse had developed a cute relationship. They were roommates.

"I thought it was your older brother who took away your motorcycle," said Jesse correcting Pat's story at lunch. Pat paused in mid-chew, pondering, then pointed his upraised fork at Jesse. "You're right. It was my older brother."

"I take it you've heard this story before," I said to Jesse.

"Oh yeah, I hear lots of stories at bedtime."

Pat was now grinning and chewing. "He does."

"Every night?" I asked.

"Pretty much," Jesse replied. "We're both in bed, lights out, and a lot of times I'm just about asleep and I hear 'Jesse, Jesse? Are you awake?' And then we have a chat."

"I'd kill him," Derwood growled.

"That's why I have the corner suite," Dave gloated. Then to me. "With the hot tub."

"You do not have a hot tub!" I exclaimed.

After that, I noticed Jesse finishing Pat's sentences or filling in a word for him when he struggled to come up with one. And it made me smile.

Chapter Eighteen

It was the first day of the basketball tournament, so there was more urgency than usual to get back after the AA evening meeting. Even Dave curtailed his mingling and dawdling. "It's tourney time! Go Hawks!" he cheered. This led to more cheers. "Go Hawks!" "Let's go! We gotta watch some hoops!" "Woo hoo!" "Go St. Mary's!" This last from Darvin. I shook my head. Poor, amateur Derwood. But his enthusiasm made me smile.

We rushed through dinner—they didn't want us eating in the TV room—and with Clint commanding control of the remote, we watched Iowa and checked in on Notre Dame during commercials. Unfortunately, Iowa was still playing when we got summoned to art therapy, but Clint snuck out during postcard crafting, then returned with the good news that both Iowa and Notre Dame had won. Upon returning to the TV room after art therapy, we found Jim sitting in the comfiest chair, feet up on the ottoman, watching the NCAA wrestling tournament, which also happened to be taking place.

"What are you doing?" I sputtered. "We want to watch basketball."

"The wrestling tournament is going on too," said Jim, keeping his eyes on the screen.

"But we have a pool." I was also aghast that no one else was saying anything.

"We can watch both," said Kyle, moving to the couch.

That's not what I wanted to hear. I did not want diplomacy. I wanted someone to rip the remote from his creepy, selfish hands.

"I'll switch after this match," he mumbled.

My dislike for Jim had intensified. I had re-evaluated my initial impression and concluded he was worse than I thought. He was always late and unapologetic for it, walking in wearing what appeared to be his pajamas. But he always looked like he was wearing pajamas. He had chosen the spot between Jesse and me for upstairs group, squeezing into the small space. And he brought candy to these meetings. *Loud* candy. Not quiet, inconspicuous candy like Hershey kisses or fun-size candy bars. Noisy, nerve-rattling Skittles, first rustling around for them in the big bag on the table, then clacking them around in his hand before they finally made it to his mouth.

He was also late getting into the van for AA meetings. There we would sit, sliding door open, chilly air blowing in, trying to figure out who was missing.

"Everybody in?" the van driver would call back.

"No, we're one short."

"Jim's not here."

At first, it occurred without comment, maybe because he was new. But it didn't last. Grumbling soon ensued.

"Close the door! Is it Jim? Is it Jim we're waiting for? It's freezing!

"Where is he? Let's go without him."

"Are we waiting for him again?"

And when he did finally walk out the front door, he was unhurried, casual, vaping away. I applaud anyone trying to quit smoking, but this device was obnoxious, at least the way Jim used it. He ate candy obnoxiously, he dressed obnoxiously, he watched TV obnoxiously. And he vaped obnoxiously. Climbing into the van, he was accompanied by a mint-scented cloud of e-cigarette smoke. Why in the world wouldn't you exhale your vape smoke right before getting into a vehicle with a bunch of people? He'd blow it in your face and say, "Doesn't that smell nice? Minty fresh."

"Do you have to blow that thing in the van?" Derwood asked.

"It smells nice. It's like air freshener," Jim replied. "It dissipates quickly."

Once at lunch while we were still eating, he took a puff before exiting the dining room, leaving a trail of scented smoke in his wake. Dave and I exchanged a look.

"I hate that thing," Dave said.

When I heard these comments, I silently cheered. Kyle defended him, saying Jim was hurting, worried about his relationship with his young daughter. I tried to dredge up some sympathy but with each late entrance, with each rustling of the Skittles bag, with each e-cigarette exhalation, it dissipated quickly, much like that fragrant cloud. And now this. TV remote stealing. I plunked down in a chair across the room from him. He finally turned it to basketball, allowing us to watch the second half of a couple of games. But he clicked back and forth between sports. I stayed silent but my head jerked toward him with each click away from basketball, hoping to catch his eye, to give him a dirty look. But he stared straight ahead at the television screen. I looked over at Dave, who was shaking his head. Clint hopped up from the couch.

"I'm outta here. You need any more chew?" he asked Dave, who said no.

"I'm going to bed too," I said. I had had enough. "Good night." I heard desultory replies as I left the room—Jim had killed the shared enjoyment of watching basketball with a press of his finger. I was hoping to catch Clint in the lobby, but he was too quick on his feet. I lay in bed and stewed, but stewing prevented sleep. I thought about Clint, comparing our tournament brackets, his gentle teasing of me for choosing Wisconsin over tournament favorite Villanova, how we looked at each other, how he kept touching my arm.

Next evening during the internal Friday AA meeting, which was always held upstairs, Jim got up abruptly and left early. My suspicion alarm bells jangled.

We had spent the day watching basketball at every opportunity, updating our brackets, teasing each other for losses, praising Derwood on the St. Mary's upset. I got Clint on the Wisconsin bandwagon, even though he didn't take them as far as I had. We heckled the player with the man-bun, all while Vape Man sat sullenly on the sidelines. And now he was sprinting out of the AA meeting. Kyle noticed it too, and looked over at me. Earlier that day, he had told me he thought I was being too hard on Jim, that I needed to give him a chance. Now, I raised my eyebrows at Kyle. Down in the TV room, he was in the same chair, watching wrestling. I stood there, silent, pissed. Kyle passed me, tossing his football, seating himself in the middle of the couch.

"Dude, can we turn to hoops?" he asked.

"After this match," intoned Vape Man, eyes staring at the screen, exhaling a scented cloud for emphasis.

I rolled my eyes at Kyle and stomped to the dining room, where I grabbed a water from the fridge, which was getting low on beverages. Still stewing, I noisily restocked the fridge with the packs stored behind the counter. Jim had been sharing more in group and even *those* were obnoxious, a lot of woe is me about missing his daughter, sprinkled with his glory days in Iowa City AA before he relapsed. Having coached at City High in Iowa City, he name-dropped University of Iowa coaches and athletes. His relapse story did stir some sympathy within me, I admit. After getting sober, he had broken his leg playing softball and while in the hospital, they gave him fentanyl for the pain. He was instantly hooked. None of that explained away his current obnoxious behavior, though. I mustered up some fake goodwill and returned to the TV room, where basketball was up on the screen. Plopping down next to Kyle, I pointedly ignored the slouched vaping figure with the remote.

"Who's playing?" I asked.

"We got Iowa State in one game and Oklahoma in another," replied Kyle, leaning over to whisper, "and we got wrestling on another." I nudged him sharply and he giggled.

"Did you bring me a water?" Dave asked, smirking from his chair. "You walked away so fast, I couldn't get your attention."

"No, I didn't bring you a water!"

"*Will* you go get me a water?" he whined, grinning.

"No, I will not," I replied, returning his grin.

Having finished his phone call to his fiancée, Clint squeezed in next to me, scooching me over toward Kyle with his hips. "Hey, make some room." I feigned irritation but was actually thrilled to be seated between these two. I particularly enjoyed Clint pressing up next to me. Vape Man switched to wrestling a couple of times, but it was quick.

Then, during a pleasant Saturday of watching basketball, Kyle decided we should watch a movie that evening—none of our favorite teams were playing—and I whole-heartedly approved of his choice, There Will Be Blood starring Daniel Day Lewis in an Academy-award winning performance. After that, Kyle and I kept addressing each other with the movie's tagline "I abandoned my boy!" Passing each other in the TV room "I abandoned my boy!" followed by a high five. Sitting down for group, "I abandoned my boy!" Going to the fridge at dinner to get a milk, Kyle bellowed at me, "I abandoned my boy!"

"What is that from?" Dan had asked. "You've been doing it all day."

"It's from the movie we're watching tonight," Kyle explained. "You're gonna love it."

It was an engrossing movie. Daniel Day Lewis was riveting in his smoldering malevolence. Just as the film was hitting its stride—it started a little slow—Vape Man paused it and switched to wrestling. Granted, he announced it before he did it, but what was he thinking? I didn't have to speak up this time.

"What the hell are you doing?" asked Clint.

"You've got a lot of nerve," Dave intoned, a little Daniel Day Lewis in his voice.

"I'll switch back," said Jim, again sounding like it was no big deal. He just didn't get it. Or he *did* get it and did it anyway. We watched the wrestling in stony silence. When he had switched to wrestling from basketball, some of the guys were engaged in the match. Not this time. Even after he returned to the movie, the mood was ruined, the rhythm of the complex story disrupted. And the movie was relevant to us. The main character, Daniel Plainview, was a drunk. Most of his actions were booze-fueled, and the drinking was progressing as he got more successful. The room stewed. And with a complex plot, you forget certain plot points, as illustrated by Pat, who said, "I forgot, why does he hate that guy?" We watched Daniel Plainview get darker and more ruthless as his oil well produced more oil. Right after he murdered the man who was pretending to be his brother, we were ordered to stop the movie and go to bed. Since it was so long and because Vape Man interrupted it a second time, we weren't even close to the end.

"Wow, he killed his own brother," Pat commented.

"It wasn't really his brother," Jesse said patiently. "I'll explain it to you when we get upstairs."

Leaving the TV room with Dave behind Vape/Remote Hog Man, we exchanged shakes of our heads. It wasn't just me anymore. Dave's disdain was out in the open and Vape Man took notice. According to Matt, his roommate, Vape Man had railed against Dave after the movie incident, threatening to punch him in the throat.

"He's a fucking idiot," said Dave upon hearing about it.

I squirmed inwardly. I was happy others now shared my disdain for Jim, yet his strong words toward Dave made me nervous. But nothing about his subsequent behavior diluted my dislike. The tardiness, the chomping on Skittles, the pervasive e-cigarette fog, all of it continued. If anything, he seemed to get cockier, more aggressive in his shares. Perhaps that was his response to the hostility. Matt relayed to us a second threat toward Dave, who dismissed it, but Matt was bothered. I'd be unnerved too if I shared a room with him. Lisa, the worry wart, asked if we should report it to staff, but no one else was alarmed.

"He's a headcase, but he's harmless," Kyle said. "All talk."

Was he?

Chapter Nineteen

I t was family day again. This time no introductions were necessary, Paula and Martha greeted like old friends by my cohorts and their family members alike. Coming downstairs after our noon briefing and their Al-Anon meeting, I came across Paula talking to Dave's wife and Pat's sister while Martha was with Kyle's wife Brittney, a striking beauty. I didn't get to talk to the sisters much before we were summoned for the main meeting. The counselor was Sterling, whom I had never met before the noon briefing. How unfortunate since I really liked him and found him attractive. He was tall and outdoorsy looking with a ruggedly handsome face, enthusiastic and engaging like counselor Andrew but without the intensity. I was sure the sisters were going to approve. Settling into our chairs, Martha asked who the moderator was, and on cue Sterling entered, striding handsomely across the room.

"There he is," I said, directing them with my eyes. "Sterling."

"Sterling?" Paula repeated, following him with her gaze. "What kind of a name is Sterling?"

"Sterling?" echoed Martha, also looking at him. "You've never talked about him. I'd say it's the perfect name."

"This is the first time I've seen him," I said. Martha made a low growling sound while Paula shifted in her chair, adjusting her scarf, fluffing up her hair.

"He's beastly," Paula commented.

"I don't see a wedding ring," Martha observed after a nonchalant but thorough inspection. "And I like his shoes."

"He said something about a girlfriend in our meeting," I reported.

Sterling introduced himself, so it was time to halt the girl talk. The first half was dominated by Dan's dad, a no-nonsense kind of guy who was clearly bothered by the heroin component of his son's addiction. "Drinking I can understand. But putting a needle in your arm and shooting up! How can someone do that to themselves?" he asked, his son next to him, who was motionless and staring at the floor. I ached for Dan, hoping he would look up so I could throw him a reassuring glance. But he didn't. Sterling stepped in, explaining that the substance didn't matter, addiction was addiction. No addiction was better or worse. But I think many of us sitting in that room knew the *perception* of the addiction differed from substance to substance.

"But his is worse!" Dan's dad continued. "He's overdosed three times! You don't OD from beer!"

"You can from vodka! I almost did," chimed in Pat, taking the words right out of my mouth.

Dan had spoken in group about his dad's shame, not of the addiction itself but of what he was addicted to. Even though heroin use had crept out to the suburbs, it still had that "junkie in the street" stigma. I know *I* had been guilty of that perception of heroin users. Until Dan. In my first rehab, if it wasn't booze, it was meth or crack. Like Dan's dad, Dave was critical of heroin addiction. The most notable example of this was during one of my favorite group exercises held just the day before. First off, Vape Man had been absent, big plus. Don't know why. Don't care. He wasn't there. It was a counselor Jo-run exercise and the minute she pulled out a rope, my cohorts scoffed. With three people holding the rope, a participant on one end created a relapse scenario for the participant in the middle, while the rope holder on the opposite end judged the strength of the plan. Participants switched places and roles along the rope. It could've been done without the rope, but who am I to judge? My threesome had consisted of Derwood, Jesse, and me, starting with me spinning a tale of road rage for Darvin. While driving to Hy-Vee on a four-lane road, I had said, a big pickup truck loomed up behind him and rode his ass until it passed on the left, abruptly changing lanes in front of him and cutting him off, the driver staring at him in the rearview mirror. I had acted out the part of Darvin driving along peacefully, then becoming aware of the pickup truck in the rearview mirror. Then I was the truck driver, angrily glaring at Derwood and flipping him off as I passed. But it hadn't ended there. My story continued at the grocery store, where Derwood spotted the offending truck in the parking lot, then bumped into the driver right by the liquor aisle in the store. I had the driver confront Darvin, shoving him and poking him in the chest.

"What do you do?" I had asked. During the telling of my story, I could tell Darvin was enjoying it, a slow grin spreading across his face. He thoughtfully considered his response.

"I grab a bottle of whiskey and bash him over the head with it," he had replied, grinning proudly.

"Good answer," Jesse said.

I shook my head disapprovingly at both of them.

"Okay," Derwood said. "I could go get the manager and have the fucker thrown out of the store. But instead I'll walk away, get my groceries, and go to a meeting because I would still be pissed."

"Approved!" Jesse claimed.

Dave, Dan, and Pat had comprised another threesome, with Dave starting off as the storyteller, Dan the subject and Pat the judge. Dave's story had Dan going to an AA meeting and getting kicked out.

"And rightfully so," Dave had said.

"Dave!" I had exclaimed.

"Woah, that's harsh," Clint had agreed.

"It's a story!" Dave had defended himself. "You know how some AAers feel about drug addicts."

It was true. Is that how Dave felt? I wondered.

"Rightfully so," Dan/Ben had repeated, a slight grin on his boyish face. "Come on, Dave. Bring it."

Dear, adorable Ben, a good sport in the face of snobby Dave whose story had continued with Dan's car breaking down, then Dan walking to a friend's house where there was pure heroin.

Acting it out, Dan had said, "I slam the door in the friend's face, and call another friend to give me a ride to an NA meeting," heavy emphasis on the "N." Ben had looked triumphantly at Dave as we cheered and Dave clapped.

Nice job, Dave. "Yes! Approved!" Pat had bellowed.

But Dan displayed none of that spunk today, slumped next to his broad-shouldered dad. Sterling commented on the hardship *any* addiction causes loved ones, deftly pivoting to the session topic, which was co-dependency. Beatnik Cody opened the discussion with more tales of his sabotaging ex-wife. She just couldn't handle his sobriety, he told us. With him sober, she couldn't justify grilling him about where he was, who he was with, what he was doing. It had taken a gradual toll.

Mona's sister spoke up. They all worried and looked after Mona, she said; it defined their family dynamic. Their father took care of things around her house, their mother was always available to look after her children.

Katie, the sister, stated this matter-of-factly, without resentment. Whenever Mona shared, she gave the impression she was the darling of the family. Her grandmother, who was dying, had given her a leather-bound mini–Big Book to bring to treatment, which she had been eager to show me. It was very nice, and I said so. Mona was also a bit of a one-upper. For example, whenever I talked about my mother's death leading to the start of my final spiral, she bemoaned her grandmother's near death and how she really wanted to get sober for her grandmother. Whenever I mentioned my time in the hospital and how sick I had been, she would talk about almost dying there, having been given the Last Rites. Also, whenever she talked about her drinking, she made darn sure to underscore that she never drank in front of her kids or when she had been running an in-home daycare. I was skeptical. Perhaps she did abstain sometimes with kids around, but I highly doubted the *never*. Plastic water bottles were a vodka drinker's dream. You just had to make sure that no one else accidentally drank out of it. For public consumption, I favored the green plastic Diet 7-Up bottles. Dump out half the 7-Up, then glug, glug, glug, fill it back up with vodka and away you go! I had a funnel for just that purpose. Mona and I got along fine—we sat next to each other at meals, teased the boys about farting, about leaving half-empty soda cans sitting around, and relentless clicking with the remote. But she and I never made that *connection*. You can't force it. She had a good rapport with the guys, but it wasn't the same rapport as I had with them, so I didn't feel threatened. Pat was gaga for Mona and wasn't subtle about it, but then Pat wasn't subtle about anything. Her seat for upstairs group was next to his and he gushed every morning about how good she smelled. Turned out they lived near each other in Des Moines, another unifying factor. Pat showered her in constant attention and she demurely basked in it. I truly was not jealous. That kind of attention would have made me feel uncomfortable. Shit, it made me feel uncomfortable watching it. Watching Mona now with her sister and parents, I got the sense she was accustomed to being the center of attention and an object of desire. She had always had a man in her life. The father of her children was a drug dealer who was in prison. He had beat the shit out of her, and she feared the day he was to be released, which was soon. When she spoke of this, she was emotional, but I got the sense she relished the drama. I expressed sympathy but did not gush.

Sterling explained that co-dependency could be just as addictive as drugs or alcohol. It was when a family member enabled an addict, or, to boil it down, put up with their shit and cleaned up their messes. There was no co-dependency in my situation. I had kept my drinking away from my sisters. You can't slur in a text. If I ever talked to them on the phone, it was early in the day, early enough for them to think I couldn't possibly have started drinking yet. Ha! It was never too early. Evening drinking melded into late night drinking, which melded into middle of the night drinking, which melded into next morning swigs. Early to mid-morning was the best time to make voice contact. It was like prevent defense. I just had to be careful to not sound too animated. Keep it simple and brief.

After the first of the year at work, we always got a new batch of PTO time and my absences had increased. During one of these absences, the sisters came to town for one of Martha's many doctor appointments at the University of Iowa hospitals. I had a heads up, but I was too far gone at that point. There was no way I was going to stop drinking for even a couple of hours. I lied and said I was at work, but I knew they would stop by. And they did. So I outwitted them. We alcoholics are wily devils. First, I made sure I had enough vodka for the day. Then I moved my car from its regular parking slot to the parking lot of the adjacent apartment complex, making sure it was between two vehicles and out of sight of my building. Then I waited. Not allowing myself to pass out, a common occurrence during the day, I remained vigilant until I heard voices. When I saw it was them, I scurried to the bedroom and dropped to the floor on the side of the bed away from the window. My apartment was on the ground floor, and you could easily peer into the bedroom window by walking around the side of the building. Although the curtains were closed, there was a crack that provided enough of a view. First, I heard knocking on the door and the playful calling of my name. I stayed down on the floor, knowing them so well, and sure enough a shadow fell across the window. The room darkened for a few seconds before the shadow moved away. I stayed down a few minutes longer, hearing them at the door again, until there was prolonged silence. I hadn't felt bad at all about hiding, just impatient for them to leave.

With Mona, it sounded like family members came over all the time, her father to mow her lawn and unclog drains, her mother to bring groceries or some item found at Target for the grandkids. "But she seemed fine. She didn't seem like she had been drinking," said Mona's mom, also an alcoholic, and also an alcoholic with an asterisk after her title. Not "I never drank in front of my kids," like her daughter. Instead "I only drank Chablis. I never drank the hard stuff." Mona shared the sharp facial features of her mother as well as the softened versions of her drinking. Her dad sat silent and stoic. You got the feeling he had to fight to get a word in edgewise.

I thought of other co-dependency in our ranks. Mona definitely, Dan somewhat. Kyle too, with his wife, as I learned from the sisters. Martha had bonded with her in the Al-Anon meeting. After Brittany complained about being fed up with getting stuck with everything—taking care of their son, taking care of the house, taking care of him—Martha told her about the ultimatum with her alcoholic husband. This was her second ultimatum, Brittany had replied.

"Martha got to her," Paula told me. "She cried, and I don't think she cries easily. She puts on a tough façade."

Dave looked over at us with a mischievous twitch of his mustache. "I bet your sisters aren't co-dependent." We exchanged looks, grinning at each other. "They didn't clean up my messes because I didn't let them know about my messes. I learned to hide my drinking from them. My other sisters too."

"There's more of you?" asked Sterling, a handsome grin transforming his serious counselor face.

"Two more," I said sheepishly.

"Which numbers are they?" asked Dan.

"Number one and two," I replied, warmed that he had broken out of his silence.

Pat started to raise his hand. "Don't do it Pat," interjected Dave, heading off Pat at the scatological reference pass. "I know where you're going."

"What?" Pat asked. "I was gonna ask if their parents drank."

Lightness and laughter descended upon the room, prompting Sterling to end the first half on a high note.

The lightheartedness continued into the second half, Pat's sister and brother telling stories about Pat and his thievery and hijinks. Knowing what we knew about Pat, I wondered how much *they* knew or if it was a dark, festering family secret. I guessed they knew but never spoke of it, pretending like it never happened, explaining away his addiction as Pat just being Pat. Several family members tried to talk some sense into Dan's dad, gently pointing out that addiction is addiction, no matter the substance, Kyle adding that opiates are more mainstream than ever. Even Mona's dad broke out of his stoic silence.

"You gotta love and support them, no matter what they're using," he said.

Chapter Twenty

Jamie gave me a book to read, *The Gifts of Imperfection, a Guide to Welcoming Your Authentic Self*, after I revealed how I chronically compared myself to others—my looks, my relationship status, where I lived, my car. Upon skimming the introduction, I realized that there was someone else who would better benefit from this book. Its message seemed to be aimed at over-achievers, go-getters, perfectionists, the ultra-competitive. I was self-critical but not consumed by perfectionism and winning. A certain Loras quarterback sprung to mind.

Clint struggled with high expectations. I suppose it was difficult for any jock in a post-jock world. The drive to compete turned into a drive to make money, to impress his peers. He measured himself in dollar amounts. Clint had turned his back on his true love, coaching, because there wasn't enough money in it. After reading a synopsis on its opening pages—"...an acceptance of imperfections and vulnerabilities..." "...difference between true belonging, which is being accepted for who you are, and fitting in which requires you to change who you are," I thought of Clint's buddies, who had abandoned him. I didn't know if he even liked to read, but I didn't care. I tracked him down in the TV room.

"Big game tonight," he said, referring to the Wisconsin–Villanova game. "Bucky's going down," Kyle growled.

"We'll see," I said, plopping down next to Clint on the couch and handing him the book. "Jamie gave me this to read, but I thought maybe you'd like it." He read the title and riffled through the pages. "It's not that long. You should be able to read most of it before you leave."

"A book!" said Dan scornfully. "Get the audio tape!" He grinned at me.

"Shut up, Ben," I said, making a face at him. Clint was looking at me. "You don't have to. I just thought you might—"

"No, I'm gonna read it," he said, smiling softly. "I'm gonna start right now. That's really nice that you thought of me. But don't you want to read it?"

"I can read it after you're gone."

Just saying those words triggered a swell of precarious emotions. He and Kyle were leaving next week, and Dave was switching to out-patient in a couple of days. I only allowed myself to dwell upon the departures when I was alone in my room at bedtime, where I didn't have to suppress the heartache. Clint scampered off with the book and I stayed on the couch, groaning as Kyle surfed the channels.

"Cops? Do you want to watch Cops?" he asked. I groaned. "South Park. How about South Park?" I groaned louder. "Snakes? Do we want to learn about snakes?" This time Dan groaned. We finally agreed on an MTV show about catfishing. Later that day, I came across Clint stretched out on the loveseat, engrossed in the book. I ached to ask him how it was, but I treaded softly to my room without interrupting him. Before leaving for the evening AA meeting, I walked again through the sitting area (Clint wasn't there anymore) and down the hall to grab a pen from my spot in the big room. Looking out the hall windows, I saw Dave and Kyle shooting baskets in the parking lot. I stopped and watched. Kyle dribbled around Dave for a lay-up, Dave grabbed the ball and dribbled to the perimeter, where he turned and released a decent jump shot. It thudded off the rim and they both scrambled for the rebound. Kyle got to it first and softly banked it into the hoop. Kyle celebrated and Dave dismissed him with a wave of his hand and a smile on his face.

Retrieving the ball, Kyle dribbled and taunted, then passed it to Dave who squared up and swished a shot through the net. Kyle writhed in mock agony as Dave strutted toward him, ending in an affectionate tussle. Tears stung my eyes. *I really had grown to love these guys.*

Whether it was the fresh air or the exercise, Kyle was rambunctious in the van as we waited for Jim.

"Who are we waiting for?" asked staffer Sam, from the driver's seat.

"Who do you think," I muttered.

"Vape Man. We're waiting for Vape Man," said Kyle from the back of the van, pronouncing it like Christian Bale's Batman. I couldn't help but giggle.

"And Clint," said Jesse who was sitting next to me in the front seat. "Clint's not here."

"Clintoris?" said Kyle in his regular voice. "We're missing Clintoris? Where's Clintoris?" Hearing Kyle's disembodied voice without seeing him somehow made it funnier for me. I rocked back and forth in laughter.

"Maybe he's reading that book," said Dan from the shotgun seat, a twinkle in his eye.

Just then, Clint hopped into the van.

"Here he is. Here's Clintoris. Where have you been, Clintoris?" Next came an "Oof," followed by the sounds of scuffling, then giggling. "No man, stop, you're messing up the hair." Giggle, giggle. "Not the hair."

Casual and unhurried, Jim pulled himself up into the van and plunked down in the middle seat, exhaling a huge cloud of scented smoke. I heard Dave mutter, "Really?" Normally, I would have been completely annoyed, but I was still laughing too hard. Kyle returned to Batman voice. "Vape Man. We've just been vaped. We've just been vaped in the van."

"Now do we have everyone?" asked Sam, in her stern, responsible voice. I looked up and saw her smiling in the rearview mirror.

"Yep. Everyone. Including Vape Man and Clintoris," announced Pat.

Head shaking, Sam pulled the rollicking van out of The Abbey parking lot.

After the meeting, Pat was last getting into the van and was resoundingly chastised for it.

"Pat, what the hell were you doing in there?" Derwood asked.

"You hate being late for dinner," added Jesse, the all-knowing roommate.

"I was talking to my nemesis," Pat said. A couple of days ago, Pat had noticed a guy at our table staring at him.

"Did you ask him why he was staring at you?" asked Dave.

"Sort of. Halfway through the meeting, I realized that I'd been sitting right under the Twelve Steps poster. He wasn't staring at me. He was staring at the Twelve Steps!"

The van erupted with laughter. My ribs hurt from laughing so hard.

"And when I told him about it, he looked at me like I was out of my mind!"

"You told him? About the staring?" sputtered Darvin.

"Yeah. I thought I'd make amends anyway."

With that, the van rollicked all the way back, too.

Wisconsin beat Villanova. It was a great game. Kyle dramatically tore up his bracket sheet and stomped out of the room. I quietly relished my victory, doubly warmed from the enjoyment of watching it sitting next to Clint.

"That probably puts you in the lead," he said.

"I can't believe Wisconsin won," Dave intoned.

"That was a really good game," added Derwood, the Nascar convert.

"I gotta go read before lights out," said Clint, hopping up from the couch. I was disappointed to see him go, but happy about the reading part. He really liked the book. Shortly thereafter, I went up to my room and tried to read my second novel, a riveting thriller, but I set it aside, instead nestling under the covers and savoring the day. How could I feel this good in treatment? How could I possibly be looking forward to the next day? I drifted into a peaceful slumber.

Upon awakening, I realized something that dampened last night's glow. It was Dave's last day. Sure, he'd be coming back every day for group, but it wasn't the same. No more Dave making us wait after the Bettendorf AA meetings. No more Dave making sardonic remarks at dinner. No more Dave leading the Catholic brigade. No more Dave trying to cajole staff into letting us stay up a little longer.

A couple of nights ago, Dave had received his one-month chip at the Bettendorf meeting, which made me cry, mostly because you could tell how proud he was. Kyle, Dave, and I had joked, as the end of our Abbey stays approached, how we were going to get up from our chairs at the Bettendorf meeting, raise our hands in the air and walk out, announcing, "I'm cured! I'm sober! I'm cured!" Of course, none of us did it but we enjoyed talking about it. Part of the reason he was switching to out-patient was because poor, pampered

Dave missed his own bed. He continually had trouble sleeping while at The Abbey, even with the corner suite and hot tub. With a heavy heart, I trudged downstairs to get my meds and start the day.

"Good morning, sunshine." Derwood greeted me as he did every morning on my trip through the TV room to the dining room for my morning provisions. His morning routine included making a strong pot of coffee, then drinking it while watching Fox News. Unfortunately, I was still off coffee. If someone else made it, we heard about it, Delvin complaining about the "pussy coffee." Instead of walking by like I usually did, I stopped. "Dave's leaving this morning," I reminded him.

"I know. I'm bummed. And I really thought he was a dick when I first met him."

"Yeah, I thought he was your typical arrogant lawyer."

"Which he is." We chuckled.

"But now, I don't want him to go."

"He's still coming back for out-patient."

"I know. But it's not the same."

"I know. It's not the same."

Upstairs for the community meeting, we sat quietly in our seats. Even Dave was already there, and he tended to stroll in right at start time. Jamie entered the room, walking straight toward me. "Can we meet for a one on one?" she asked. My stomach clenched.

"Is it alright if we do it later? We're saying good-bye to Dave."

"Oh, sure. I'll come find you later."

As Jamie left, Vape Man entered, carrying a couple bags of candy. He sat down and slapped the bags on the table. I caught Derwood scowling at him and rolled my eyes. Karen and Eff Jeff took their seats at the head table, bringing us to attention. Eff Jeff looked right at Dave. They exchanged a smile and tears stung my eyes.

"I understand we have a good-bye this morning," Karen said.

"This should be good," added Eff Jeff, soft chuckles rippling around the room. Vape Man stuck his hand in the Skittles bag and rustled around. I couldn't take it. I grabbed his arm.

"Please. Not now," I pleaded. He pulled his hand out and deposited a handful of Skittles into his mouth. I closed my eyes and prayed for strength. When I opened them, Eff Jeff was grinning at me.

"I'll start," said Pat.

The good-byes were a combination of humor and nostalgia, two of *my* favorite things. Pat brought up the dongs and emotionally thanked Dave for re-introducing him to the Catholic Church. Pat's voice broke during this and I strained to look at Dave. Only his profile was available to me as he staunchly stared straight ahead. Darvin also thanked him for getting them to Mass and for helping him with some legal issues. "You're a pretty good guy for a lawyer," he said. Kyle recalled the no smoking placards, acknowledging what a good sport Dave had been, stressing that they should get together in Cedar Rapids and go to a meeting together. Clint also mentioned getting together in CR and how nice it was to have a "chewing" buddy. Dan reminded him about the glitter mess ("I'm still finding it") and thanked him for the scapular that Dave had given him. "I'm going to miss you. And rightfully so," he added. I kept mine short and sweet, prevent defense from crying. When I got to the part about missing him, the tears trickled. Eff Jeff got in one last dig. "Just remember, Dave, the pronoun 'I' when talking to your wife, when talking to your kids."

"*I* will do that," Dave replied with a grin.

Jamie found me during afternoon group. "Inside or outside?" she asked. I looked out the window, seeing sunshine and blue sky. "Outside." Protected from the wind on a balcony, we sat at a patio table with a view of the Mississippi River. It was time to talk about post-Abbey, to work on a plan. I had been set up with a temporary sponsor, who was also Kelli's regular sponsor. She was nice enough, but I didn't feel a connection, too many AA clichés and too much Christianity. We worked out of the Big Book, which I liked, going over some of her favorite passages. The Big Book had a lot of good stuff in it. The Abbey arranged these temporary sponsorships in preparation for our return to the outside world and continuation of the 12 Steps. Eff Jeff had set up an outing for me to attend an AA meeting in Iowa City. "You're gonna get along great with those Iowa City broads," he told me, showing me a pic on his phone of one of them dressed as a pink cloud at a Halloween party. "Pink cloud" was an AA term referring to the early honeymoon days of sobriety. "She's pretty," I said of the slender blonde woman in the photo. "She's my ex. Here's my current," he added, swiping to a photo of another pretty thin blonde woman. On the balcony, Jamie and I cobbled together a post-Abbey plan that included meetings, meditation and prayer, and exercise. I timidly proposed another post-Abbey activity: writing. I told Jamie I wanted to write about my Abbey experience. I watched her closely. And what I saw made my heart soar—a genuine spark of interest.

"A book? You mean a book?" she asked, beaming.

"Yes, a book." I felt a stinging in my eyes. Just then a flash of red caught my eye, solidifying into a shape, a crowned bird shape. The cardinal landed on a lantern that hung from the balcony ceiling. "I don't believe it," I murmured. Jamie turned to see what I was looking at. We had talked about the cardinals. I sensed her turning back to look at me, but I couldn't take my eyes off of him, his head tilting, hanging onto the lantern as the swinging slowed. As abruptly as he appeared, he flew off, a blur of fluttering red wings.

"I don't think I've ever seen a cardinal out here before," Jamie said.

"Really? Right when I'm telling you I want to write about this. I can't believe it."

"That's your Higher Power talking to you, you know."

I nodded, not trusting myself to speak.

"Do you have a name for your book? A title?"

I nodded, looking off to where the red beacon had flown, shoring up my inner resources so I could speak. "I do." A pause for effect. *Come on! This was a dramatic moment, the first time I'd ever told anyone!* I looked straight into Jamie's blue eyes. *"Get Me to The Abbey."* Her eyes widened, then softened, her mouth upturning into a warm smile.

"I absolutely love it."

I basked in the glow of my revelation. I basked in the magic of another cardinal sighting.

I kept coming across Clint in different spots, reading the book. I'd scamper down the steps and he was in a chair in the lobby. I'd saunter into the dining room and he was at a table, feet propped up on a second chair, one elbow on the table. At the top of the stairs, I came across him again stretched out in the loveseat, this time asleep with the book face down on his chest. I longed to touch his face, to cover him with a blanket. I did neither, just stood there a moment quietly looking at him. I started going to the noon meditation sessions, I admit, because Clint went to them. The sessions were overseen by Eff Jeff. Wearing headphones, six of us listened to constant, steady binary tones, which were supposed to bring you to a deeply meditative state. Clint swore by it, Pat said it was great for a quick nap, Mona said it really relaxed her. I really tried to get there but I kept sneaking peeks at Clint. I never reached that complete meditative state—the awareness of trying to empty my mind never left me—but I got close, like an elusive orgasm. Almost there, reaching for it, reaching for it—don't peek at Clint—but alas, not quite there.

It had gradually dawned on me that Clint resembled my ex, the same muscular build, blue eyes, and sparse hair with a hint of ginger. Before this realization, I had flat-out asked him, "Do you have red hair?" He instinctively rubbed his bald head and grinned. "Yeah, when I had hair. I'll show you a pic." The next day, he had come up behind me in the TV room, leaning over my chair, holding a photo in front of me. I was flustered by his closeness, and tried to focus on the photo, a head and shoulder shot of him in a football jersey, thick ginger curls atop his head.

"Look at you with your red hair!" I teased. His face had been closer than I expected. Thankfully, he straightened up before I did something insane like grab his face and kiss it. Dear Lord, the impulse had been there, a quick flash, then the moment of madness passed, leaving me laughing at myself.

Departures were looming, and I hated it. I hated Kyle and Clint's excitement, their preparations. Eff Jeff kept reminding Kyle to tell his wife to get that spilled Adderall out of the couch.

"You *have* to get it out of there," he told Kyle in group. "You're fucked if it's still there and you get a craving. Get rid of it. Even better, get rid of the fucking couch!"

"I know," Kyle agreed. "I can see myself tearing that couch apart if I feel a relapse coming on. I'll remind her tonight when I talk to her."

Kyle also worried about seeing his siblings and parents. He had a younger brother who was considered the golden child and while in The Abbey, his parents had given that brother a flat screen television that Kyle had wanted. From previous discussions, it sounded like there was a history of sibling rivalry between the two brothers. Eff Jeff chuckled and shook his head. "Resentments are exhausting," he said. "They take up too much energy. You gotta let it go."

"You don't have *any* resentments?" Dan asked him.

"No. I don't have to let them go because I never pick them up in the first place." We all chewed on that one.

"I read something like that," Kyle said. It said something like 'You've got to forgive others, not because they deserve forgiveness, but because you deserve peace.'"

Eff Jeff considered that, nodding thoughtfully. "Not bad. But when you say it, you should say...?"

"*I've* got to forgive others," picked up Kyle. "Yeah, yeah, yeah. Because I deserve peace." Everyone else laughed while tears sprung to my eyes. *I'm going to miss him so much.*

During a Higher Power discussion, I reminded Clint of something he had said about fellowship being part of his Higher Power and how much that had impacted me. "It hasn't been a big epiphany for me. It's been little signs along the way, like candles being lit rather than a big explosion of fire."

"Little signs?" Jo asked. "Like seeing a cardinal?"

"Yes. Like seeing a cardinal."

"Cardinal?" Dan asked. "What about seeing a cardinal?"

Jo was smiling at me. "Yes, Lisa. What about the cardinal?" she said.

I shot her a mildly dirty look, then looked at Dan even though I was addressing the whole group. Looking only at him steadied me. "Have you ever heard about seeing a cardinal and how they represent someone you know who has passed away?" Given the response, no one had. "For me, that's a sign."

Jo wasn't done. "Tell them about your cardinals," she pressed.

I hadn't shared the cardinal sightings with any Abbey cohorts—Jo didn't know about the second one—and now here I was, exposed. And suddenly, I wanted to tell them. I got through it without crying, even though my voice quivered near the end. When done, Dan smiled softly at me, and Kyle looked at me with a glisten in his eyes.

Clint was excited about seeing his fiancée—she had agreed to give him a second chance—but not about moving in with his parents. "It's good for my sobriety but not for my self-esteem," he said.

"Stay sober and things will fall into place," Eff Jeff advised him. "It may not happen as quickly as you want it to, but you stay sober, things will work out like they're supposed to."

Clint ceremoniously handed over the scoring of the brackets to me. Kyle did the same with his beloved football, except he presented it to Dan, getting down on one knee and bowing his head as Dan laid on the couch. Dan scrambled to an upright position to accept. "Dude, I'm honored," he said, respectfully accepting it.

Initially, Clint had been scheduled to leave Sunday on family day—Paula had baked a new batch of cookies with him in mind—but now his parents were picking him up on Saturday, so he and Kyle were leaving the same day, a double whammy. My dread filled me with a heaviness. Those few days before their departure, I crammed in every possible moment with the two of them, spending little time in my room. Dan must've been feeling it too because he was often there. One afternoon during an hour of free time, Kyle and I contemplated what television show to watch when he suddenly suggested, "Hey, do you want to watch the rest of the movie?"

"You mean 'I abandoned my boy?'" I asked.

"Yeah. We have enough time."

Kyle scampered up to put the movie into the DVD player. We settled in as he fast forwarded, then watched in rapt fascination as Daniel Plainview devolved into a drunken, sweaty mess, alone with his servants in his sprawling, gloomy mansion. We giggled at the growly slur of his speech, his alcohol-fueled malevolence.

"That is one drunk motherfucker," Kyle commented.

"He's gonna die from drinking at this rate."

"We'll see," he shrugged evasively.

When Daniel Plainview's estranged, deaf son comes to visit his father in his vast study, Kyle nudged me. "This is good." After his son announces that he's starting his own oil business, Daniel Day Lewis, drunkenly hunched down over his desk, growls at him that he's an orphan and not his real son. *"You're a bastard from a basket! Bastard from a basket! Bastard from a basket!"* Daniel Plainview howled at his son.

My jaw dropped and I looked at Kyle, wide-eyed. "Oh my God."

"Just wait. It gets better. Or worse, depending how you look at it."

And it did. Plainview's nemesis, the charlatan, self-righteous preacher, returned, looking for a handout. Plainview sneeringly humiliated him before bashing in his head with a wooden bowling pin. Kyle rewound to the shaming part since it was hard to understand the heavily slurring Plainview. *"Stop crying, you sniveling ass,"* he snarled. *"You're just the afterbirth, Eli.* [Eli was a twin.] *You slithered out of your mother's filth. They should have put you in a glass jar on the mantelpiece."*

I squirmed in horror and made Kyle fast forward through the head-bashing. He enjoyed my reaction, not in a mean way but in the way you delight in sharing something. After it was over, we sat together, basking.

"I'm so glad I got to see the rest of it!" I exclaimed. "He so deserved the Oscar!"

"Bastard from a basket! Bastard from a basket!" Kyle recited in a pretty decent Daniel Plainview impression.

"It's almost better than 'I abandoned my boy.'"

Also laughing, Kyle agreed. "You slithered out of your mother's filth," Kyle growled and giggled.

I shivered and cringed. "What an awful thing to say! What an image!"

It was a special shared experience, a shining illustration of how our relationship had evolved to this level of warm companionship. Lying in bed that night, I reviewed the Kyle and Clint highlights reel in my head, smiling in the dark, tears sliding down my cheeks. Sleep was elusive that night.

Chapter Twenty-One

I woke up gloomy and sluggish. Looking at the weekly schedule in the lobby while waiting for my meds, I realized with growing alarm that Mona and I had to go to a women's AA meeting in Davenport at 10 o'clock. The community meeting/goodbye to Clint and Kyle meeting was at 9. I knocked on the office door, which was opened by the weekend staffer who had driven us last Saturday.

"Is Karen here? Or a counselor?" I asked, trying to control the alarm in my voice. I didn't succeed.

"No. They don't usually come in until 8 or 8:30 on Saturdays," he said. "Is something wrong?"

"No. But I have to talk to them about the women's meeting. I'll come back."

After getting my meds, I trudged up to my room and got ready. I took a little extra care with make-up and chose one of my favorite and most flattering tunics. After all, this may be the last time I see them. That thought stopped me cold in front of the mirror, mascara wand in mid-air. *They both live in Cedar Rapids! You'll see them all the time!* I said aloud to my reflection. But I knew how this worked. We had talked about getting together—going to meetings on Melrose Street in Iowa City, me going up there for meetings—but often times, you pick up the daily details of your life and those plans and good intentions fall by the wayside.

Walking toward the stairs, I came across Kyle dragging his bedding down from the third floor.

"We have to strip our beds?" I asked.

"Yep."

"What's Jesse gonna say about that?"

Earlier that week, Jesse had confessed that when he first got to The Abbey, he thought there would be maid service, like at a hotel. "It *used* to be a hotel," he said defensively in the TV room as we chuckled. "I thought they might make up the beds."

"And turn-down service?" Dave had teased.

"No, I didn't think *that*," Jesse grinned.

"He did think they'd bring up food if we called down here," Pat interjected.

"Pat!" Jesse had exclaimed.

From thereon out, we gently teased him about it. "Did you have a chocolate on your pillow last night?" "Hey, Jesse, did you get fresh towels?"

Hanging on to his sheets, Kyle chuckled at my Jesse comment. "He will not be pleased with this. Hey, hold on a sec. I'll run these down and then I gotta show you something."

"Show me something where?" I asked.

"Upstairs. Wait here."

I paced around the sitting room area then heard footsteps on the stairs. "I've never been on the boys' floor before," I said.

"You never snuck up to visit Jim?" Kyle teased.

"Oh, Kyle!" I cried, smacking him on the arm. I followed him up the stairs, struggling to keep up, pausing at the top to catch my breath. Instead of a cozy sitting area on this floor, we walked across a utilitarian, sparsely furnished landing. I followed him down the hallway that replicated the path to my room one floor below. Kyle stopped and pointed to the door of the room right above mine. "This is Dan's room."

"He's right above me! The Cary Grant room!"

"Yep. The Cary Grant room. This is mine," he said, pointing to the open door across from Dan's room. I glimpsed inside, observing twin beds and mid-packing disarray. Inwardly, I sighed. We continued on to the room next to his.

"Whose room is this?" I asked.

"The nun's room," Kyle replied dramatically before opening the door.

"The what?" I asked, baffled.

It *was* a nun's room, preserved from the abbey days like a museum display, complete with a stark, barracks type bed and a nun's habit hanging on a wire hanger in front of the window.

"Right next to your room. No wonder you have nun ghost visits," I said.

Kyle claimed he had experienced a couple of ghostly encounters in his room. The first had occurred at night while lying in bed; his closet door opened slightly, then stayed open a couple of seconds before closing again. The second time had involved his toothbrush. He found it on the floor of the bathtub after he placed it on the sink the night before. Some were skeptical; after all, this was the guy who thought meditation led to demonic possession. But I believed him. This was an actual abbey, it stood to reason that there would be some spiritual residue. My grandpa had been the janitor at our parish, and he told us stories of nun ghost encounters. He had been a sensible, stoic man, not known for wild theories or flights of fancy. The staff nurse, Bette, had shared with Kyle that once she caught a glimpse of a nun behind her while looking in the downstairs bathroom mirror. The image had been fleeting, but vivid. In my opinion, being right next to the nun's room bolstered Kyle's claims.

"Did they pay you one last visit?" I teased.

Kyle was startled. "How did you know that? They did." He had been lying in bed and felt a presence, then felt a gentle brushing on his forearm.

"It's like they knew you were leaving," I murmured.

We stood there in reverential silence, careful not to touch the habit or rosary, not to sit on the bed. I loved that he had brought me up here to show me this room. "Thanks for bringing me up here," I said to my dear, nun-haunted friend. I was going to cry. "Well, you better get packing." I scampered off to find a counselor. I knocked on the office door, and Karen appeared.

"Good morning," she said. "I heard you were looking for me."

"Yes, good morning. I was wondering if we have to go to the women's meeting," I tried to keep desperation out of my voice. "We're saying goodbye to Clint and Kyle this morning and I don't want to miss that."

Holding my gaze with her warm, understanding eyes, Karen assured me that I wouldn't miss my chance. "You can leave a little later and you and Mona can go first," she calmly said. "We'll make it work."

I walked away partially satisfied—I had hoped to be released from the meeting. Part of saying goodbye was hearing everyone else's goodbyes. But I could tell Karen wasn't going to budge. It was bad enough having to say goodbye to these key figures who had played such a huge role here, but now there was a sense of urgency. I was the second to take my seat, after Jesse. We greeted each other with sad smiles.

"This is a tough one," he said.

"I know," I replied. "Did you know we have to strip our beds when we leave?"

Jesse pretended mock horror, his hand covering his mouth as he gasped. "That's barbaric." We laughed.

Mona, Pat and Darvin solemnly filed in, taking their seats. "This is a bad one," Pat said.

I nodded silently.

"We have to go to the women's meeting," Mona said to me.

"I know. I tried to get us out of it, but Karen wouldn't budge. She said we can go first."

"I'll go before you. You'll make me cry. You always make me cry."

I smiled softly at Mona. Right then, the two stars of the meeting walked in, smiling, handsome, just short of swaggering. They were excited to be going home. Clint squeezed my shoulder as he passed and I quickly grabbed his hand, covering it with my own for a moment. My lips trembled, my eyes burned. Clint took his seat. Sitting in his usual spot for the last time, Kyle looked over at me, his expressive blue eyes reflecting the usual mischievous sparkle with a hint of something else. There was also quiet there, sadness, perhaps a smidgen of fear.

"Two of the heavy hitters are leaving us," Pat said.

"This really sucks," said Dan, who held the football.

"Guard it with your life, Ben," Kyle said. "I won't let it out of my sight," said Dan/Ben, clutching it to his chest. "I'll eat with it. I'll sleep with it."

"He'll shit with it," Pat added.

"Oh dear, what did I just walk in on?" asked Karen as she came into the room. "Good morning, everyone." Now seated, her warm, brown eyes scanned the tables. "I understand we have a couple of goodbyes this morning. Because of that, and because the girls have to leave for their women's meeting, we'll skip the reading and any regular business. I'll go first." Her steadying presence fortified me. She addressed both men.

"You've both brought a strong presence to the group and because of that, your absence will be all the more felt," she said in that calm, warm tone that also contained a girlish lightness, belying her age. The few times she had to get stern with us, I'd been struck by the incongruity of that girlishness in her voice. "Who's up next?" she asked, glancing between Mona and me.

"I'm going first," Mona said.

As she spoke, I thought how this goodbye really was twofold—they were saying goodbye to me too. This thought had occurred me to me earlier, resulting in poignant goodbye fantasy scenes that sober Lisa quickly squelched. (Drinking, self-pitying Lisa would've wallowed for hours in these scenes, dramatically sobbing at my starring role.)

It was my turn. My smile trembled. To Kyle, I said, "I really thought you were a jerk at first and was fully prepared to avoid you." I paused for the chuckles. "Then it changed. I saw how thoughtful you are. Stuff that you said really had an impact on me." *So far, so good! No tears!* "And I really enjoyed hanging out with you. You made me laugh. You helped make my time here so much better." *Uh oh, eyes filling, mouth fully trembling. Gotta wrap this up.* "I'm really gonna miss you." I switched gears. "And you really need to pursue your art. It's a gift."

We smiled at each other, a sparkle in Kyle's eyes.

"You have an infectious laugh," he said, surprising me with his opening volley. "It was my goal every day to make you laugh. I hope I succeeded." I nodded, the burning behind my eyes cooling into pools of tears that streamed down my cheeks. "Your sisters are cool. Be sure to use them for support. I'm gonna miss you too. I love you."

That last part truly took me by surprise, but somehow I managed to whisper back, "I love you, too." I took a deep breath, wiped my cheeks, and turned to Clint.

"Clint, you helped me with my Higher Power and accepting it. When you talked about fellowship and your Higher Power, something clicked. I'm so grateful for that. I've appreciated your honesty and openness and you must pursue coaching. You have so much to offer young kids, especially now. I think for your sobriety's sake, you need to teach and coach. Anybody can make money." *I was going to get through this tear-free!* "I wish you all the best with everything, especially your sobriety."

"I wish you the best," Clint said. "You deserve it. You've given me a lot.

You're gonna do great. I hope you find someone to share it with. You deserve that too. I love you."

"I love you, too," I whispered again. It was time to go. I got up and out of the corner of my eye I saw Clint also get up. He advanced toward me and I faced him, taking him into my arms. We hugged hard, leaving me wobbly. I reluctantly pulled away, aware of the eyes in the room and the ride we had to catch. I turned away but was stopped on the way out by Kyle.

"Hey, what about me?" he asked, extending his arms. We hugged warmly but it was different, our bodies weren't pressed together like with Clint. And it was easier to pull away. I wanted to get out of there. After a distressing goodbye, I wanted it finalized, kaput. As I walked down to the van, I began mentally distancing. Thankfully, Mona was sensitive enough to leave me alone. I looked out at the sliding landscape, first older spacious homes, then a Kwik Trip, fast food restaurants, Walgreens, the Augustana College campus. Then the landscape changed to an older stretch featuring small, shabby houses, a check cashing place, a Dollar Store, a liquor store. Then the buildings became more contemporary, strip-mall style. We were getting close. The women's meeting was in a church that didn't look like a church, a nondescript building that shared a parking lot with a strip mall. Our driver pulled into the parking lot, then let Mona and I out. We walked into the front room, which resembled a school cafeteria. A sign taped to the door announced a craft sale today, which explained the array of knickknacks on the long tables. The meeting room was off to one side, emitting a rectangle of light and the murmur of voices. Inside, Mona and I were greeted warmly as we found empty seats. The small room quickly filled. It was an eclectic group, most middle-aged like me, most dressed in Saturday morning casual, with a couple of the women more gussied up. One of these was a California born transplant, sparkling in a glittery leopard print top and heavy dangling pendant earrings. Her colorful shares matched her bold and colorful appearance. She and another "character" in the group had monopolized large chunks of time at last week's meeting; the other was her polar opposite fashion-wise, a mentally unsteady, homely woman who detailed her woes with pills, booze, and hospital stays. Mona was the youngest and showed the most cleavage, and last week she talked more about motherhood than she ever did at The Abbey. I half listened as the meeting proceeded, replaying the goodbyes in my mind, still surprised that they'd told me they loved me. It warmed and saddened me.

Back at the Abbey, I walked into the TV room and picked up the basketball tourney sheets from their usual spot. Dan and Matt were watching South Park and I joined them. I looked at the TV screen, then over at Dan who was sprawled in his usual spot on the side couch, cradling the football. He looked at me and I tilted my head toward the TV, rolling my eyes at him.

"What?" he exclaimed. "It's a great show!"

I had to admit the show was funny and edgy, but it was too caustic for me. I leafed through the tourney sheets, and smiled when I saw they had been updated by Clint. Matt was in first place and a quick perusal indicated that there was no close challenger. Just then, Clint walked in and headed to the seat next to me.

"They're all up to date," he said, tapping the sheets on my lap.

"I saw that. It looks like you're gonna win, Matt."

"How much do I win?" he asked.

"Seven dollars."

"Alright. I'll take it."

"Well, I better get back to packing," Clint said, looking at me. "Just came down to get something to drink."

"Good. Now I get to say goodbye again."

We hugged a second time, an awkward, twisted hug, but satisfying. On pure impulse, I kissed his neck. "You can do this," I whispered. He squeezed me in response.

Jesse joined us, sitting next to me on the couch, bringing with him a sense of comfort.

"It's gonna be weird, isn't it," Jesse said.

"Yeah, it's gonna be weird."

"When do you leave, Lisa?" Dan asked.

"A week from Monday."

"That's not very far away."

"No. It isn't." The mere mention of it triggered a tummy lurch. Kyle and his wife returned, him scampering up the stairs while she remained in the lobby. She paced into our line of sight, then out of it. Into our line of sight, then out.

"I wonder what she's thinking," commented Jesse.

"Probably a lot of different things," I replied.

"She's probably got a long list of shit for him to do," chimed in Matt.

"Do you think she cleaned out that couch?" asked Dan.

"Do you think she even knows about it?" Jesse pointed out. We all murmured our assent.

I had never spoken to her, but Martha had, and somehow that felt like an opening. From what Kyle said, she was a hard ass, but that was from his perspective. I got up from the couch and walked out to the lobby. She looked at me unsmilingly as I approached, her beautiful bronze face expressionless.

"Hi Brittney. Big day today," I said.

"Yes, it is," she replied, a small smile slightly defrosting her expression.

"I just wanted to tell you how much Kyle has meant to me here. He's said a lot of things that have really helped me. Just his friendship has helped me a lot."

"Thanks for telling me that," she said, her smile widening, fully defrosted.

"I wish you guys all the best. I'm really gonna miss him."

I returned to the TV room and shortly after sitting down, I saw Kyle walk by for the last time. We heard voices, footsteps, then silence.

"Almost time for lunch," Jesse said absently.

"Our first lunch without them. Who's gonna take my salad?" wondered Dan.

"Pat!" Jesse and I said in unison. We all chuckled.

"Yeah," Dan said. "It's gonna be weird without them."

I sighed. "Yep. It's gonna be weird."

Chapter Twenty-Two

There was a palpable shift, not seismic but noticeable. Even Vape Man seemed a little less obnoxious, though not less tardy. Family day was uneventful, and after family members were gone, the mood was even more subdued than usual. I started hunkering down in my room more during free time. I preferred to read in my room, allowing periodic thoughts of Clint and Kyle to drift across my mind, than to hang out with the modified group. My three best Abbey friends were gone. This was how I soothed my sad soul—wallowing in my room, away from prying eyes and conversations. Monday brought two new residents to whom I was indifferent, though one had some potential. His name was Jeffrey, and he was an addict/chef with a nervous, quick-witted air about him, irreverent and blunt. My initial impression of him was good, but I wasn't in the mood to make new friends, so I wasn't particularly welcoming. Along with my wallowing, I was preoccupied with my field trip that evening to Iowa City. A Bettendorf AAer with ties to Iowa City was driving me over to the AA meeting where an Abbey alumnus, who also worked at ACT, would be in attendance. Eff Jeff advised me to talk to the alumnus about returning to work and how to handle it. When I walked out to the lobby to meet my driver, I recognized the man standing there from the Bettendorf meetings. Don looked to be in his 60s with a good head of white hair and a kind face, a face that put me at ease. We walked out to his car, a gray Prius, which also put me at ease. As we started off in the fading light of dusk, winding through the Bettendorf streets, Don talked about the bells and whistles of his newly purchased Prius.

"I still don't know what half the stuff is for," he said, pointing at the lighted computer screen and other various lights on the console. Reaching Interstate 80, the conversation shifted to Iowa City, where Don had lived for a few years before returning to his hometown of Bettendorf. I told him about my trepidations about staying sober in Iowa City.

"Iowa City is a great place to get sober," he said. "It has a great AA community. You know, some of the biggest party towns have the best AA."

I mulled that over. It made sense. Lots of drinking, lots of alcoholics hitting rock bottom. I wondered if Madison, Wisconsin, where I had lived for over twenty years, had a strong AA community.

"You can be a drunk anywhere. There's booze everywhere. It doesn't matter where you end up living," said Don, as if reading my thoughts.

"Yep. There's vodka everywhere now," I replied. "Even at Walgreens!" That launched us into a reminiscence of when the state of Iowa only sold hard liquor at state-run stores, which was how it was set up during my early drinking years, when the legal drinking age was nineteen. After Prohibition was repealed in 1933, Iowa's 1934 legislature passed a sweeping bill entitled the Iowa Liquor Control Act, which took effect on March 8, 1934. The state assumed direct control over the wholesale and retail distribution of all alcoholic beverages except beer. As the result of a massive state government reorganization in 1987, the state started selling its 220 liquor stores. Now you could buy it everywhere—grocery stores, drug stores, and convenience stores.

We rode along in companionable silence. Closer to Iowa City, we talked about Iowa football and the connection to drinking and tailgating. I told Don that for me, sitting in a bar and watching football had been one of my favorite pastimes.

"That's part of staying sober," he said. "Seeking out non-drinking activities."

That is what I truly dreaded: life without drinking. Life with "non-drinking activities," reminding me of one of the most annoying AA cliches: Different playgrounds, different playmates. What a bore. Booze was a social lubricant. All those types of get togethers—meeting friends in bars on a football weekend, hanging out with work friends over drinks, going on the bike ride across Iowa—were over for me. Life without drinking seemed dreary, boring, mediocre. But life *with* drinking wasn't an option anymore. I think I had accepted that, but I hadn't yet accepted that life *without* drinking could still be fun and exciting.

Passing the Tipton exit sign, an indicator of getting close, apprehension flared in my belly. Don pulled off at the Dodge Street exit, taking us by my workplace, which triggered a second flare-up. There's Market Street, the turn for George's of the infamous burgers, where I'd go drinking after work. Next, we turned onto Burlington Street, drove through downtown Iowa City, crossing the river and up a hill toward the university hospital complex. Across the street from the hospital sat the modest house that served as a home to AA meetings, dubbed the Melrose meeting after the name of the street on which it was located. The one and only AA meeting I'd attended after moving back to Iowa City was at Melrose, where I'd noted the irony of going to a meeting just down the street from the launching pad of my early drinking career, Kinnick Stadium. Beyond Kinnick was my apartment, close enough to walk to tailgating, carrying a six-pack of Blue Moon and a diet 7-Up half-filled with vodka. I had been "managing" my drinking during football season, which meant drinking beer before switching to vodka. We pulled into the driveway alongside the house and Don turned to me. "Are you ready?"

The nervousness had become a steady gnawing. "Ready."

We walked in the back door, through a small kitchen where the coffee was brewing, then into the main room, which was almost completely full. It was a long room with windows along one side and a long table in the center. I followed Don to a couple of empty chairs and looked around the room, wondering if I would recognize anyone. I didn't. Don greeted someone down the row from us. Leaning forward and looking down the row, I saw a pretty, blonde woman who smiled warmly at me. She looked familiar.

"That's Jeff's other friend Tammy," explained Don, distinguishing her from the Tammy who had just died. That's why she looked familiar—she was the one in the Pink Cloud costume on Eff Jeff's phone. I think he had said something about her being an ex-girlfriend too. I stole another glance, this time noting her tan face and well-toned body.

One of the two people seated at the end of the long table brought the meeting to order, opening with the Preamble, then How It Works. A latecomer walked in and acknowledged Don, who whispered to me, "That's Jerry, the guy who works at ACT." I looked back at Jerry, and we smiled at each other. He was nice-looking with dark brown hair and a salt-and-pepper mustache. He wore wire-framed eyeglasses that appeared quite strong, magnifying his eyes. The moderator asked if there were any newcomers to the meeting. I looked at Don who nodded. I timidly raised my hand.

"I'm Lisa, I'm an alcoholic." A collective murmur of voices greeted me. "I'm here from The Abbey."

"When do you get out?" the moderator asked.

"A week ago today."

"Well, be sure to come back," he said kindly, then opened the Big Book and read a passage. After reading, the moderator opened the meeting for discussion.

The hour flew by, filled with humor, pathos, and relatability. Some commented on the reading, some didn't. When it was my turn, I admitted my growing trepidation about leaving The Abbey and how this meeting had reassured me. After I was done, there were several callouts to come back, which warmed my insides.

After the meeting, Don introduced me to Tammy, whose glowing kindness instantly put me at ease. Jerry walked up and introduced himself. "When are you going back to work?" he asked.

"The Thursday after I get out." Just saying it set my belly roiling.

"That's a good idea, have a couple days to decompress. What department are you in?"

"Test administration."

His face brightened. "I used to be in TA. I was the manager."

"Really?"

"Yep," he nodded. "Colleen, Moser, Natasha, Grace. I was their boss." These were some of my co-workers, who were also friends.

"When you went back to work, what did you tell people?" I asked. With some of the people he had named, I planned on full disclosure. It was the rest of the team I worried about.

"I told the people I felt comfortable with. Everyone else, I didn't say anything. If they asked, I told them I had been sick and left it at that. Tell whoever you want. Or don't tell."

Looking into those magnified eyes, hearing those words, the roiling in my belly subsided. On the drive back, Don left me alone with my thoughts and impressions. For the first time, I felt something besides stress about post-Abbey life. I couldn't wait to thank Eff Jeff.

It was an intense week. Just when you thought Pat had turned a corner, his anger surged. He gave a memorable performance at the Sunday evening Bettendorf meeting. He was the last to share, and since he was such a wild card, I waited with bated breath. He started off talking about a dwarf star, a star in a solar system 40 million miles away with eight earth-size planets, three of which may have water. Jesse and I had exchanged a questioning look. *Where was he going with this dwarf star shit?* Dan caught the look and broke into a grin. Pat had discussed the dwarf star and these possibly life-sustaining planets with a guy at work, but when his son came home, Pat said nothing to him.

"When I'm drinking, I don't even talk to my kid. Fuck the dwarf star!" Pat finished.

Oh Pat, he nailed the landing. In the van we paid homage to Pat on a job well done.

"Fuck the dwarf star!" chanted Dan from the shotgun seat.

"Fuck the dwarf star!" Jesse and I chanted in unison.

"Yeah, fuck it!" Pat shouted.

"What are you talking about?" asked a very confused Sam.

He'd gotten better, but Pat still struggled with his old demons, resentment and anger. He still slipped into rants about being betrayed by his ex-wife and by AA. When he railed against AA, we pointed out that his resentment was directed at a particular group within Des Moines AA, not AA itself, that AA could still help him. We pointed out that Des Moines was large enough for him to find a new group. He conceded it was his home group that was the object of his anger, not AA as a whole, and that he needed to find a new meeting. We tolerated but respected his rants. During an afternoon group with counselor Mark, he used the c-word and "fat cow" as part of his share. I felt compelled to help him get over it. I had been overcome by a revelation. "Pat, did you ever think that maybe all this happened to you, with your wife, with AA, to bring you to this point in your life? To this exact place? That it all happened for a reason, a good reason?"

Pat looked at me, mulling that over, his grimace softening. I sensed Mark also looking at me.

"What?" I said to Mark.

"That's really wise. That's a great way of looking at it," he said. "Have you ever thought of that, Pat?"

"No, I haven't," he replied, the redness of his face fading.

"Acceptance is huge in this program," Mark continued. "Think of the Serenity Prayer, accept the things I cannot change. You can't change what happened to you, Pat, none of us can. But you can change how it affects you. You can change that. Remember, you have no control over what happens to you, but you have control over how you react to it."

"I love that," I said. "You can use that for everyday stuff, like standing in line at the grocery store."

"Or driving," Derwood said.

"Or at work," Jesse added.

Pat smiled at me. "Thanks Lisa."

Darvin hit a rut in his sobriety road that week. He had transitioned to out-patient, and he was not adjusting well. Maybe leaving us and returning to the outside world had unhinged him.

"It really might help to talk about it," Andrew said. "It really can help."

"I was feeling good and now I'm feeling shitty," Derwood grumbled. "I've hit a wall. And I don't want to talk about it."

Andrew moved on. I tried to catch Derwood's eye, to give him a reassuring look, but he wouldn't look at me. When he got gruff, he stayed gruff until he wasn't gruff anymore. Before it had been something tangible that set him off—a phone call with his insurance agent, counselor Jamie defending cops, any mention of politics. This felt like an intangible gruffness, that overall unease and anxiety that you can't shake. Dave could usually draw him out when he got like this, but Dave wasn't here. As an out-patient, Dave pretty much made his own schedule. *Please don't let Derwood drink,* I implored my Higher Power. There. That's what I could do for him. I could pray.

A couple of days later, Delvin walked in carrying a paper sack from McDonald's, a spring in his step, a glint in his eye. He met my eyes and grinned. My heart lifted.

"I had a panic attack at my son's last night," he said, "and at McDonald's they kept saying biscuit rather than muffin. I ordered a sausage McMuffin but he kept saying biscuit. I thought I was going to explode." A pause. "Both times I kept saying to myself 'Get me to The Abbey, get me to The Abbey.' It kept me from blowing up."

I was bursting at the seams. Darvin had been chanting the title of my book. I couldn't wait to tell the sisters. Certainly, I had chosen the right title.

"Oh, Derwood," I murmured to myself.

"So, did you get a biscuit or a muffin?" Dan asked.

Darvin rustled around in the sack, pulled out a wrapped sandwich and slowly, tantalizingly unwrapped it. "Muffin!" he cried triumphantly, holding it up.

We cheered. I beamed.

Later that afternoon, in group during a discussion about coping skills, Derwood repeated his biscuit-versus-muffin story. Sitting next to him, I grinned and nodded, recalling his usage of my book title. I realized he was looking at me.

"I love you, Lisa," he said.

I was taken aback by this unexpected declaration but also warmed by it. "I love you too, Derwood," I replied sincerely.

"I mean it. I love you," he repeated.

Mischief poked me. Nodding and smiling at Darvin, I replied, "I don't."

My comedic timing was impeccable, and I basked in the glow of the laughter, Derwood's included. It felt good to make people laugh.

That last week, the feel-good vibrations continued. Good-looking Brent returned for an internal AA meeting, friendlier and happier than I had ever seen him. Via eavesdropping, I had learned he was living in sober housing and was dating a girl he had met in a bookstore. I was glad that he was moving on from his broken marriage. Rehab counselors strongly recommend that you have a year of sobriety under your belt before entering into a relationship, but with his good looks, meeting someone new was probably effortless.

After the meeting, he surprised me when he walked up and greeted me. I almost looked over my shoulder to check if he was addressing someone else.

"Hi, how are you doing?" he said. "You look great."

Of course, I was flattered, even a little flustered. "Hi, thanks! Good! How are you?"

"I'm doing good. Living in a sober house. It's not ideal but it got me out of here. What about you? You must be leaving pretty soon."

"I am. Sunday after family day. Back to Iowa City. You're from Iowa City, aren't you?"

"Yeah. I decided to stay away from there. Too complicated. I didn't think it would be good for my sobriety. Anyway, I wanted to wish you the best." He surprised me again by moving in for a hug.

One evening that week, I sat in the lobby, watching Dan and staffer Sam, who were sitting on the floor, flirt over a chessboard. Dan didn't know what he was doing but didn't seem to mind Sam's command of the board; her moves were swift and bold. Another evening that week, I almost began to like Vape Man after tossing the football back and forth with him. Some of us were watching TV, Jim in the prime chair, me as far from him as possible on the opposite couch. Vape Man faked like he was going to throw it at me, and I responded by holding out my hands. He lobbed it to me, which surprised me since I had expected a bullet throw. I easily caught it, impressing Jim and several others in the room. Then I really impressed them when I tossed it back. It wasn't a perfect spiral, but it was on target.

"Not bad," Jim grudgingly praised. We tossed it back and forth a few times, each time my spirals getting a little tighter and his throws coming back a little bit harder. I ended it. That was enough Vape Man time. *Maybe he's not so bad after all. It's my last week, I should cut him some slack.*

Jeffrey, the new guy, was really struggling with the Higher Power concept. With my battle, I had been forced to surrender, but I didn't feel defeat. I felt liberated. I yearned for Jeffrey to feel the same. Nobody really knows what guides the universe. Nobody knows what happens to us after we die. Nobody knows why some people can't stop drinking after one drink, while others can have one or two and walk away. I ached for him when he eloquently and passionately expressed his inner struggle. I bristled when others got irritated with him. One morning he showed us some sketches that looked like a cross between a mathematical formula and ancient hieroglyphics. As he held up the sketches and enthusiastically attempted to explain their meaning, I noted the glazed looks of my cohorts, along with some barely disguised irritation. I gently interjected, wanting to alleviate some of his vexation, to offer my simpler revelation.

"When it happened to me, it wasn't a big dramatic explosion of light. It was more like candles, one lit here, one lit there, a gradual lighting of candles," I described, thinking of the cardinal sightings, Clint's comment about fellowship, Kyle calling addiction a gift. Jeffrey looked at me, brow furrowed in thought. He wasn't ready to accept a simpler and quieter explanation. Jeffrey generated mixed feelings amongst my fellow residents. Pat, Dan, and Jesse were okay with him while Jim and Matt frequently exchanged looks whenever he shared. Being part-timers, Derwood and Dave hadn't developed strong impressions either way. Kyle probably would've been irritated by him. Mona got along with him fine.

Until the Incident.

The Incident transpired during an ordinary afternoon session, all of us seated in a circle in the TV room. Overseen by counselor Mark, we were having a cordial discussion about dealing with family members. Mona had been talking about her dad who was always coming over for maintenance stuff—to mow her lawn, to fix her screens, to change her furnace filter—and she was concerned about his health. She didn't want him always worrying about her.

"How does he find out that you need something done, that you need something fixed or you need a filter changed?" Mark gently asked.

Mona was confused by the question, but I thought I saw where Mark was going with it. "Well, I don't know, he asks, and he checks on me. He can drive by and see if the yard needs mowing," she replied.

"Right, but how does he find out about the inside stuff that needs fixing?" Mark pressed.

"I guess when I talk to him. I tell him things and then he wants to help."

"So, if you didn't tell him about things that needed to be fixed, he wouldn't know, so then he wouldn't come over," Mark summarized.

"But he likes doing it," Mona countered.

"You said earlier that he complains about it all the time," Vape Man reminded her.

Mona was getting flustered. She *had* said that. Vape Man was right. "He does. But he likes helping. He likes helping me and his grandkids."

Jeffrey, sitting next to me, was getting agitated. He was shifting a lot in his chair, crossing and uncrossing his legs. Hell, *I* was getting agitated.

"Do you want him coming over?" I said. "If he likes doing it, then let him. But if you're worried about his health, then don't tell him about stuff that needs fixing."

"But it makes him happy," she defended. "I think it makes him happy."

"OH MY GOD!" Jeffrey sputtered. "You sound just like my sister! She asks for my parents help all the time! And says they *like* doing it! And she acts like she's the perfect mother just like you do, even though she's a coke-snorting mess! Like you've never gotten wasted in front of your kids! PLEASE!"

Uh oh. He attacked Mona's mothering skills, her pride and joy. Her face reddened with rage.

"Don't you *ever* say anything about my kids," she hissed. "I *never* did anything to hurt my kids. I love them more than anything."

"And that's what my sister always says," retorted Jeffrey.

Mona leaped up from her chair, stabbing her finger at him. "Fuck you! Don't you *ever* fucking talk to me about my kids!" She stalked out of the room.

"I'm sorry but she reminded me so much of my sister. I couldn't take it," said Jeffrey after a moment of silence.

"Saint Mona," Matt mumbled.

"Yeah, she's a martyr," added Vape Man.

Pat, Jesse, and I exchanged alarmed looks as Mark tried to salvage the discussion. I was sure Pat would look for Mona after group to try and comfort her. Poor Jeffrey sat hunched over in miserable silence. He was going to beat himself up over this. I was surprised by Matt and Vape Man's comments—I had assumed all the guys were gaga over her—but their comments crystallized feelings I had been stifling. She was always going on and on about how her kids were everything to her and how much she loved them and how she never did anything in front of them. I didn't doubt her love, but I was skeptical about the last part. Once we alcoholics started drinking, nothing stopped us. Except running out of booze. She rarely alluded to anything unpleasant in her homelife except issues with her parents or the father of her kids, a drug-dealing meth head, who had once beat the shit out of her. Just once. They had mostly argued when he was high. The drug dealer father had recently gotten out of jail and she feared for her life, she had told us.

After The Incident, she was a no-show for the Bettendorf meeting and for dinner. Jeffrey skulked around sheepishly, telling anyone in earshot how bad he felt. He'd tried to apologize to Mona, but she had walked away. We're in rehab where emotions run high, I had said, and Mona shouldn't hold a grudge, it wasn't helpful to her recovery. Personally, I thought she was milking it for sympathy, but I kept that to myself. After dinner, I saw her upstairs talking to counselor Jo, crying about how she'd been "attacked" and how "nobody says anything to me about my kids!" She was not coming to art therapy, she wept. I envisioned Mona lying prostrate on a chaise lounge, the back of her hand held up to her forehead, whimpering in anguish. I giggled as I scampered down the stairs, where I ran into Jesse.

"What's so funny?" he asked.

"I can't say. It's not nice." I rationalized that by not saying it out loud, I was not being mean. That thought reminded me of a quote from the movie The Big Chill, uttered by the self-absorbed Jeff Goldblum character in defense of his selfishness. "I don't know anyone who could get through the day without two or three juicy rationalizations." This was my daily juicy rationalization.

Chapter Twenty-Three

started to pack. I washed a load of clothes so everything would be clean. I'd worn just about everything Martha had packed except for one sweater. During the wash cycle, I laid my big suitcase on the bed and placed into it the clean sweaters and shirts from the drawers. I liked packing, especially if it wasn't hurried or pressured. This packing was bittersweet, with excitement, worry, and melancholy all jockeying for prominence. But underlying that emotional turmoil was a layer of peace. I was excited to get back to my place, to sleep in my own bed, to start going to meetings at Melrose. It was when I thought about going back to work that the excitement stopped short, like stomping on the car brakes when a squirrel runs in front of your car.

Walking to the laundry room, I came across Jeffrey and Vape Man playing Scrabble, with Pat at another table, hunched over a legal pad, scribbling away.

"Hey Lisa!" Jeffrey called. "Do you want to play Scrabble? We just started."

Scrabble with Vape Man? "No. I'm doing laundry." To Pat, I said, "What are you writing? A letter?"

Pat grinned mysteriously. "Not a letter."

"A story? Are you writing a story?"

He continued to grin at me. "I'm writing something for somebody."

Was he writing something for me? "You have fun with that."

I transferred the damp clothes to the dryer, setting aside a bra and a tunic to air-dry. Long ago in college, a roommate had told me that her mother taught her to *not* put her bras in the dryer so they would last longer. I'd been doing it ever since. I draped the bra over my arm, covering it with the damp tunic for the trip back through the TV room. Pat was still writing, and Jeffrey and Vape Man were engrossed in their game. "That's not a word! I'm challenging that!" I overheard Vape Man say. I knew he'd be that kind of Scrabble player.

I laid low the rest of the day, soothing my simmering nerves with a visit to the chapel to make a last-ditch plea for strength and peace outside the Abbey walls. I quietly enjoyed my last dinner, relishing the gourmet salad with sliced almonds. I was really going to miss this food! I watched part of the wizard movie Fantastic Beasts and Where to Find Them, but retired to my room before the end. Crawling into my king-size bed for the last time, I lay in the dark, eyes adjusting to the familiar bedtime sights—the windows softly illuminated behind the drawn curtains, the silhouette of the entertainment center, my array of greeting cards on top. I tuned into the familiar bedtime sounds—a distant train whistle, the muffled voices and footsteps of my cohorts heading to their rooms.

I recalled the morning goodbyes in my mind. My emotions had stayed under control. Tears had stung my eyes from the warm words of Pat and Jesse. Staffer Jules' surprise appearance and her kind words led to a spillover. Dan kept it light, and knowing that I'd see him in Iowa City kept my tears at bay. Later, when I saw what he had written in my big book, the tears flowed. After his home address and phone number he wrote, *Visit anytime. Rightfully so!*

I knew anxiety would return, but for now I had peace. I was ready to go home.

I sprang out of bed, hurrying downstairs for my last round of meds. Nurse Jan placed my meds in a Ziploc bag to take with me. After signing the meds binder for the last time, I flipped back a couple of pages through four weeks of signatures. All those signatures, all those mornings coming down to the nurse's office, and now this is it. The last day. I walked through the dark, empty TV room to the shadowy quiet of the dining room to get a Diet Pepsi and a breakfast bar. I set them on a table and walked over to look out at the walled-in yard, the covered swimming pool and twinkling lights along the river. It was now April, and the shades of morning gray tinted the sky earlier. I had been at The Abbey the entire month of March. I walked back to my room, my heart momentarily heavy.

This time when I showered and put on my face, I also packed up my make-up and toiletries. I cleared off the sink, placing toothbrush, toothpaste, mascara and blush into my flowered cosmetic bag. I carefully folded and packed the remaining tunics and pants, wondering who would occupy this room after me. I looked out the windows, at the shrub, at the portico, but no cardinals appeared to say goodbye. I looked out at the white van in the parking lot. I walked back into the bathroom and stripped out the bathmat and dirty towels to take downstairs, coming back later for the sheets. Down near the office entrance, I ran into Jules and she unflinchingly took the dirty towels from me. "You can leave the sheets outside your door," she said.

"Are you sure? The guys brought theirs down."

"You can leave them in the hall," she said, smiling softly. She always smiled softly. I felt emotion welling up as we looked at each other. That beautiful, serene face. The very first face I had seen when I walked into The Abbey. I was so happy she was here on my last day.

During our noon pre-family briefing, counselor Mark suggested that we discuss creating a post-rehab plan. Not only was I leaving, but Pat, Jesse, Dan, and Mona were leaving soon, too. Derwood was here and so was his ex-wife. I thought it was great she was there and could tell that Derwood was happy about it too. The vibe between Jeffrey and Mona was still frosty. Mona's children were there, too. They weren't little kids—her daughter was as tall as she was, and her son's head reached her shoulder. Jeffrey's girlfriend was also there, so at least he had a loved one at his side.

When we took our seats in the big circle, Martha sat next to Jeffrey and immediately struck up a conversation with him. I knew she would like him. Mona and her family sat to Paula's left, a couple of non-Mona people in between. Dan and his parents sat directly across from us, his dad waving cheerfully, in a much lighter frame of mind than the first time. Impossibly cool Cody launched the discussion, sharing his strategy upon leaving The Abbey. "I scheduled every hour of every day and hung the schedule on my refrigerator," he said, the casual, smooth timbre of his voice incongruent with the excessiveness of such a schedule. "It kept me on task to fill my time, so I didn't have down time to think about drinking."

I sensed that Martha was trying to catch my eye, probably to signal to me her support of such a schedule. I avoided looking at her. I had discussed this with Jamie: I would develop a weekly routine, with loose daily schedules mostly for weekend days. During the week I would be at work most of the day, then go to meetings in the evening. It was the weekends that would be tricky. For those days, Jamie suggested a daily schedule split into three increments for morning, afternoon, and evening. That seemed reasonable but it wasn't something I felt I had to post on the refrigerator. I predicted Martha would disagree. There was a range of opinion about the hourly schedule, but all agreed that free time was our nemesis and it must be managed. Mona said she would fill her time by spending it with her children, emphasizing it by gazing at each of them; they both stared straight ahead, probably bored out of their minds. I yearned to lean forward and look at Jeffrey, but I restrained myself.

At halftime, the sisters and I talked to Dan and his dad. Dan and I promised to go to meetings together—we *were* going to see each other again. He hugged me and it was no ordinary hug, surprisingly strong and all encompassing, leaving me wobbly and breathless. This hug from the pale and fragile creature whose heart had been dangerously racing from withdrawal. My, what a difference three weeks had made. His dad looked at me and grinned. "He gives quite a hug, doesn't he?" he said.

"Yes, he does," I replied, watching him crush the petite Paula, who stumbled after release.

"Okay number four, it's your turn," Dan said, turning to Martha.

The second half of the meeting focused on the importance of going to meetings and having a support network. "That's why we have you go to so many meetings when you're here," counselor Mark explained, "to develop a habit."

They had drilled it into us: AA meetings daily, sometimes twice a day. At my first rehab stint, internal AA meetings were held a few times a week, but nothing like this. Here they partnered you with a temporary sponsor. I had only met a couple of times with my temporary sponsor, and even though I hadn't developed a strong connection with her like Kyle had with Cody, the prep work had been done.

Martha shared some family member perspective with us, sprung from her observation of our strengthening relationships. "You guys have to keep in touch with each other," she implored. "You have to reach out to each other, check on each other. From what I've seen, from what Lisa's told us..." She faltered. "You need each other."

Dan and I smiled at each other across the circle. I was moved by Martha's impassioned plea. She was absolutely right. We needed each other.

It was time to clear out my room, and Jesse offered to help. He was the only fellow Abbeyite who had ever been in my room, and he was impressed. I was almost embarrassed by my fancy digs.

"Your room is *huge!*" he exclaimed. "Look at all these cards!"

"Is it really that much bigger than yours?" I asked. The only rooms I'd seen on the third floor were Kyle's and the nun's room.

"Yes, it is. And I room with Pat."

The sisters and I giggled, and I was reminded of Jesse thinking that there would be room service at The Abbey. I had to share with the sisters.

"You did not!" Martha yelped.

"I really didn't think it was that unreasonable to expect it," he said.

Jesse dragged my big suitcase out to Martha's car while the rest of us carried the smaller bags. Paula and I exchanged a look while she rearranged the trunk to make room for the smaller bags. Martha's "junk in her trunk" was a known phenomenon in our family, right up there with her chronic dawdling. Once all bags were loaded, we walked back into the lobby, where Karen and Pat were waiting for us by the check-in window.

"Look what your sisters gave us," Karen said, holding up a framed print

Displayed inside a black frame was the AA symbol, a triangle within a circle, and below that, seven lines of printed words. It read:

recovery
Such a simple little symbol
for such a monumental task...
getting one's self back again.
It's the brave souls who will
admit they need help,
and then do the hard work
to get there.

I looked up at the sisters, my eyes filling with tears. "Where did you get this? It's perfect."

"It's a card I found," Martha said. "I thought it was so spot on, I framed it. I was going to give it to you, but Paula and I decided we should give it to The Abbey."

"We'll find a good place for it," Karen said.

Pat, who had been chomping at the bit this entire time, handed me a large manila envelope, inside of which were sheets of paper. "I wrote a story for you. I had Karen check it for spelling and stuff. You can read it when you get home."

I looked at Karen, who was conspicuously expressionless. "What did you think?"

"It was very...Pat," she said, a smile tugging at the corners of her mouth. We all laughed.

"I'll bet," Jesse added.

It was time to go. Karen came out from behind the counter and there was a flurry of hugs. Pat hugged the sisters, I hugged Jesse, Pat hugged me, the sisters hugged Karen, Jesse hugged the sisters. Then I stood before Karen. We looked at each other, then embraced, and she murmured in my ear, "You're strong Lisa. You can do this. I believe in you. You have a lot of people to turn to. Use them. Use your sisters. I love you. Please take good care of yourself."

"I love you too. I love this place." I reluctantly pulled away and turned to the sisters. "Let's go."

I quickly walked out. I heard more good-byes but I didn't look back. Another emotional goodbye followed in the parking lot with Paula, who was going back to Madison. We hung on tightly to each other, crying and murmuring. Finally, after buckling in and glancing up at the golden dome, Martha's black Impala pulled out into the streets of Bettendorf.

Emotionally drained, I was quiet during the drive back to Iowa City. I don't remember if we had music playing. I ticked off the Interstate 80 landmarks—Rhythm City Casino just outside of Davenport, the child trafficking truck stop, exit signs for Durant, Tipton, West Branch. We drove past the Melrose Street house ("Do you want to stop for a meeting?" kidded Martha) and the fire station, then down the hill on Emerald Street to my apartment building. Unbuckling, I looked over at Martha.

"We're here!" We smiled at each other in the dim light.

"Yes, we are," said Martha, popping the trunk. I got out and hauled out the big suitcase from the back seat, pulling out the handle for dragging while Martha grabbed most of the bags from the trunk. "I'll come back for the rest," she said, shrugging the various bags into better position on her shoulders.

"Keys?" I asked.

Martha glared at me before fumbling around in her purse. She found the keys and I picked up a bag she'd dropped, then followed her across the parking lot, past my beat-up Toyota, the suitcase clattering and thumping behind me. My ground-floor apartment was in the first building. I looked at the flowerpots outside the door, dead leaves and stems outlined in the shadow. I couldn't wait to plant flowers. Martha unlocked my door and pushed it open, then dropped the bags on her way to the floor lamp. The warm light illuminated a recently cleaned living room.

"You guys cleaned! It looks nice!" I dragged the suitcase into the bedroom, clicking on that room's overhead light, revealing another recent cleaning. "In here too!"

"We washed the bedding, including the bedspread," said Martha, standing behind me. "There was blood on it."

My hand reached for the spot on my head where I had bashed it after a nasty fall. "Oh, that's right. I forgot about that."

In the kitchen, I flicked on the light and looked at the floor where I had been found five weeks ago. My gaze landed on the refrigerator and a thought crossed my mind. I walked over and opened the freezer door, and sure enough, a frosty liter of Smirnoff vodka was in there lying on its side. I called out to Martha. "You guys left something in the freezer." She scurried past me, grabbing the bottle and hiding it behind her back as if her swift action would erase the sight of it from my mind. I pressed my lips together to suppress a giggle.

"I'll be right back," she said, hurrying out the front door.

While Martha was out, I picked up the remote, hoping that cable TV still worked. A handsome MSNBC news reporter peered out from the screen. I had paid the bill while in the hospital but had still been worried about it after being gone so long. I pressed the digits for CBS and there was Leslie Stahl, impossibly beautiful. She always wore great earrings.

Martha returned.

"What did you do with it?" I asked.

"I got rid of it. That's all you need to know." She noticed the TV. "Good. It works." We took our seats, me in the comfy gray chair, she on the red loveseat. It felt a little odd sitting here without a drink in hand. We chose to watch Law and Order: SVU reruns, and I unpacked during commercials. It felt good to return my clothes to their places in the dresser drawers, to hang tunics and pants in the closet, wrestling with the temperamental sliding door. Bending over the bag of books in the living room, I spotted Pat's envelope. I pulled it out and removed the yellow sheets of legal pad paper from it, filled with Pat's grade schooler printing. Martha was watching me. "Do you want to hear it?" I asked.

"Sure."

Also, in the envelope was a note written on a smaller white slip of paper. It read:

"Lisa No time to proofread and if I would have looked up every word I couldn't spell nothing would be done." I chuckled. *"If you don't like where the story is going let me know, I'll change. If it gets to scary just repeat it is only a story over and over. Love Pat P.S. I write like a child so read like one."*

Tears stung my eyes as I passed the note to Martha. I sat down in the gray chair. "Okay, here we go." I read aloud:

"Lisa leaves the Abbey, by Boyd Mildred Stanek, aka Pat Meyer, or Pastor Pat." We chuckled.

"Lisa awakened laughing in the car Paula was driving with Martha sitting in the passenger seat, Lisa had her hand on side of Martha's seat she realized she was telling stories." I stopped, reread it to myself, satisfied I'd read it correctly, then continued. *"The laughter was comming from a lotus part of their souls, creating a warm vibration that filled them form the bottoms of thier feet to the top of thier heads."* I stopped. "I like that," I commented. "Me too," Martha agreed. *"Lisa continued her story thanking Paula and Martha for getting her to the Abbey and how much it helped. 'The Abbey?' says Paula. Lisa smiled and again said 'yes it meant so much to me.' Maratha* (I pronounced it like that) *rolled with laughter and said 'Lisa you never cease to amaze me.' Lisa sat back into the comfort of her seat the warmth in the car felt like sunshine through a window on quiet day. The girls all sat back in the warmth of the car catching thier breathes* (again pronouncing it like that) *and wiping the water from thier eyes and smile lines as the car continued down the interstate. The laughter was replaced by smiles and warm sighs as the miles passed, and the memorizing beat of the tires over sain cuts of road."* I stopped again. "I think he meant 'mesmerizing' instead of 'memorizing....'" We giggled, not unkindly but endearingly. "And I can't make out this word before 'cuts of

road.'" "That's okay. Keep going," Martha said. *"...sain cuts of road replaced the conscious thoughts to a warm yet comfortable emptiness of mind where thoughts of the past float by like scents in a warm breeze. Lisa looked forward and became aware of her sisters, both lost in thought to the thump, thump of road and soft smiles of thier faces. She felt safe, accomplished, affluent, and joyful. She felt a gratitude for her sisters which swelled in her heart soften her soul that she felt she could float on that feeling alone. Dump, dump, dump was the only interuption of the hum of the car gliding* (pronounced as written) *down the road."* We smiled at each other. *"Lisa began to talk about the Abbey again, Martha chuckled as Lisa told them about a foul mouthed man who wanted to see spirits of the dead."* I stopped here, saying to Martha, "He must mean Kyle." I continued. *"'I mean to tell you that guy needs more than the Abbey has for help' Lisa said in fond memories of the Abbey passing through her mind. Martha continued to chuckle and just said 'Lisa you and that creative mind of yours.' Lisa continued with stories of the desperateness of the people that entered including herself and seeing joy re-enter thier lives. About what a honor it was to witness this and what a blessing it was to experience it first hand."* Tears stung my eyes. *"She said 'It saved my life thank you guys for getting me there.' Suddenly she realized Martha was not laughing and Paula had a familiar look of concern on her face. Martha said 'Lisa are you okay,' Lisa chuckled and said 'yes' and asked 'did I say something that troubles you guys, you look concerned.' 'Well' Paula responded 'what Abbey are you talking about,' a concerned look with awkward smile was on Paula's face. Lisa knew the look well, 'what do you mean? what Abbey?' Lisa said continueing 'The Abbey you just picked me up at. The Abbey of Sisters of Mt. Carmel.' Martha turned in her seat to look at Lisa, Paula gave quick glances in the mirror and back to the road and repeated it a couple times. The sisters looked at each other with the same thought on thier minds which was, 'What the fuck, she is serious, has she lost her mind.' Martha thought for a second 'she has final lost herself in one of her books. Paula puzzled considered that the stress of fame as a writer has gotten to her. 'All the book signings all the talks, everything that has happened in her success.'"* I stopped again, murmuring, "Oh Pat," warmed by the sweet sentiment of his story. *"Paula look in the mirror at Lisa, wondering if she needed to pull off the road, to focus on her sister. Martha thinking that maybe Lisa was writing her next book said 'I told you before I don't want to be in one books! Anyway if we just left the Abbey, who was the person signing books?' Lisa giggled a little and thought I was signing books, but didn't they just pick me up at the Abbey. She wondered had I been dreaming, I remember all those people."*

Martha interrupted, "Is this gonna be like Bobby Ewing in 'Dallas'? It's all just a dream?"

"Yeah. Or like that little kid in St. Elsewhere, looking into a snow globe. That was a dream too."

"No, that kid was autistic, he made them up in his mind. I hated that ending. All those characters just made up in a little kid's mind? Come on!"

"Okay, where was I? Here we go." I found my place. *"Lisa in a startled state said but you just picked me up at the Abbey in Bettendorf, the Abbey of the sisters of Mount Carmel which was turned into drug and alcohol treatment center. Martha mouth just about droped off her face. Being a keeper of information Martha knew of the Abbey and it's history. Martha said aloud come on Lisa...."* I stopped reading and looked over at Martha. "You just said 'come on.'"

"I realize that." We looked at each other a moment.

I cleared my throat. *"Martha said aloud come on Lisa everyone knows that Abbey was burnt down by the—"* I covered my mouth and giggled as I read ahead. *"The Klu Klux Klan some 75 years ago."* We had a long laugh. "Oh dear, okay." I continued. *"All eyes were on Lisa she felt the crazy that her sisters were thinking. She decided that a chuckle and oh you guys would buy her time to contemplate what was going on. The sound of the road returned dump dump dump now pierced the uncomfortable silents. Paula turned on the radio, Wait Wait don't Tell Me came on the air"* To Martha, "Have you ever heard of that song?" Martha shook her head and gestured at me to continue. *"...the announcer just ask what was most likely to true if Donal Trump won the presidency A. Repel the Affordable Care Act, or B. Build a wall between Mexico and U.S. All the grils broke out in laughter. Donald Trump President, a wall between U.S. and Mexico, now that was funny. End chapter one maybe?"* I flipped over the sheet, which was blank on the other side, and looked at the next sheet, the first page. That was the end. "That's it."

"I want more."

"I know. Where would he have gone from there?"

Story time was over. I was ready for bed. I pulled out the blow-up mattress from the closet in the second bedroom, which I used mainly for storage and furniture remnants. In the closet hung out of season clothes. A low, wide dresser, inherited from my mother, sat across from the closet. I liked watching the mattress inflate, the heavy plastic undulating before slowly rising, morphing into an over-sized swimming pool float. I spread a fleece blanket over the top and grabbed a pillow from the closet shelf, completing Martha's bed. Now five weeks sober, I was awakening to the contentment derived from simple tasks. It had started at The Abbey—making my bed every day, rolling up silverware in napkins and changing the tablecloths for my assigned chores, doing laundry—and it now continued in my own home. As my drinking had progressed, ordinary tasks had become a nuisance.

"Your bed's ready," I announced.

I was excited to crawl into my own bed with its clean sheets, but I had nothing to read. The last book I had been reading at The Abbey, The Girl with the Dragon Tattoo, was still there. I walked past Martha to the bookcase. "I need books," I told her.

"Okay. We'll go to the library tomorrow. A meeting and the library. What else do you want to do?"

"I'm not sure." I pulled a P.D. James mystery from the bookshelf and bid good night to Martha, who would be up for a while. I turned on the bedside lamp and crawled between the clean sheets, then surveyed the room, enjoying the point of view. I'd never read at bedtime in this apartment on a regular basis. I couldn't focus on a book when I was drunk. During the last few days of my drinking, I hadn't even bothered to turn on a light before stumbling into bed. Unlike Pat, I couldn't pass out on the couch because I only had an armless loveseat, so no place to set my head. I kept a vodka bottle on the floor next to me for middle of the night swigs. Facing me was my antique vanity with the octagon-shaped mirror, also inherited from my mother. I'd had it forever. To my right was the matching dresser, which had been used by my dad up to his death; I'd claimed it after their house was sold and Mom moved to assisted living. It wasn't until I had brought the two pieces together that I realized they were a set, with their matching gilded handles and scalloped wooden trim. Looking at the matching vanity and dresser brought me comfort, warm reminders of my mom and dad. I started the P.D. James mystery but didn't even get to the murder before sleepiness overtook me. I set the book on the bedstand and turned off the lamp.

Chapter Twenty-Four

I slept in to a luxurious 6:30 a.m. I was almost to the point of wanting morning coffee but not quite. But I added it to my mental grocery list. I grabbed a tall Diet Pepsi from the fridge, continuing my Abbey morning ritual. I turned the TV to MSNBC. With Martha's bedroom door shut, I could turn it up without waking her. Dear Lord, Donald Trump was the President. I had kind of set that awful truth aside while at The Abbey. Now here it was before my eyes, full frontal reality. I shuddered. How the hell did this happen? Recalling Pat's story, I wished it had been a horrible dream, the part about a reality TV star becoming president.

I decided to deal with my own personal reality and check my car. I stepped into the slip-on shoes set near the outside door. Would it start? I grabbed my Abbey sweater from the coat tree and the keys from the shelf, and walked out into the morning chill. *Right about now, they're piling into the van to go to an AA meeting.* My car was locked (Martha) and the driver's seat was pushed back farther than normal, the result of Martha's husband trying to start it and finding the battery dead. I harbored the faint hope that he hadn't pushed in the clutch pedal when trying to start it, but Dennis was too car savvy for that. He knew how to start a stick shift. After making sure it was in neutral, I pushed in the clutch with my foot and turned the key. Click. Silence. Click. Silence.

I lifted my foot from the clutch, turned off the key and waited. I said a quick prayer, pushed in the clutch pedal and turned the key. Deafening silence, except for the chirping birds. My thoughts spun. *Spring birds are so boisterous. Where's my Higher Power now with a divine spark for the car battery?* I was not upset, though. Before, I would've been pounding the steering wheel, lamenting my misfortune. Now I calmly got out and pushed the door firmly shut, without slamming it. I would find a tow truck company and call them for a jump, then go about my day. I would not let this inconvenience consume me.

The bedroom door opened, and Martha emerged. She was freshly awoken but not looking too fresh.

"Good morning!" I greeted her cheerfully. "How did you sleep?"

She groggily walked past me to the loveseat. "Like a rock. That air mattress is comfy." She eyed the open phone book on my lap. "What are you doing?"

"Well, my car didn't start, so I was looking for someone to jump it and look what I found." I turned the book toward her and pointed to the listing where my finger had stopped.

"Is that the one you're going to call?"

"Of course!"

"You know what I'm going to say, that it's a sign."

"It's definitely something. There's no way I could *not* call it." The listing I had shown her was Whitey's Towing and Starting Service—Whitey was her husband's lifelong nickname. To my surprise, they were able to have someone over in an hour, which meant I had to get cleaned up, or at a minimum brush my teeth and put on a bra. We continued to watch Morning Joe, critiquing each panelist until my phone rang. The Whitey's guy had arrived.

His tow truck was parked in the parking spot adjacent to mine. I handed him the keys, and after confirming the battery was dead, he said, "You may need a new battery. Even after not driving it for a few weeks, you should get some response."

"Oh." This was going to cost me.

"Do you know how old your battery is?"

"I have no idea." Alcoholic broads don't know that kind of shit.

"I'll try and jump it. Otherwise, I have batteries with me so we can get it all done right here."

Even if I needed a new battery, at least I was getting it all taken care of this morning. "Okay. I'm gonna go in. You can let me know what you find out?" I didn't want to hover over him while he worked.

"Sure. It won't be long."

I returned to my apartment, still unphased, and updated Martha.

"How much does a new battery cost?" she asked.

"I don't know. I didn't ask. I'll find out when I go back out."

About ten minutes later, the tow guy called to say he was ready. Walking out, I reminded myself of Paula's fortune cookie philosophy: "Expect nothing and you'll never be disappointed." I was informed that I needed a new battery. From the range of prices, I opted for the low end $60 model. He agreed it was adequate and didn't try to pitch a pricier option, which I appreciated. With the labor, the total was $85. I could handle that.

I found Martha in the bathroom, closely inspecting her face in the mirror. I relayed the price information to her reflection in the mirror, and her reflection agreed it was reasonable. "It's done," her reflection said to me. "Your car is fixed."

"Yep. All done."

We watched The View even though Martha despises it—a generous gesture for her newly released sister—then The Young and the Restless before our first scheduled appointment, the noon Melrose Street meeting. We left at five minutes before noon—the meeting start time was 12:10—and even though it was a two-minute drive, we carried on the Avelleyra tradition of getting there early enough to score a good parking spot and a good seat. This tradition heralded back to nine o'clock Sunday mass, my mother mastering the organization of five young girls for a departure time of twenty minutes before nine, even though the drive to Corpus Christi Church only took seven minutes. Mom had spearheaded getting us ready for church, but it was Dad who set and enforced the departure time. In retrospect, I was once again amazed at my mother's ability to maintain order amid chaos. Granted some of the organization was motivated by fear of Augie, but it had become a tightly choreographed routine. It started the night before, when the girls were booked for bathroom time because in the morning, the big bathroom was Augie's domain. No one bothered Dad when he was shaving. And my mother knew how to delegate. So Phyllis concentrated on Martha and me, brushing and styling my long hair. Through second grade, I had worn my hair in two long braids that reached down to my rear end. I have warm memories of that morning routine, standing at the kitchen sink, Mom brushing and braiding my hair. I would stare out the window overlooking the gnarled boxelder tree. As she brushed and yanked, I watched the squirrels descend to the corn cobs and nibble their breakfast. Mom brushed and yanked my hair with a no nonsense, gentle firmness, not painful but not painless either—an embodiment of her mothering style. I loved those morning brushings, and as I got older, I used special occasions as an opportunity to ask her for help with my hair. To this day, I love having my hair brushed, as evidenced by the untangling by Paula in the hospital. That multi-day grooming session had allowed Paula and me to slowly rebuild our affection for each other during stressful, confrontational circumstances. It had been therapeutic. Although no-nonsense like my mother, Paula had been sensitive to inflicting pain and I had repeatedly assured her that it was okay, I could take it. And how did our mother manage Martha on those Sunday mornings? By keeping her on task with frequent check-ins. During a recent Paula rant about having to wait for Martha again, #4 flashed back to those Sunday mornings, reluctantly confessing to memories of being the last one in the car, the rest of us nervously waiting for her, Augie scowling behind the wheel.

"Even back then..." Paula had bemoaned.

"We waited," I completed. Martha had grinned and shrugged.

Today she had not kept me waiting—she was excited about going to this AA meeting, which was open to visitors. I was feeling some low-grade apprehension. Yes, I had been to a meeting here a week ago, but this was different. Martha's presence alleviated some of my apprehension, but I had a feeling all first time post-Abbey activities were going to stir some worry. With Martha driving, we pulled out of the parking lot onto Emerald Street, and a red flash caught my eye. There in the grove of lilac bushes across the street from my apartment complex, a male cardinal perched among the bare branches.

"Look Martha! A cardinal!" I pointed. She stopped the car in the middle of the street, and we watched him as he flitted to a different bush, a bright red spot in the brown, early spring branches. We watched as he flew off, then looked at each other.

"It's Dad, saying 'Good luck with your first meeting Lisa!'"

I nodded, my eyes filling, my worry washed away. We proceeded up the hill and turned right onto Melrose Street, past the nice houses of a near-campus neighborhood, past the quiet hulk of Kinnick Stadium and its empty parking lots, past the gleaming curved tower of University Children's Hospital, then turning into the driveway of the modest AA house. We parked and walked through the back door into the kitchen, where a full pot of coffee was ready to go. It smelled appealing. My tummy concurred. I was ready to rejoin my fellow coffee drinkers.

I chose a cartoon dog mug, shook a layer of powdered creamer onto the bottom, then covered it with the steaming dark, brown liquid. I inhaled the rich aroma and took a sip. It wasn't fancy but damn, it tasted good!

I chose the exact same chair as a week ago. In the brighter light of daytime, the well-wornness of the room was more apparent, the orange vinyl cushions indented by hundreds of alcoholic butts, the wooden arms smoothed and faded by hundreds of addicted forearms. The regular noontime crowd started filling the well-worn chairs, a rich cross section of working people using their lunch hour for an AA meeting. Construction guys clomped in wearing heavy work boots. Office workers sauntered in wearing business casual. The mood was light and companionable. I kind of felt like an outsider. Anxiety returned, this time about speaking in front of people. The worrying just never stopped.

"It really filled up," Martha murmured.

"Yes, it did."

The moderator brought the meeting to order with the soft pounding of a gavel and requested a moment of silence for those still suffering, followed by the Serenity Prayer. The strong chorus of voices reciting the prayer was soothing. Next was the question about visitors/newcomers to the meeting; Martha and I cautiously looked at each other. I raised my hand.

"This is my first time at this meeting," I said.

"And you are..." the moderator gently prodded me.

"Oh! I'm Lisa. I'm an alcoholic." Tears sprung to my eyes, and my introduction ended on a quavering note.

Martha raised her hand. "I'm her sister. I'm here to support her." We were both warmly welcomed.

The hour flew by, just like a week ago. The shares ranged from light-hearted to somber. Compared to Bettendorf, the shares here were more *interesting*. You couldn't deny it, Iowa City was different from Bettendorf. College towns have their own palpable feel so why wouldn't that spill over to their AA community? Even the meeting locales demonstrated the difference. Bettendorf was sterile and utilitarian with its florescent lighting, drop ceiling, and metal folding chairs, while Melrose was shabby-chic, a cozy bungalow furnished with vintage chairs. When it came to my turn, I kept it brief, not trusting my emotions, touching on my return-to-work anxiety. By the time the meeting wrapped—again we recited the Serenity Prayer standing with hands clasped like the residents of Hooville (Bettendorf closed with the Our Father)—I was already looking forward to the next. More and more I was feeling that staying in Iowa City was the right thing to do.

In the car, we rehashed our favorites. Martha's was a woman who sat to our left, who'd made her presence known the moment her rear end hit the vinyl cushion, announcing to someone at the other end of the room to not worry, she'd had her meds adjusted. During her share, she elaborated on that and the "don't worry" warning made sense. Mary was angry and unabashedly willing to talk about it. She was pissed at a co-worker, she was pissed at her roommate, she was pissed at her doctor for failing to adjust her meds sooner. But she was funny, not whiny and petulant. The reaction to Mary varied, ranging from amusement to barely contained irritation. I was in the amused camp, but this was my first time hearing it. I could see how it would wear thin.

My favorite had slipped in late, taking the last vacant chair. He was small and wiry, dressed in the uniform of the trades, jeans, sweatshirt, ball cap pulled low over his brow. He wore sunglasses throughout the meeting, and a plaster cast on his right forearm. Ronnie was a week sober, and grimly admitted that every day was a battle to not take a drink. He had been going to meetings every day, he told us, sometimes twice a day, and each day was a little bit better. There was determination in his boyish voice, and you could feel the entire room pulling for him. After his share, he was met with a resounding response. "Glad you're here!" "Keep coming back!"

"Did you notice his black eye?" Martha asked, ever vigilant as me. "He kept his sunglasses on to cover it up."

"Did you notice how much more welcoming they were to him than me?" I asked, tongue planted firmly in cheek.

"They were not! It was just different, a different kind of welcoming..." noting that I was grinning at her, she grinned back. "Oh, Lisa."

I pulled my phone out of my purse, searching the contacts first for Dave, then for Kyle. I had added their phone numbers from my AA book last night. It felt good to have them in my phone. I started to text.

I'm free! I texted. *Just went to a meeting with Martha.*

My phone remained silent until we pulled into a parking spot near the library. It was Kyle. I had given all my Abbey contacts the same jazzy alert tone.

Freedom! Did you go to the one at Melrose? he texted.

Yes. I really like those meetings, I texted back.

Dave and I went to a mens meeting Thursday. Do you want to go to one tomorrow?

To Martha, I said, "It's Kyle. He wants to know if I want to go to a meeting up there tomorrow."

"In Cedar Rapids? Say yes. I'll drive you up there."

What time is the meeting? And where is it?

We were about to enter the library when a muffled jazzy tone emitted from my purse. *5:30 at Friendship Hall. It's on 1st Ave easy to find.*

"Okay, good," said Martha. "Now turn off your phone."

I was going to see the boys! How exciting! My thoughts stopped short. *Would it be weird?* I texted Kyle back while standing in the entryway. *What about Clint? Is he going to meetings?*

I silenced my phone and headed to the fiction section, Martha to the art books. In the L's looking for author Stieg Larsson, I felt my purse vibrate. I pulled out my phone and looked at it. *Yes. I'll let him know.* I found a trade paperback of *Girl With the Dragon Tattoo*, then browsed for some of my favorite authors: John Irving, P.D. James, and John Le Carre. All had titles unfamiliar to me. I had stopped reading, but they hadn't stopped writing. It was time to check out and get a new library card. It was much more high-tech than the last time I had gotten a card. I followed the prompts on the computer touch screen and a few minutes later I had a new plastic card. Feeling satisfied, I tucked the new card into my wallet, right behind my driver's license.

After the library, I wanted to go home to read my book and maybe doze off. We spent a nice evening watching TV, going back and forth between the Housewives of Beverly Hills and MSNBC, back and forth between the alcohol-fueled antics of vapid, Botox-riddled California women and the latte liberal musings of Chris Matthews, then Rachel Maddow.

"They drink constantly!" Martha noted of the housewives.

"Day drinking. It's a thing." I shrugged.

We discussed the stark contrast of Rachel Maddow with her natural beauty and sexy intelligence. "If I was going to be with a woman..." I said about Rachel. Martha frowned at me as I knew she would; she was still prudish. I welcomed the arrival of bedtime and reading, and relished the healthy sleep that overtook me.

Even though I had broken through the coffee-drinking barrier, I started the

222   GET ME TO THE ABBEY

next morning with a Diet Pepsi, mainly because I didn't have any coffee. The grocery store was on the itinerary for today. Martha joined me for the last hour of Morning Joe and after that I ventured out to the grocery store, an errand I loathed. My car started right up, and I was off to the nearby Fareway, a smaller, homier option for groceries, preferable to the sprawling modern layout of a Hy-Vee. Fareway had just what I needed in compact aisles between vegetables and dairy. And the meat department was downright quaint. I backtracked for birdseed, because I hadn't fed the birds in weeks, months! Would they return to the small ground feeder built by Martha's husband, and to the hanging feeder my high school friends gave me when my mother died? Upon my return to Iowa City after living with my Mom, the ground feeder had brought me happiness in the early months of 2016. It had attracted a wide array of creatures from squirrels and chipmunks to cardinals and blue jays and eventually a pair of ducks I had dubbed The Quackenbushes. But like everything else, that simple pleasure, the desire to feed the birds, had disappeared as I was slowly swallowed whole by my addiction. Eventually the only desires remaining were the desire to drink and the desire to acquire drink.

I heaved the bag of birdseed into my cart and headed to check out. A tall, thin young man pushed my cart to the car.

"How's your day going?" he asked.

"Good. Getting my grocery shopping out of the way," I replied.

He looked up at the sky. "It's cloudy but at least it's not raining," he commented.

"Yep. And it's getting warmer. Spring's finally here."

"Yeah, finally." He placed the three plastic sacks (an Iowa term) and oversized bag of bird seed in the back seat. We wished each other a good day and I drove away smiling, partially because this chore was done and partially from the residue of a pleasant human interaction.

"Do you need any help?" asked Martha, back at my apartment, peering down at her phone.

"Nope. I just have birdseed left in the car. I can get it."

Unpacking the groceries, usually an unpleasant extension of the chore, was also enjoyable and satisfying. I neatly placed bread and Triscuits and corn chips in the pantry. Then I neatly arranged milk, cheese, sandwich meat, mixed greens, and cherry tomatoes in the refrigerator. The last time I had any fresh food in the fridge was the day before my collapse, some soup from Brian after I had declined to go out to lunch with him. I had found out later that his pop-in visit occurred because of phone conversations between him and Paula. Oh Brian. What was it going to be like seeing him? I was so thankful for his unexpected part in all of this, but also sheepish about dragging him into it. He had sent me a card, which warmed my heart and made me laugh.

"Time to feed the birdies," I announced to Martha, waving a pair of scissors. I cut open a corner of the bag and lifted it carefully, still feeling the lingering weakness, and went out to the green space behind my building. Just around the corner sat the barren ground feeder, the tube feeder hanging crooked and forlorn. I poured the seed evenly over the screen bottom of the ground feeder, then turned to the tube feeder, a clumsy Hawkeye gold contraption. I looked up into the barren branches of the mature twin oaks, hoping to see a potential customer perched on a branch or hear the scratching sound of a squirrel, but there was only the far away caw-caw of a crow. Down a short slope, a tree-lined creek wound itself behind the apartment buildings, a water source for the wide array of creatures. During the dark months of January and February, on those bitter cold nights, I had often contemplated sauntering, or most likely staggering, down the slope to the banks of that creek, and laying down on the snow to quietly freeze to death. That's how Teresa McGovern died, Senator George McGovern's alcoholic daughter: found in a snowbank. Looking at that creek now, its banks brown and muddy, I thought about how easy it would've been, but something had held me back, that same something that compelled me to call work that Friday, insuring I wouldn't be fired.

I walked back into the apartment. "Creatures are fed," I announced to Martha.

We attended another noon meeting at Melrose, this one co-chaired by Martha's darling, Prozac Mary, as we had dubbed her. She managed to fit in a rant about her boss before starting the meeting. Many of the faces were familiar, including Ronnie, who was again wearing sunglasses. The honesty, the camaraderie, the relatability of each share warmed my heart. I spoke again of the trepidation about returning to work, but also addressed the positive impact of these meetings. I recounted what they had told us at The Abbey, about those going to a meeting within 24 hours of leaving treatment are more likely to stay sober. With each meeting, I felt more and more comfortable expressing myself, even when emotion overtook me. Did it make a difference having Martha at my side? Probably. I would find out after she left at the end of the week.

I had been texting with Kyle and Dave, though the latter didn't respond right away. We were meeting in front of Fellowship Hall, which turned out to be right across the street from a bar called The Irish Democrat where I had once met my ex. Kyle had texted that we could park in the adjacent Hardee's parking lot and that Clint was coming. I was excited.

It was a half hour drive to Cedar Rapids, the meeting was at 5:30 so naturally we left at 4:15; neither Martha nor I were familiar with the area. A mix of anticipation and nervousness quieted me on the drive up. I tried not to be so painfully aware of the numerous semi-trucks, those looming steel monsters of careening doom. Whenever Martha passed one, I clenched and tensed, that vast metal wall way too close for comfort, swaying just inches away from our vulnerable, tiny sedan. I unclenched after passing the latest behemoth, only to tense up again upon seeing two of his good buddies in front of him. Martha noticed. "What? The semis? Are you worried about the semis?"

"Yes! Look at them!"

Martha was fully aware of my highway driving phobias. The last time I had driven this stretch of Interstate 380, dubbed by me the Corridor of Doom, was when my Mom had died. The drive hadn't been bad at all because I was half drunk. I had found out at work that she was being moved to hospice so I left work at noon in tears. Instead of driving straight to Fort Dodge that afternoon, I waited until the next morning. I knew I wasn't going to be able to drink in Fort Dodge, so I had to take advantage of this drinking window. I packed before I got too drunk, Paula's ominous words of "Pack nice clothes..." echoing in my ears. I also packed for a longer-than-weekend stay, anticipating the worst. I drank until I had passed out in my bed. Upon waking the next morning, I stood in the kitchen and swigged straight from the bottle, reasoning that this would be the last drink for days. Considering I was still partially drunk from the night before and swigging the next morning on top of that, I now realized I wasn't half drunk the last time I drove on this stretch. I had been fully drunk.

We were at the outskirts of Cedar Rapids, which meant a slower speed limit, but cars a continued to zip past us.

"What is their big toot?" I asked, using one of our mother's catchphrases. "So, you get there a couple of minutes sooner."

"I hope they get a ticket. Doesn't Cedar Rapids have cameras?" The largest city in Iowa was notorious for its traffic cameras on I-380. We were approaching our exit, which was also the exit lane for 29th ST NE/Coldstream. At the top of the exit ramp, we turned onto 29th NE, past a Walgreens, a BP, Hy-Vee, through a couple of stoplights, until our surroundings changed to a modest residential area.

"We must be getting close!" I said.

Martha pulled into the Hardee's parking lot Kyle had told us to use, adjacent to Fellowship Hall. The hall was an old fashioned, red brick aberration on a street lined with steel and glass structures. It looked like a former church. *We're here, parked at Hardees,* I texted Kyle.

Ok be there in 15, he texted back.

Martha went into Hardee's to use the bathroom, and I texted Dave. *I'm here. Kyle is on his way.* I waited, and waited, staring at my silent phone when Martha returned with a large fountain drink. Still no response. "Dave's a bad texter. I let him know I'm here."

"He's older." She sipped through her straw. "He's busy."

I nodded. "I'm gonna go wait for them."

"Okay. Tell them Hi. I'll be here."

I slipped my phone into my purse, climbed out of the car, and headed toward Fellowship Hall. A couple of men walked toward me, turning up the sidewalk leading to the hall. I stood outside, allowing myself a line of sight up and down the street. As the minutes ticked by and a few more people streamed into the building, I started to feel conspicuous, so I went into the foyer. From there, a flight of stairs ascended to an open double doorway and another flight descended to a dimly lit corridor. A hodgepodge of notices covered a bulletin board on the foyer wall. I glanced at my watch. Almost 5:25.

Muffled chimes came from my purse. It was Dave. *Running late.*

I texted back. *Ok. I'm here. Waiting for Kyle.*

Then there they were, Clint and Kyle. My Abbey guys. I saw them before they saw me, and my heart swelled. They looked so big and strong. And handsome. Clint saw me first, and enfolded me in his arms before I could say anything. Goddammit he felt good, the crush of his chest and burly arms dizzying. We pulled apart, beaming at each other.

"You look great," he said, blue eyes sparkling.

"So do you!" I patted those big strong shoulders. I couldn't help myself, randy old broad that I was. "It's so great to see you!" I turned to Kyle, who was patiently waiting. "You do look great, Lisa," he said, moving toward me for his hug. Although not as burly as Clint, the hug was solid and comforting, his musky cologne tickling my nostrils.

We pulled apart, looking at each other. "You smell good," I said.

"I always smell good," he said, a cocky grin spreading across his face, hair gelled perfectly into place.

"You do," I agreed, remembering him making me sniff cologne samples from magazines. "You made me smell those scratch and sniff things."

He chuckled. "That's right. I did."

"Dave's gonna be late. Should we go in?" I suggested.

I followed them up the stairs, pausing at the open doorway at the top, but the guys kept going. I looked into the expansive room and saw people sitting around tables at the far end. "Where are you guys going?" I asked. "We don't go in here?"

"No," Kyle replied. "We go to the one upstairs. It's better."

I followed them down a narrow hallway, past closed doors to another flight of stairs, up to another hallway and toward the murmur of voices. The small room was about half full, mostly men scattered around the tables arranged along each wall. Kyle tilted his head toward three vacant seats along the opposite wall. Like an usher at church, Kyle gestured to the middle chair for me, thereby nestling me between my two handsome escorts. I enjoyed the curious eyes following us around the room and staying on us as we took our seats. I'd wonder about us too if I were them.

"How have you guys been?" I asked.

"Good." Clint grinned, his nearness leaving me a little breathless. "I've been working out, going to meetings every day. What about you? You really do look good."

I stole a quick glance at his muscular forearms. "That's nice to hear. I feel good. Martha's staying with me until the end of the week. I'm going to meetings. And I'm nervous about going back to work."

"Yeah, that's a big one," Kyle said. "It was a little weird, but no one really said anything to me, no one asked."

"Hmm," I murmured.

The man to the right of Clint motioned to the room, a binder and Big Book sitting before him on the table. "It's 5:30 so let's get the meeting started," he said. Kyle leaned toward me and whispered, "He's the chair, he's a good guy."

"Hi everyone. I'm Kevin and I'm an alcoholic." A soft chorus of "Hi Kevin" greeted him. "Let's open this meeting with a moment of silence for those still suffering." Now when I heard those words, I always said a quick, intense prayer for those still in despair, those still not aware that there is hope. During the reading of "How It Works," the door slowly opened and you-know-who slinked in, luckily finding a vacant seat right inside the door. Dave scanned the room and his dark brown eyes stopped when they got to us, a grin pushing up the tips of his mustache. I wished I could see us from his point of view, me squeezed in between my strapping young Abbey lads. Ever the schmoozer, Dave acknowledged some others in the room. Clint and Kyle were among the youngest, most in the stuffy windowless room around Dave's and my age. Among the attendees were a couple of retirees, a hipster, his hair fashionably shaggy, wearing a black Nirvana shirt and black horn-rimmed eyeglasses, and sitting to our left an older black guy who was celebrating 20 years of sobriety. He was cool and looked like he'd been cool all his life with his salt and pepper hair and husky build, wearing purple and gold aviators. His deep, rich late-night radio voice matched his cool outward appearance as he accepted his chip and commented about the difference between performing as a musician sober versus performing while high.

"It's nice remembering the whole gig," he chuckled deeply.

The middle-aged male configuration of the room leaned more toward a Bettendorf vibe than Melrose, but the four other women present were all strong, obviously comfortable in this group. When sharing came around to the three of us, we acknowledged each other like co-winners at the Oscars, commenting on the importance of fellowship to our recovery. Pride and affection swelled within me. Even outside The Abbey, here in this stuffy room our connection held strong. I spoke quickly before the swell of emotion rose to my eyes and spilled over in tears, but not before my voice shook.

Dave piggybacked on our shares. "I was with them at The Abbey," he said, nodding toward us. "Something special happened there and it's up to us to keep it going, for each other and for others trying to stay sober."

Holding hands while closing with the Lord's Prayer, I concentrated fiercely on the strong touch from each side, reluctant to let go at the Amen. We wound our way through the lingering meeting-goers to the schmoozing Dave, pulling him out into the hall.

"Do you want to go over to Hardee's?" he asked. "Get something to eat?"

"Sure," I replied. "Martha's out there waiting in the car."

"I can't," Clint said. "I'm meeting my parents at Red Lobster. Their treat so I can't say no." He grinned.

My stomach lurched in disappointment. I hadn't realized how much I had been counting on hanging out after the meeting. I covered my disappointment. "Keep in touch," I murmured in his ear during our goodbye hug. That was the last I would see or hear from Clint for a long time.

The reunion at Hardee's was enhanced by Martha's presence. I had recounted thumbnail sketches of some of these stories to the sisters, but Dave and Kyle breathed life into them over burgers and fries. Steering the narrative, I brought up Kyle's pranks and nun visits. Martha lapped it up like a thirsty kitten, as I knew she would.

"You really think there were nun ghosts?" she asked.

"I know there were," Kyle stated. "They came to my room. I was right next to the nun's room. Tell her, Lisa."

"Yep, he showed it to me," I concurred.

"Did you ever see ghosts?" Martha asked Dave.

"No. They probably didn't approve of my hot tub." "You had a hot tub in your room?" Martha asked. I groaned.

"No," Dave smirked. "But Lisa thought I did."

"It was a former hotel!"

Martha joined their laughter.

"I seem like a hot tub guy?" Dave asked me.

"You do have a pornstache," Kyle teased.

"No," I explained. "You seem like you'd *demand* a room with a hot tub."

"Oh, well. That's different," he chuckled. "I'm okay with that."

We all laughed some more.

"Did you tell her about the cards?" Kyle asked me.

"The cards..." I wasn't sure what he was talking about.

"When Dave was sleeping..." Kyle prompted.

"Oh yeah! The cards!" To Martha. "Dave had fallen asleep in a chair in the TV room..." I gestured to Kyle to pick up the thread.

"And I had a bunch of these No Smoking cards—"

"Where did you get them?" Martha inquired.

"Oh, they were all over the place," replied Kyle. "And I set them on Dave while he was sleeping."

"Were you there?" Martha asked me.

"Oh yeah. Dave slept through the whole thing. And he didn't wake up for a while."

"What happened when you woke up?" Martha said.

Kyle and I looked at each other and laughed.

"I didn't really notice them at first. Then I saw them on my legs and on my chest..." Dave recalled.

"And there was one on his head," Kyle added.

"And on his crotch. Finally, he just got up and they all fell off," I concluded.

"What were you guys doing?" Martha asked Kyle and me.

"We were all laughing," I answered, "but I have to admit, I was a little worried that you'd be pissed."

"Yeah, me too," Kyle confessed.

"I got him back," Dave smirked, mustache devilishly upturned.

"What did you do?" Martha asked.

"I put crackers in his bed," Dave proudly replied. "But they were in the packet. I didn't want to be a dick about it."

"Vape Man wouldn't have left them in the packet," I interjected.

"Vape Man would've put a dead animal in my bed," Kyle said. "But they still stuck to the back of my legs. And they made a weird crackling sound when I got into bed. You know, when I first got to The Abbey, I had crackers in my bed. I never told anyone about this, but I found crackers in my bed that first night. And they were Club Crackers..." Kyle stressed, looking pointedly at Dave and me. We looked at each other and back at Kyle, the point he was trying to make escaping us. "They don't have Club Crackers at The Abbey." Dave and I exchanged another confused look, still not getting it. "They were outside crackers," Kyle explained, slightly exasperated with us.

"Were you going through withdrawal?" I asked, half joking.

"No!" Kyle replied. "Well, yes, but that wasn't it. Somebody left those crackers in my bed."

"Maybe the previous person in your room left them for a joke," Dave suggested.

"Yeah, like a welcome present," I added.

"But The Abbey doesn't have Club Crackers!" Kyle repeated.

After consideration, I murmured, "I don't think they *did* have Club Crackers."

"So what?" countered Dave.

"Who brings their own crackers?" Kyle said. "Anyway, I ran down to the office with the crackers and yelled that I found them in my bed and asked who had been in the room before me."

"So what did they do?" I asked.

A sheepish beat. "They took the crackers from me and told me to go back to my room." We all laughed. "Yeah, maybe I was jonesing a little bit," he chuckled.

For two hours we swapped Abbey stories, with Martha our rapt audience. I loved rehashing stories—family stories, high school stories, Ragbrai stories, what happened the night before stories—and sharing them with a third party, or in this case a fourth party, made it even better. I loved seeing Martha's reaction to our exploits. It was wonderful.

Driving home I was quiet, basking in the warmth of a visit that exceeded expectations. We still had it, the camaraderie created from shared emotional rawness, from living in close quarters, from spending so much time together. We still had it outside The Abbey walls. I was at peace.

Chapter Twenty-Five

Back to work. My world the last few months had consisted of my apartment, a hospital, and The Abbey. Face-to-face interactions had been limited to liquor store cashiers, hospital staff, addiction counselors, Abbeyites, and the sisters. These people all knew my truth—even the cashiers had some idea what was going on. I had been gone for three months. Lying in bed, my stomach lurched, then settled into a steady churning as I walked to the kitchen to make coffee. I stood there waiting until the coffeemaker rattled and gurgled. As I walked out to the living room to turn on Morning Joe, I compiled a mental list of people at work who *knew*. Obviously, the department director and two managers knew—they would have been notified by human resources—but my co-workers, my cubicle neighbors? I knew that Colleen, who was also my ex's cousin, had to know because she had been dragged in when my ex got dragged in after I stopped showing up for work. He had probably given her some sugar-coated version, finding it to be an embarrassing and messy nuisance. Unlike her cousin, Colleen was compassionate and non-judgmental, understanding of human frailty. I was comfortable sharing with her the unvarnished truth. There were a couple of other co-workers I felt this way about.

For my return-to-work outfit, I went with comfortable and dressy casual, a pair of gray trousers and a light, transitional season sweater. I tried to focus on the antics of the Morning Joe gang and away from my anxious thoughts. Yesterday I had grown increasingly quiet throughout the day, the prospect of going back to work weighing on me. Martha had intuitively adjusted to my disquiet, not trying to coax or joke me out of my reticence. Sipping my coffee, I heard the bedroom door open and a sleepy sister emerged. "How'd you sleep?" she asked through a yawn and a stretch.

"Not good. But I wasn't up all night. I got some sleep."

"Good." She shuffled off to the kitchen, then returned with a diet Pepsi.

"Barnacle boils it down again," I commented.

"Yep. They should let him talk more. Joe needs to stifle."

"I love their music choices," I noted.

"Mmm hmm." A pause. "How are you feeling?"

"Nervous. But ready to get this done."

Time to go. After a strong hug from Martha, followed by our signature European air kiss on each cheek, I was out the door, then sitting in my car, waiting for the windows to clear from the heavy morning dew. I had a feeling after a couple of days at work—maybe even one day!—I would feel like smoking again. Tuned to my regular morning radio station, I steered my car out of the parking lot. Strangely, the closer I got, the calmer I felt. Taking a left at the Scott Boulevard fire station, I made my final approach to the ACT campus, three buildings nestled in a woodsy, beautifully landscaped setting. I turned right at the first building, down the driveway to the rear parking lot, finding my usual slot in the second row. With the car still running, I pulled my badge from the bin between the seats, draped the lanyard over my head and waited for my favorite lyrics from the Peter Frampton song, "Baby, I Love Your Way," playing on the radio. *Here it comes.* I turned up the volume and sang along. "I can see the sunset in your eyes, brown and gray, and blue besides." Fortified, I turned off my car and climbed out, walked briskly to the stairs, swiping my badge over the scanner and awaiting the green light. I pulled open the door, its weight heavier than I remembered, a subtle reminder of my weakness and where I had been. Our department was in the basement, so sticking to my normal routine, I click clacked through the hallway to the descending stairwell on the far end, then down the stairs.

I entered the warren of cubicles in a windowless, fluorescent-lit space where it was impossible to get a cell phone signal. Another Lisa, the team "secretary"—a term I despised, fraught with old fashioned sexism—was stationed at the welcome cubicle, empty now since she came in a little bit later at 8:30. Lisa B was a spitfire, a petite, tough broad, gravelly voice of a former smoker, the go-to person for getting things. You need a new phone headset? Ask Lisa B. She'll scrounge one up for you. Plastic silverware so you don't have to go upstairs to the break room? Ask Lisa B. She'll know where to look. She was the go-to person for office gossip, too, so I would not be confiding in her. I spent a lot of time at her cubicle, partially because Colleen, who also came in at 8:30, sat across from it. I heard voices, coming from the next row, the row where my cubicle was nestled. Facing Colleen's cubicle was the white erase board where days off were displayed, an entry in red marker, reading "Lisa A—ret 4/7." Here I was, just steps from my first encounter. I turned up my row and was greeted by Andrea. "Lisa! She's back!"

So much for slinking past. Across from Andrea was Grace, my work buddy. She stood up and when she stood up, especially with the low ceiling, her height was, well, heightened. Grace was six-foot plus, ever conscientious of her weight and painfully self-conscious of her height. I was pretty sure Grace, who was good friends with Colleen, knew where I had been.

"Welcome back," she said in her low, alto voice, reaching out for a hug.

"You've lost weight," commented Andrea, still seated, a non-hugger.

"Yeah, I guess I did," I replied after the hug, starting to feel uncomfortable, wanting to move on down the row to the safety of my cubicle.

"It's good to see you guys," I said, inching away. Thankfully the next cubicle was empty which belonged to Hillary, one of the office know-it-alls, but not the one across from her where Moser sat. Known by her last name, Moser was popular, an ACT rock star. She was also a valuable resource. A self-proclaimed hippie, her cubicle was decorated with peace signs of every size and color.

"Welcome back!" she called out boisterously. Moser did everything boisterously—working, raising her sons, taking care of a sick friend, getting coffee in the breakroom. Underlying the ebullience was an ever-present calm, which was extremely useful with agitated callers and co-workers. She never got angry, which fascinated me. Although a lover of peace, Moser was not a lover of hugs.

"Thanks," I replied. "It's good to see you again." We looked at each other, a current of unspoken communication flowing between us. She knew. And I was glad she knew. I smiled. "Now I have to see if everything still works," I said.

"Let me know if you need anything," she offered warmly.

Entering my cubicle, I first noticed the objects d'art I had brought from home, their presence soothing me with their familiarity—the two small 8 x 10 Parisian landscapes, the framed photo of me with my parents outside Estes Park, the laminated Sugar Bowl poster of the classic Notre Dame vs. Alabama game in 1972. I sat down before the darkened, dual computer screens, pressed a key on the keyboard and the screens flickered.

"How you doing over there?" Moser called out.

"Pretty good. All logged in." I slid my chair out into the aisle, addressing Moser's cubicle, which was kitty corner from mine. "Is there anything new I should know about?"

Moser also slid out. "No. There was a test on Saturday so payments, returning materials, reschedules. The usual stuff."

"Okay. Thanks."

I stared at the multiple computer apps we used for test readiness issues, for assisting already overworked teachers, principals, and guidance counselors with the myriad of guidelines and rules required to give an ACT test. Most of the test coordinators were reasonable, a pleasure to talk to and help, understanding of a mishap such as a missing shipment or a downed computer system. But there were a few—there's *always* a few—who were either downright hapless or just plain mean. For those few, no explanation or alternate solution was acceptable.

I set my phone to "Ready" status, waiting for that first call. It was a brief wait, my phone trilling, red light flashing. "Test administration. This is Lisa. How can I help you?" It was an easy one, pretty typical for post-test week, a test coordinator notifying me that their test materials hadn't been picked up yet. FedEx was contracted to pick up test materials for up to three days after the test. It was now Thursday so I had to reschedule a pickup. "Okay, I'll go ahead and reschedule a pickup for you." The gears in my brain slowly creaked to life, sending out pings of memory. *Ask how many packages. Verify their address. Ask about their school hours.* "How many packages are there? Okay, one polymailer, two boxes." I groped around on my desk for a pen and scratch paper to jot that down. I was a jotter-downer, aware that details may dissolve between now and the time I type the info into the FedEx website. "I'll reschedule that right after I get off the phone. Thanks for calling."

Logging calls had been an ongoing topic at almost every meeting since I started; Moser was a fervent proponent, though Colleen and Grace were not. Moser railed often when she couldn't find a call log related to a call she had just taken. When I first started, I had surreptitiously asked Colleen and Grace if they logged every call and they both gave a non-committal response. "If it's really needed." "It depends on the call," they replied. I had developed the habit of logging every call. If anything, it allowed a break between calls. I pasted the FedEx confirmation number into the log, closed it and took a deep breath, setting my phone to Ready. It trilled immediately.

"Test administration, this is Lisa. How can I help you?"

The caller was a test coordinator who hadn't paid one of her proctors. I assured her it was okay, I would email her a form that she could fill out with the payment information. A pleasant call with a satisfactory outcome. Most of my morning unfolded that way, straightforward queries with one speedbump when I was unable to find a school on the state and district testing website. Frustrated, I placed the caller on hold and walked over to Moser's cubicle. "I can't find the school and she insists they're doing state testing," I whined.

"What state?" Moser calmly asked.

"North Carolina."

"Now remember some smaller schools and charter schools participate in district testing," she gently reminded me. "Did you check district testing?"

"No, I didn't," I replied sheepishly.

"Check district. You're doing great."

I returned to my cubicle and clicked on district testing from the dropdown list. Voila! I informed the test coordinator and proceeded to help her modify the student roster. The rest of the morning passed without major incident. Right before lunch, Grace entered my cubicle. "Do you want to help check in international?" she asked.

Grace had been at ACT for fifteen years, winding her way through different jobs in test administration before landing at international testing. She was a whiz with spreadsheets and computer savvy. Checking in international meant unpacking the test materials, counting the answer sheets, matching them up with the student rosters, and confirming the proper paperwork had been returned. It meant getting away from the phones and going to the warehouse where ACT packed up and shipped out test materials—a nice reprieve from any phone craziness.

"Yes, I would," I replied.

"Okay. I'll go tell K.J." K.J. was Kathy Johnson, our supervisor who annoyed some people with her unsophisticated, small-town ways, though I appreciated her forthright, no-nonsense style. You always knew where you stood with K.J.

Grace returned to my cubicle. "We can start after lunch if that's okay with you."

"Sure. That's fine." Being back on the phones had been okay but I was looking forward to the minimal human interaction and physical exertion of checking in materials. It was also a great opportunity for Grace and me to talk openly without being overheard. After eating lunch at my desk and perusing Facebook for the first time in months (Kyle's on Facebook!), I drove down to the warehouse on Scott Boulevard, along the eastern border of Iowa City. Or at least it used to be. Constructed years ago to serve as an eastside north-south corridor, Scott Boulevard had been considered a country road until urban development crept up to it from the west, then jumped over it like a fire over a firewall. The first stretch going south from ACT was still relatively unsullied, the graceful hills of a prairie reserve on each side providing a riotous landscape in the summer of yellow and purple wildflowers, before giving way to suburbia at the top of a hill, on which loomed a giant stone Buddha. He sat on the hill, overlooking the road as if to serenely remind drivers to relax, slow down, drive 25 mph like the signs tell you. But of course, there were always the assholes who refused to heed the Buddha. I passed Buddha and proceeded through the four-way stop, entering the developed stretch. Next came a brief respite of greenspace before a stretch of newer cookie cutter houses and a trailer park until crossing the railroad tracks introduced the industrial park segment. At the last building on the end, I turned into the driveway, up a small incline to the half-full parking lot. The warehouse was a large one-story nondescript structure, surrounded by brown scrubby fields, the low hum of traffic on nearby Highway 6 punctuated by the bright chirping and chatter of birds. I entered the foyer, badged through the door into the empty reception area then walked past the half dozen offices into the vast, brightly lit main space. I headed to the rear of the building, past the vacant makeshift computer stations on the right, toward the whirring and clanging of the machinery as it sorted and packed test materials. Grace sat at a long table in our check-in area, peering at her laptop, a pallet of stacked boxes behind her.

"We've got boxes!" I noted.

"We do! I'm just about to print the list."

I took a seat at the table. The check-in process was a pleasant balance of physical and mental exercise. Hoisting, cutting open, and unpacking each box blended perfectly with the counting and matching up of tests to rosters. It was nice to be away from the phones. I had returned to my co-workers, dipped my toe into the office waters. Grace returned from the printer with the list and we got down to business.

The smaller boxes on top of the pallet were from the smaller test centers in Europe, Canada, and Latin America, light enough to lift with one hand. We flew through the top half of the pallet, taking five boxes at a time to our seats at the table, quickly counting and reconciling answer sheets with rosters. We worked steadily until mid-afternoon, when Grace broke the rehab ice.

"How was it coming back to work?" she asked.

I set down my pencil and gave her my full attention. "I was really nervous about it." I paused. "But once I was there and saw you and Andrea and Moser, it was okay. It helped that this counselor, Eff Jeff...." I stopped to chuckle.

"Eff Jeff?"

"We called him that because he used the f-word all the time. He'd walk into group and say 'How ya doing, ya drunk fucks.'" We giggled at that. "Yeah, he was one of my favorite counselors. Anyway, he set it up so I could go to a meeting here and meet someone from ACT. That person gave me some good advice, but I can't tell you who it is."

"I think I know who it is." Of course she did. Between Grace and Moser, they knew just about everybody at ACT. And he had been their boss.

"Talking to him helped a lot and now it's just a huge relief to not have that weighing on me anymore."

"I'm just glad you're back."

We spent the rest of the afternoon catching up, Grace updating me on office scuttlebutt and on her long distant relationship with her Spaniard fiancée. Grace had been with Alex seven years, though they were no closer to living in the same country as they had been when we'd met. And she had been my drinking buddy even though she wasn't a real drinker. She was a careful, moderate drinker, often a no-show to my favorite socially acceptable boozing event—Friday happy hour. That was her scheduled time to Skype with Alex, and she refused to reschedule no matter how much I harangued her. Grace was more familiar with my public drinking persona, with rare glimpses of my "real" drinking, occasions when I had gone home via Uber or Grace herself had driven me.

My last public drinking event had been on New Year's Eve at Colleen's house for her early Ireland New Year's party, celebrating the new year at 6 o'clock central time. This had allowed me to do some controlled day drinking—we had the day off from work—so I had a decent buzz by the time Grace picked me up. At Colleen's, the booze flowed so my buzz seamlessly fit in. I drank freely, blending in with everyone else's drinking, no hint of what was yet to come.

After the first of the year, something had clicked in my mind. It wasn't an instant click like a light switch—it was like a dimmer switch, the light of an idea turned on, then the dial slowly turning, the light imperceptibly dimming, ending with an abrupt twist of the dial to darkness with the purchase of two bottles of vodka. Mom was not alive to worry, not around to call me and anxiously wonder why I didn't pick up. She was not alive for the shame. Her absence gave me permission to completely succumb. When I was still going to work, I had used her death to justify not wearing makeup and calling in sick. I had taken advantage of the sympathy. What started off as using sick time to extend weekend drinking transformed to drinking every awake moment.

I returned to my apartment from the warehouse tired but in good spirits, anticipating Martha's interrogation and excited to share the revelation that had been growing all day: I was okay. I was going to be okay.

"How did it go?" she asked, muting the television like she had done in the hospital.

I sat down and looked at her, a little surprised. "It was easy, seamless. Nobody asked any questions. Everyone welcomed me back, they were all really nice."

We discussed what it was like taking calls, and the welcome reprieve of checking in international tests at the warehouse. "That'll be good, having that time with Grace," Martha commented. The TV was tuned to the handsome Ari Melber on evening MSNBC.

"I'm gonna go to a meeting," I said.

"Do you want to go alone?"

"You can't go. It's a closed meeting."

"Oh, that's right." A beat. "But you want to go by yourself, don't you."

Oh dear, intuitive Martha. "Yeah, I do. I gotta start cutting the cord."

I got to the meeting ten minutes early, grabbed a prime seat along the righthand wall and settled in, trying not to plan out what I was going to say. AA advised you to be in the moment, listening fully to those sharing before you. Voices from the front porch drifted in, three guys out there yukking it up. I pulled out my phone and texted Kyle. *At a meeting.*

A good texter, Kyle replied immediately. *Way to go! I need to come down for a meeting.*

The room started filling up. There was Ronnie, still wearing a cast, a mechanic named Chris who had also just gotten sober, familiar faces, unfamiliar faces. Halfway through the shares it was my turn. I piggybacked off an earlier comment about relishing drama when drinking. I described how my ex's ex would show up at events, knowing we would be there, and how I would wallow in the sympathy from his friends, soaking up the attention along with the booze, always hoping someone would confront her and tell her to leave. That had never happened and a couple of times I had stormed out of the room in a dramatic, drunken huff. "Looking back on it," I concluded, "I think on some twisted level I was enjoying the drama, being the center of attention of the drama." A beat. "I was an idiot." A sprinkling of laughter warmed me.

A few shares later, one of the porch guys—I'd noticed his swarthy good looks, long, dark hair pulled back in a ponytail—piggybacked off of my share, admitting he had also been drawn to drama. It was always rewarding when someone responded to your share. His voice was deep and mellow.

Another good-looking long-haired guy, more yoga instructor than rock star, shared something that stuck with me long after the meeting. He talked about noticing things, simple everyday things like making scrambled eggs, and appreciating them like he never had before.

"I'd forgotten how good they tasted, how good they *smelled*, how satisfying it is to make myself something to eat. It was weird," he said.

Simple things, being aware of them and finding pleasure in them. I knew what he meant. I thought of how I felt when I was feeding the birds, the simple task of pouring the seed, then watching from the bedroom window as the creatures gradually returned, the squirrels and chipmunks right away, followed by the maligned sparrows, then the special early morning visitors, a pair of cardinals who dined at dawn to beat the morning rush. Rounding out the array of returnees were the tree trunk-hopping nuthatches and the chattering chickadees with occasional cameo appearances from the noisy and magnificent blue jays and a red-bellied woodpecker.

Back home, I debriefed Martha. I summarized the eggs share and how it had struck a chord with me. We settled in with snacks for one of our favorite television shows, The Blacklist, me with Triscuits and sliced cheese, her with a box of Chicken in a Biscuit. The show starred James Spader in a career-revitalizing role as a charming, droll, likable anti-hero. He killed and beat up people all the time, yet you rooted for him. He was also sophisticated, often drinking expensive whiskey from heavy looking, richly carved tumblers. But he never got drunk. I wanted him to drink more, to get noticeably drunk.

"Does it bother you to see people drinking?" asked Martha.

I pondered. "Bother me? No, not bother. But I notice it. I'm aware of it. What bugs me is that they never show them getting drunk."

"I could always tell on the phone when you'd been drinking. There was something different in your voice."

"I know. I should've never called you when I was drinking. But after having a few drinks, I thought I could outsmart everyone."

"Are you okay with me leaving tomorrow?"

"Yes. It's time. But I'm really glad you were here this week."

"Me too." We smiled quietly at each other.

I woke up sad, knowing that Martha was leaving today. But it was time for her to get back to her husband and for me to do this on my own. I hated to admit it, but it had been nice having someone to come home to. I didn't like feeling that way. I had been around someone—my sisters, hospital staff, Abbey people—the past few weeks and now I was really going to be alone for the first time since getting sober. I'd be with work people during the day and going to meetings in the evening. But I had two weekend days ahead of me. All of a sudden, I was excited to have two days to myself. I would miss Martha's companionship, but I was ready to be alone. I sprung out of bed.

Driving to the warehouse, tears stung my eyes as I replayed our goodbye in my mind.

"I believe in you," she had said, looking at me intently, holding me at arm's length.

"Thank you for *everything*," I replied before hugging her extra tight.

Chapter Twenty-Six

The weekend flew by. Who knew that puttering could be so satisfying? Between grocery shopping, roaming the aisles of a consignment store aptly named Stuff, and going to meetings, I easily filled my time. At home, I straightened up Martha's room and went through a couple of bins, switching out some winter sweaters for spring tops. After arranging some spring tops on my closet shelf, I eyeballed the room, the bed a stark reminder of sleepless hours in the dark, lying among the twisted sheets, tormented by my battle to not drink in the morning. Surveying the room with a fresh, sober eye, I realized the room was large enough to reposition the bed. I got to work.

Thankfully the rear legs of the bed were on wheels, so I easily swung out the foot of the bed and pushed the headboard up against the wall next to the window, leaving the end table and lamp in the same corner. With the head of the bed next to the window, I would be able to hear the birds when it was warm enough to leave the window open—an unexpected bonus. I laid down to try out the new perspective, head near window, facing the closet. I loved it! Lying there I noticed the open space the foot of the bed had formerly filled, space enough for my parents' old rocking chair, now in the second bedroom, boxes stacked on its seat.

Next I rearranged the furniture in the living room. I switched the red loveseat with my gray drinking chair, placing the chair in front of the window where the loveseat had been. It took a little more effort than moving the bed, but the result was rewarding, and the chair now sat in the natural light from the window. I sat in it, sunlight pouring over my shoulder. *I never drank while sitting over here. And I never will.*

At the Tuesday 6 o'clock meeting, I was rewarded with an appearance by Eff Jeff. The room crackled with energy when he entered. Lowering himself into the chair next to the doorway, he looked my way and our eyes met, his grin widening.

"How are you?" he asked.

"Good! How are you?"

"Same old shit...." Then someone else grabbed his attention.

His share was surprisingly thoughtful—I anticipated something more comedic—but sprinkled with his signature word. "Serenity's fucking great! But you have to work it, exercise it every day with prayer, with meditation. You can't take sobriety for fucking granted."

After seeing Eff Jeff, I disobediently pre-planned one part of my share. I couldn't resist. I spontaneously talked about taking what I had learned at The Abbey and rolling it over to my daily life, praying, going to meetings, structure, then wrapped up with my planned statement. "And now that I'm feeling good, I have to keep reminding myself—" Here I turned to Eff Jeff, also part of the plan. "—that I can't take my sobriety for fucking granted." Did he get it? His mouth twitched, then slid into a slow grin. He mouthed "I" and pointed at himself. He left the meeting early, but seeing him plus our inside joke moment alleviated any disappointment.

At work Thursday, my phone chimed. "It's Dan!" I squealed. During one of my stories about Dan, Grace's brow had thoughtfully furrowed.

"He's from Iowa City?" she had asked.

"Yes."

"Tall? A baby face? Kind of shy?"

"Yes. What?"

"I think he worked here at the warehouse." After a few more details, we had confirmed it was Dan, Grace recognizing his last name.

Meeting tonight? he texted.

You're out! Sure! 6 o'clock at Melrose? I texted back.

Yep. They sprung me. See you then.

See you then!

"We're going to a meeting!" I announced. "My first one with an Abbey person!"

"Yay!" Grace clapped her hands, happy for me.

Later that afternoon while perusing Facebook, I came across Dan's feed, his profile photo of him wearing a Cubs baseball cap. His relationship status had changed to "In a Relationship." I spotted a comment from Vape Man. "Congrats bro. Best of luck to you and Mona."

No. It couldn't be. It had to be some dumb Vape Man joke. How could that possibly have happened? I had only been gone a week. She's older and has two kids. I furiously texted Kyle.

Dan changed his relationship status on Facebook and Vape Man said something about wishing him and Mona good luck. It can't be, right?

I stared at my phone, willing it to chime. It did.

What? It has to be some kind of joke. Its Vapeman. Mona? No way

They must have concocted this post to mess with people. Dan was a prankster, more subtle than Kyle, but mischievous, nonetheless. It *had* to be a prank. The alternative was too disturbing.

Upon turning into the Melrose driveway, I saw Dan, smoking a cigarette at the bottom of the stairs, standing next to a young regular named Spencer. I remembered Spencer's name so readily because it was unique, as was he, a smart and eloquent hipster with shaggy hair and black horn-rimmed glasses. Dan squinted at me through a cloud of smoke, his mouth breaking into a big smile.

"Dan!" I greeted him, reaching up for one of his signature hugs.

"Lisa!" We hugged tightly, then broke away to look at each other. "It's good to see you."

"When did you get out?" *And are you really in a relationship with Mona?*

"Sunday, after family day. How's it going with you?"

"Good. I'm back at work, Martha stayed with me that first week, which was really nice." I wanted to ask the big question but not in front of Spencer.

Seated next to him in front of the windows, I worked up to the main question. "How's Pat?"

Dan smiled and chuckled. "He's Pat. No, he's doing pretty good. He's staying on for a couple more weeks."

"He is? That's good. How's Derwood? Is he still coming for out-patient?"

"Yep. He's doing really good."

It was time. "I saw on Facebook that you changed your relationship status." A pause. "Then I saw a comment from Jim wishing you and Mona good luck." I was careful with my tone of voice, trying to keep it as even as possible. "Was that a joke? Or are you in a relationship with her?"

He turned and looked at me. "No. It's not a joke."

I fought to conceal my emotions, wanting to say, "Are you out of your ever-loving mind? What are you thinking?" I wanted to smack him upside the head. But some deep instinct advised me to tread carefully. "I'm not sure how I feel about that," I replied evenly, but dishonestly. I goddamn well knew how I felt about it. It was insane, not only entering into a relationship but into a complicated, messy one with a fellow addict who is also fresh out of rehab.

"I get that," he said.

The meeting was called to order. I hoped that someone would bring up relationships and getting sober, but no one did. For my share, I acknowledged my gratitude for The Abbey and for the Iowa City AA community. For his share, Dan also expressed gratitude for The Abbey and the people he met there, nodding at me (and probably thinking of Mona!). Then an older woman welcomed Dan and warmly praised our support for each other.

"Keep coming back, Ben," she said.

Dan and I exchanged a look, then giggled. Flustered, the woman apologized, realizing her mistake but we quickly alleviated her discomfort.

"I've been called Ben before," Dan/Ben chuckled.

Compelled to elaborate, I explained, "There was a guy at The Abbey who had trouble remembering names and he called Dan Ben all the time. Sometimes we called him Ben!"

Dan/Ben nodded. "They did."

Standing outside afterwards, Dan revealed that Mona's sponsor had dumped her because of the relationship.

"Hmmm. That seems kind of harsh," I replied, still covering my strong disapproval. "Is it okay for me to say that I'm concerned?"

Our eyes held. Dan smiled. "Yes. That's okay."

I reached out for a hug and was rewarded with another satisfying one. *No change in hugs! He's still with me!* "Take care, keep in touch. We'll go to another meeting soon," I said as I started for my car.

Driving out, I waved at Dan as he waited for his mom to pick him up because he had lost his license. Once home, I began texting furiously, first the sisters, then Kyle and Dave. *Dan's in a relationship with Mona!!! What are they thinking??*

The replies varied but all were of the same vein.

Hes thinking with his dick—Kyle.

Don't they tell you not to get into a relationship?—Paula.

He's too young for her. What do his parents think?—Martha.

No response—Dave.

I reiterated to all, except Dave, about how I was being careful, about not wanting to jeopardize my friendship with Dan. They all agreed that was the best strategy.

The following Tuesday I ran into Eff Jeff again at the 6 o'clock Melrose meeting. He caught my eye and scampered straight toward me, plopping down in the chair next to me.

"How ya doin'?" he asked.

"Good. How are things at The Abbey?"

"Same shit. A bunch of drunks." He waved at someone across the room and grinned at me, softening the content of his words. "I'm leaving in July."

"What? Why?"

"It's time. I'm gonna do my own thing." He nodded at someone else who had just sat down.

"What kind of thing?"

"Counseling." He looked at me. "There's a lot of fucked up people out there. You look good."

"So do you. You have nice legs." He really did, muscular but too muscular. Hairy, but not too hairy. It didn't feel weird complimenting him on his legs, I felt that comfortable with him. And I knew it didn't make him feel weird. I followed his gaze to a tall, thin, blonde woman in workout clothes who had just entered the room. "Isn't that your girlfriend?" I recognized her from photos he had shown me on his phone. She sat down a few seats away from us even though there was an empty chair next to him. "You don't sit by each other?"

"You're sure asking a lot of questions," he smirked. "It's not high school. This isn't fucking study hall."

"Mm, hmm, and I have another question. What's up with Dan and Mona? How did that ever happen?"

He broke off eye contact. "These things happen. We caution against it, but it still happens." A pensive beat. "It's not good."

I sensed he was done talking about it. Once again, Eff Jeff's share was thoughtful and eloquent, only one f-word used. Throughout the meeting he kept checking his phone, which bugged me. It bugged me when *anybody* did it.

Two days later, Dan texted me, *Meeting tonight?*

Yes, I texted back. *See you tonight!*

This time at Melrose, we sat across from the windows.

"How have you been?" I asked.

"I'm okay. I'm kind of bored. I need to get a job or something. Maybe go back to school."

"Yes, you should do something. Boredom is not good." A cautious pause. "How are things with Mona?"

"Good. She's coming here this weekend. Maybe we should all go to a meeting."

I tried to inject some enthusiasm into my voice. "Yeah, maybe we should." I guess it didn't work.

"I thought you liked Mona."

"It's not about how I feel about Mona." Which wasn't entirely true. I was pissed at her for allowing this to happen. Yes, technically Dan was an adult, but he was still young, too young to be ensnared with a fellow recovering addict with two pre-teen kids. "It's just that I'm worried."

I stewed through the meeting. I didn't want Dan to turn away from me because I didn't approve of his relationship. His share eased my skittish mind. He disclosed about how, now that he's sober, he worries about staying sober, about failing his family and himself. "I've always had high expectations for myself, for everything." He turned to me. "What's that saying, your sister's saying? She got it out of a fortune cookie."

My mind blanked for a second, but memory kicked in. "Expect nothing and you will never be disappointed."

"That's it! Expect nothing and you'll never be disappointed. I have to keep saying that to myself."

I leaned into Dan, bumping his shoulder with my shoulder, and squeezed his knee. Dear, sweet Dan. He was still with me.

Via text, I periodically checked in on Dan, while also checking with Kyle about his checking in on Dan.

Have you said anything about Mona? I texted.

Yeah I told him Im happy for them.

What??? Happy for them?

I also told him to be careful. Like you said we dont want to push him away.

I had finally heard from Dave, the old-fashioned way via a phone call. "I got a bad feeling about this," he intoned. "I don't see it ending well. I wonder what his parents think."

"I asked. He said they really like her."

"Well, she can be charming. And she is attractive." I rolled my eyes. "Dan's talking about moving to Des Moines."

"What? When? Did you talk to him?"

"No. Derwood told me."

"Derwood?" I was confused.

"Yeah. He still goes there for out-patient and it was a guys group and they were talking about what they're going to do after leaving The Abbey."

"Oh, no."

"Yeah, and you're going to love this. Pat pipes in and says, 'That's a good idea unless you're moving there just for pussy.'"

"Oh dear." Bless Pat and his crude way of making a point.

"And Jamie was the counselor."

"Yikes."

"Yeah. I guess he apologized for using that word, but his point had been made. And Derwood said Jamie had agreed with what Pat was trying to say."

"I'm glad he said it. He could've phrased it a little differently."

"Lisa. It was Pat."

"Yeah, it was Pat."

"You just keep going to meetings with him and stay connected."

"I will. Do you ever see Clint?"

"Not lately. He doesn't go to the men's meeting I like."

"I've texted him, but I don't ever hear back. He's worse than you."

I had also emailed Clint but had received no response. From his Facebook posts, I gathered that things were not going well with his fiancée, many of his posts about not being accepted or understood, or song lyrics about break-ups and heartache.

"Keep in touch," Dave signed off. "I may not respond right away but I will eventually." At least he was a self-aware bad texter.

That Thursday, Kyle texted me, *Coming down for a meeting. Picking up Dan.* I happened to be at lunch with Grace when I got the text.

"Kyle's coming down for a meeting and he's picking up Dan!" I exclaimed.

"Yay!" she enthused.

6 o'clock at Melrose? I texted.

Yea, he replied.

"I'm so excited!" I gushed. "My first outside meeting with Kyle and Dan!" I immediately texted the sisters. *Going to a meeting with Kyle and Dan tonight!*

Melrose at 6? Martha texted back.

Talk some sense into Dan, Paula responded.

This was a golden opportunity for Kyle and me. Between the two of us, maybe we *could* talk some sense into him.

After parking at the house on Melrose, I spotted Dan and Kyle standing next to a black SUV, both grinning at me. My step quickened. "Hi you two!" I called out, my heart swelling at the sight of them, tall and handsome, boyish Dan next to sleek, hip Kyle. I hugged him first.

He affectionately looked at me after our hug. After a Dan hug, we approached the back door, me keenly aware of my young, good-looking escorts. Ascending the steps, I was greeted by a couple of regulars.

"Hey Lisa."

"Hi Jim. Hi Mark." Thankfully, I remembered their names.

Reminiscent of the meeting in Cedar Rapids, I felt proud sitting between my two Abbey guys, and kind of cool when meeting-goers greeted me. "I guess you've been coming to this meeting a lot," Kyle commented after another greeting.

"Four times a week," I said. "I wish Eff Jeff would show up, but he goes to the Tuesday meeting."

"Yeah, I'd like to see him," Dan said.

"I wouldn't," Kyle added.

"Oh, Kyle," I chided. Kyle was not so enamored by Eff Jeff.

I was hoping for a good meeting and we got one. When it was Kyle's turn, I was a little nervous, acutely aware of his volatility and unpredictability. He was volatile alright, and used the f-word as a verb, noun, and adjective all throughout his share. But the room was attentive, embracing his impassioned declaration of fear.

"Now that I'm sober, I'm fucking *feeling* again, but I'm fucked because I'm more aware of the fear, fear of taking care of my family, fear of not being able to stay sober and disappointing everyone again." He glanced at me. "But now I'm better able to deal with that fear. So I do have that going for me."

My heart swelled with pride. Good looking and eloquent in his street-smart way. After the meeting, a couple of people came up to us.

"You guys were at The Abbey together?" one regular asked. "That's really cool you're going to meetings together."

"It's great you have each other for support," commented Tammy, Eff Jeff's ex.

Outside standing next to Kyle's vehicle, I sensed our reluctance to leave each other.

"Hey, you wanna get something to eat?" Kyle suggested. "I'm starved. I didn't have time to eat."

"I ate but sure, I'll go," I said.

"I got nothing else to do," Dan added with a grin.

"Good. Let's go to the Village Inn," Kyle said. "It's right down on Riverside."

"Okay. I know where it is. It's close," I agreed.

"Ride with us. I can bring you back here."

"Are you sure? But you have to take Dan home."

"It's no big deal. Get in," Kyle ordered.

I smiled at his bossy, take-charge tone and hopped into the backseat while Dan climbed into the front. There was something about riding in the car with people who are familiar, the unexpected conversations, the possibility of hilarity. I couldn't help but comment on Kyle's immaculately clean SUV.

"Your vehicle is very neat and clean," I said.

"Yeah, you can't tell that you have a kid," Dan agreed.

"That's the kind of guy I am, neat and clean," said Kyle, meeting my eyes in the rearview mirror.

At Village Inn, we slid into a booth next to the windows, the guys on one side, me on the other. Kyle looked around the mostly empty restaurant. "Same ugly décor from 15 years ago. It's not very busy. But I bet the food's still good. Basic comfort food."

"They decorated in orange because back in the 70s there was some study that said orange affected people's appetite, made them want to eat more," I explained. "Hardee's were also decorated in orange for the same reason."

"How do you know that?" asked Dan, looking skeptical.

I shrugged. "I don't know."

"I remember hearing that," Kyle said. "Think of all the fast-food restaurants. The interiors are orange and brown."

A waitress approached our booth bearing three thick, plastic menus, setting one down in front of each of us with a heavy slap. "Does anyone want coffee?" We all looked at each other and shook our heads.

"Too late in the day for me," I said. "I'll just have water."

"Yep, too late for coffee," Kyle agreed. "I'll have a Coke or Pepsi."

"That's still caffeine," I interjected.

"But it's not coffee caffeine," he explained.

"I guess."

"Coke for me," Dan ordered.

They ordered burgers and fries while I ordered onion rings with a side of ranch dressing. Kyle looked at me, then at Dan, a question brewing behind his dark blue eyes. "So how are you really doing, Dan?"

Dan looked from Kyle to me and back to Kyle. "I knew this was coming."

"Well, we care about you," I said. "You have to understand why we're concerned."

"Yeah, getting into a relationship right out of rehab and with someone from rehab. It's a lot," Kyle added.

"I know, I know," Dan conceded. "We're taking it slow."

"You're not going to do something like move in with her, are you?" I asked.

"Yeah, that would be a little nuts, this soon," Kyle added.

"I don't know. I'm bored," Dan lamented. "I need to get a job or something."

"Dude, don't move there because you're bored," Kyle admonished.

"Yeah, boredom is bad for us addicts. I'm sure you can find a job here," I encouraged. "You could get a job like at Ace Hardware. I love Ace Hardware. I've always thought it would be a fun place to work."

"Or Best Buy," Kyle suggested.

"Best Buy. Why Best Buy?" I questioned.

"Why Ace Hardware?" Kyle countered.

"I like the Ace Hardware idea better than Best Buy," Dan interjected.

"See!" I grinned at Kyle. "Maybe Menards. Or Home Depot."

"Maybe ACT," Dan said, looking at me. "You know, I worked there at the warehouse."

"You did?" I feigned ignorance.

"Yeah, on the line, packing up test materials."

Our food arrived, interrupting our job coaching session. Their burgers looked and smelled good but so did my thick golden onion rings.

"Ranch dressing?" Kyle asked, chewing a bite of burger.

"It's good with everything." I dipped one of the rings, taking a tentative bite. It had cooled sufficiently. "Better than ketchup," I said, nodding at the red pool of sugary paste on his plate. "You should try it."

Kyle dipped a couple of fries in the mini paper cup. I watched him chew thoughtfully, the chewing slowly transforming to a grin.

"Not bad," he said. "You know, I've seen people dip fries in mayonnaise and I thought it was weird. Now I get it."

When the waitress returned, we requested more ranch. Then we reminisced about The Abbey—the basketball tournament, Vape Man, art therapy, Pat's rants.

"What happened with Sam?" I had to ask. "I thought you liked her."

Dan shrugged. "I did. She's cute. But it just wasn't happening."

"How did it happen with Mona?" I hoped my voice sounded even and neutral.

He shrugged again. "I don't know. It just happened."

Kyle shot me a warning look. I backed off.

"Well, as long as you guys are taking it slow," I smiled at Dan, who smiled back and held my gaze.

The following week I heard from Kyle that Dan had moved to Des Moines, that he had moved in with Mona.

Chapter Twenty-Seven

still didn't have a sponsor. I'd approached Eff Jeff's ex-girlfriend, the spirited and lovely Tammy, but she had hedged, citing her realtor schedule of evenings and weekends, the opposite of my work schedule. I had quickly and genuinely told her it was okay. She probably had a ton of sponsor requests. Eff Jeff assured me that it would happen, not to force it or worry about it, I'd find a sponsor.

"Just sit back and listen at meetings," he advised. "It'll happen. You'll know. Have you ever been to the Saturday morning women's meeting? It's at Wild Bill's. I've heard it's one of the best broads' meetings."

Tammy had also mentioned that meeting. Eff Jeff wasn't sure of the start time, so I looked it up. It started at 9 am, right away in the morning to allow for running errands afterwards. It was only five minutes from my apartment, so I got there 10 minutes early that next Saturday. I wasn't sure where to park—only three parking stalls in front of the building—so I parked on the dead-end street on the downhill side of the building, forced to make a clumsy Y-turn to be on the parking side of the street. Walking toward the entrance, I saw bookshelves and paintings through the front windows.

Upon entering, I heard voices coming from an adjacent room to the left of the main space. Peeking through the doorway, I saw a long, smaller room, two couches halfway down along the walls facing each other. Rows of plastic patio chairs had been set up on the two ends of the room. Two women sat on the couches, facing each other, while a third unstacked some chairs to complete a row on the far end. Paintings, from what looked like local artists, hung on the walls. I ducked back out and walked toward the counter at the other end of the main room, past bookshelves, filled with an array of used hardback and paperback books. I set my Big Book from The Abbey on the counter, the AA schedule pamphlet indicating this meeting was a Big Book Study meeting. On the counter was a cake stand displaying a half dozen chocolate chip cookies and a glass jar designated for tips. A tall, older man emerged from the back room.

"Can I get you something?" he asked, smiling gently.

"Sure. I'll have a cup of coffee."

"There's half-and-half over in the cooler if you want it," he said, gesturing. He set down a steaming mug before me. "It's a dollar seventy-five."

I pulled my billfold from my purse, slid out a couple of singles and handed them to him. He turned and walked to the back room. I liked this place already with its quaintness and simplicity. It was casually comfortable and welcoming.

"And here's your change," he said, smiling gently again as he dropped the quarter into my palm.

"Thanks." I dropped it into the tip jar, the quarter landing softly and quietly on top of a bed of dollar bills.

I chose a seat in the middle row at the near end. A few more women had slipped in while I was getting coffee, all about my age, chatting like old friends. As the room filled, the volume of chatter increased exponentially. From gussied up with full make-up and styled hair to no make-up and low maintenance hair, from young to old, the attendees covered the spectrum. Except for race. They were all white faces. But this was Iowa after all, where 90 percent of the population is white. The meeting was brought to order by a blonde, curly-haired woman seated in a wing chair next to one of the couches. She explained the format of the meeting, reading a passage from the Big Book, then commenting on it or whatever was on the reader's mind. The hour passed swiftly, filled with heartache, humor and rawness. Years of sobriety were packed into this little room, from fresh open-wounded sobriety still oozing sticky fear, to seasoned, scabbed-over sobriety, nurtured and fortified by time, yet still vulnerable to being picked off, exposing the ever-present disease underneath. I basked in the wisdom, some basic and plain spoken, others cerebrally eloquent. These were the broads of Iowa City. Despite his chronic political incorrectness, Eff Jeff was correct once again.

After the meeting, I chatted with a woman who had also rehabbed at The Abbey, then turned to another who had been standing by expectantly.

"You don't remember me, do you," she stated.

I hadn't, but then I did, the last mental Rolodex card flipped over. "We worked together at The Arc. Joni."

"I saw you across the room and tried to catch your eye, but you didn't see me," she said.

"I saw you, but it didn't register until just now," I admitted. "How long have you been sober?"

"Seven years."

"Seven years! Wow! So when we were working together..."

Joni nodded. "I was about two years sober then. So you just got out of treatment?"

I nodded. "I'll be coming up on two months at the end of April."

"And you're going to meetings. This is a great one."

"That's what I was told." An impulse sprung up from deep inside me, manifesting itself in a bold question. "Do you sponsor?"

She smiled. "I do. But I haven't for a while. I just had a baby in January."

My mind flashed back to when I had worked with Joni—her earthiness, her vegetarianism, talking to her about Cozumel before going on a trip there with my ex, meeting her girlfriend at The Arc chili cook-off fundraiser. Returning her steady gaze behind the purple, rectangle-framed eyeglasses, I recalled her patience and compassion as a job counselor for The Arc's special need clients.

"Would you sponsor me?" I dared to ask.

She smiled. "Yes, I will." We hugged. "You know, I've been thinking recently about how I'd like to sponsor again."

"How long has it been?"

"Over a year."

"Wow. And then we run into each other at this meeting."

"The universe is talking to us."

A delicious chill scampered up my spine. We exchanged numbers and made a tentative plan to get together after next Saturday's meeting.

And just like that, I had a sponsor.

The first time we got together, Joni and I met at a coffee shop on the east side of Iowa City, which was convenient for both of us since she lived on the east side and I worked on the east side. I drove to the Java House after work, a little nervous but also excited, kind of like going on a first date. *I have a sponsor! And I know her!* The sisters had been ecstatic when I told them.

"You worked with her?" Martha had exclaimed on the phone. "No way. And you didn't know when you worked with her that she was in AA?"

"No. How would I know? It's not something you talk about at work. But I do remember how serene and kind she was."

"Oh, Lisa, I'm so happy for you!" Paula had responded. "And the way it happened! It just seems like it was meant to be. What made you ask?"

"It was pure impulse. I didn't even think about it. I just did it."

"That is so great."

Sitting outside at the Java House in the chilly April air, we ironed out the preliminaries. Having an infant restricted Joni's schedule more than mine, so we decided to meet after the Saturday women's meeting when Joni already had regular childcare, which she would extend for another hour. She outlined the structure—reading out loud to each other from the Big Book starting with the Preface through all of the Forwards and The Doctor's Opinion. I liked it. I liked reading out loud and hearing the written word spoken aloud.

For our second meeting, we sat outside Wild Bill's. It was a little warmer than our first meeting but not much, and Joni insisted we sit outside whenever possible. We didn't get to reading, instead I gave her the Cliff Notes version of how I ended up at The Abbey. I included a synopsis of my first stint in rehab, since it was related to my abrupt departure from The Arc. Joni nodded and smiled knowingly, her hazel eyes and wide generous mouth expressive. She was a natural beauty, clear skin, soft brown hair cut short. Our third meeting, also in front of Wild Bill's, we just talked, sharing histories, discovering we drank for similar reasons—introverts wanting to transform into extroverts. The fourth meeting we got down to business, forced by rain to sit inside Wild Bill's at the long table in the front window. Joni pulled her Big Book out of her crossbody bag, the blue binding lovingly covered with flowered fabric, worn and frayed from hours of handling. Inside, the pages were covered with doodles, scribblings in the margins and highlighted passages. After reading the Preface—only two pages so I read the whole thing—we started on the Forewords, moving to our one page each format. The initial Foreword appeared in the first printing of the first edition in 1939, the much longer second Foreword in the 1955 second edition. I jotted down notes in the margins of my book.

Our next meeting was outside Wild Bill's again, but instead of reading, Joni showed me a drawing in her Big Book on the title page of the AA symbol, a triangle within a circle, with single words and phrases written inside and outside of it. She wanted me to draw one in my Big Book. So beneath the title ALCOHOLICS ANONYMOUS, *The Story of How Many Thousands of Men and Women Have Recovered From Alcoholism, Fourth Edition*, I sketched the AA symbol. Inside the triangle I wrote "AA" with "Unity," "Service" and "Recovery" along each of the three sides. Outside the circle next to "Unity," Joni directed me to write "Fellowship" "Mind" and "Obsession," indicating the shared disease of uncontrollable drinking. Next, she told me to write down "Spirit—working w/ others" adjacent to "Service," explaining that could mean anything from refilling coffee cups to chairing at a meeting. "This is how you develop emotional sobriety," she said.

Finally, below Recovery under the base of the triangle, I wrote "Repair body—start Steps." Around all of that I drew a second circle, to represent the progression of drinking, writing at the top of this circle, "Pick up a drink." Some of the platitudes and clichés in AA drove me crazy and "Don't take that first drink" used to be one of them. As over-simplistic as it sounded to non-alcoholics and resistant alcoholics, it is a hard truth that I had grudgingly, then gratefully accepted. It was a hard truth to swallow, much harder than vodka straight from the bottle, but it was sticking this time unlike after my first rehab. Having accepted that truth, now I had to figure out how to live without taking that first drink.

Copying Joni's drawing, I drew arrows counterclockwise on the second circle, dividing it into five sections. Between the first set of arrows outside the circle, I wrote "Fixed mind, thought process," the next phase after taking that first drink. She explained that this was the phase when we are preoccupied with drinking, thinking about it, looking forward to it and planning for the next drink. Outside the next three segments, I wrote "Obsession," "Drinking and more drinking" and "Guilt, shame, remorse, hopelessness," respectively. One segment of the circle remained.

"We're gonna leave this part blank," Joni said. "Can you guess why?"

We had rounded the circle, now back to "Pick up a drink." There was nowhere to go from here.

"Because it's the end, death," I replied.

"Could be. Or this is where you can break the cycle. So write that off to the side—'If you can break the cycle here, you can live.'"

We smiled at each other. "So the guilt, shame, hopelessness part is your rock bottom," I said. "I think of my kitchen floor as my rock bottom."

"It's a great visual, your kitchen floor."

I looked down at my rough but decipherable drawing. "*This* is a great visual."

Along with meetings and a sponsor, I had developed a morning routine of prayer and reading a passage from "Daily Reflections." Joni suggested that I read aloud, giving the words a little more power. There was something ceremonial about speaking those words out loud in the morning quiet of my apartment. And I had started writing longhand in the notebook I had taken to The Abbey. I had always known how I was going to begin: with my rock bottom, the kitchen floor. After my first rehab stint, I had considered writing about it, scribbling out a few pages about the intervention and the transport to the hospital in the back of a squad car. But it never went beyond that. This time I yearned to write about it.

Chapter Twenty-Eight

Ever since Dan had moved to Des Moines, Mona had been posting photos of them on Facebook, kissing and canoodling, declaring he was the love of her life, her soulmate, a father to her children. I texted my dismay to Kyle.

Have you seen her posts! They're gross!

Yea. I don't need to see them making out on the couch. My eyes burned.

I railed to Joni about the relationship and my anger toward Mona. Sitting in her backyard, she reined me in, advising me to pray for them.

"You have to remember, she's sick," she said. "You need to pray for her and get rid of the anger. I know it's hard to do."

I sputtered a little more. Joni knew full well about the lure of getting into a relationship right after getting sober. After leaving the hospital, Joni had gone to her first meeting where she saw Jenny, her future spouse. It was love at first sight, she recalled; Jenny had a similar reaction. But Jenny had seven years of sobriety under her belt and knew not to act on it. She had laid down strict ground rules.

"She wouldn't allow us to be alone together for a year," Joni told me. "We'd text and talk on the phone and get together with other people, but she would never be alone with me. It was really hard, but she stuck to it. Of course, I got into a relationship with someone else because I was still emotionally sick, and it was unhealthy. It turned abusive. I was sober but my emotional sobriety was not there yet."

After that conversation with Joni, when I got down on my knees and prayed in the morning, I included Mona. I had always prayed for Dan. Per Joni's suggestion, I now prayed on my knees at the side of the bed, elbows on the mattress just like when I was a little girl. A recovering Catholic herself, Joni understood that some features of Catholicism could still provide comfort. For example, crossing myself—right hand to forehead, then right hand to heart, left shoulder to right shoulder—was now a physical reminder to keep my shit together.

It was a perfect day in May, sunny and warm but not too warm, a soft southerly breeze fluttering the leaves in the trees behind my apartment. I had unfurled a blanket on the grassy slope, with my phone, a Diet Pepsi, and a book lying next to me. Sitting there with my arms wrapped around my knees, the one o'clock sun on my face, I watched a pair of mallards peacefully bobbing in the creek until I felt drowsy. I laid down, eyes closed, the singing birds and softly quacking ducks merging into a lullaby. As I drifted off to sleep, my meandering, unfettered thoughts morphed into the elements of a dream story, the thought fragments linking into an alternate reality, the jazzy notes of a piano adding a soundtrack. My eyes flew open. It was Martha's text alert tone. I sat up and groped around on the blanket for my phone.

Where does Joni's wife work in the hospital? she texted.

I don't know. Why? I texted back.

Martha had been in the University of Iowa Hospital for a couple of days for a procedure and was getting out today. *My nurse this morning her name is Jenny and she was talking about how her spouse just had a baby in January.*

Oh I see. What floor are you on? I'll text Joni and ask.

Women's post-care unit.

Ok. I'll find out.

I texted Joni, and it turned out it was her Jenny. I excitedly texted Martha. *It's her! That's where she works and she's working today!*

Wow! What are the chances? It's a sign.

There are no coincidences as Kyle would say. Just then a flash of red caught the corner of my eye. It was a cardinal hopping around in the grass not six feet away from me. I texted furiously. *You're not gonna believe this, there's a cardinal hopping around right next to me.*

No way! Another sign! Dads happy were talking to each other.

My Higher Power is talking to me today! I watched the cardinal, a bright splash of color in the green grass, his upturned tail twitching in sync with each bright chirp before fluttering off. I settled down for another attempt at a siesta until my phone intervened again, this time by the Messenger alert ping. It was The Abbey group, started by Mona with some other Abbeyites who had arrived after us. These Abbeyites were much more enthusiastic about her relationship with Dan than me, as indicated by their comments on Facebook. I had reluctantly joined, mainly to keep tabs on Dan. He was returning my texts but the replies had become delayed and vague. This message was from Mona. And it was long. Shit!

I think I have everyone on my Facebook group but I'm really worried about Dan. He just left my house to go back to Iowa City. I think he's been using. He's not acting like himself. I'm really scared. Can any of you PLEASE help me and reach out to him. I love him so much. Even my kids are crying.

I definitely will, messaged someone named Brandi.

I will try to get a hold of him. How was he acting? I messaged.

He can't remember things. Repeating himself. Trouble walking or with general motor skills. Slow speech. Dilated pupils. Basically all of his behavior is nothing I'm used to.

Shit. I'll try and call him in a sec—Brandi

Crap! That doesn't sound good. I'll try and call as well. Is he driving?—Me

Yes. I'm really scared because he showed up like that around 3 yesterday and told me he almost went off the road twice.—Mona

Oh crap—Kyle

My phone continued to ping. No one could get a hold of Dan. I texted Kyle.

I'm not surprised this is happening. But this soon?

Yea I'm surprised by that too. The poor kid.

Later that evening, Mona notified us that he was at his parents, having spoken to his sister Emily. *She says without a doubt he's using. Everything I described to her is how he acts. She's heading over to their parents house now.*

I called Dave who provided a blunt, realistic perspective. "He'll go back,"

Dave predicted. "He thinks he loves her. They're playing house. She can probably be very persuasive, if you know what I mean."

I sighed. "Yeah, I know what you mean."

Dave was right. Within a week Dan was back in Des Moines and Mona was again posting canoodling photos on Facebook along with "family" snapshots.

I couldn't slip anything past Joni. When we discussed a plan for the Twelve Steps, she instructed me to start compiling a list of people to whom I would make direct amends. When reading my list to her, she stopped me at the naming of my ex.

"Wait. Why your ex?" she asked.

"Well, when I lived with him, I was drinking all the time and then I just left him without warning..."

"Do you really need to make amends to him or are you using it as a way to see him, to show him how good you're doing?"

I paused, mulling that over.

"He's not in your life anymore, you certainly don't have to do it in person. If you really feel you need to make amends, you can write him a letter," she continued.

Once again, Joni saw through my bullshit even when I didn't realize it was bullshit. She was absolutely right. I wanted to make amends to my ex to flaunt my sobriety, to flaunt how good I was doing.

I smiled. "You got me. He's off the list."

I wished Dan had a Joni.

The Friday before Memorial Day, while eating lunch with Moser, my phone chimed, The Abbey text alert tone. It was Kyle. *Mona just called me. Dans using again.*

I frowned and shook my head. "I gotta make a phone call." Kyle answered on the second ring.

"Now what's going on?" I asked.

"He's using, they got in a fight and he took off again. He comes back to Iowa City because his dealer is there."

I sighed. "Okay. Have you tried to call him?"

"No. Not yet."

"I'm gonna try and call him. He's driving again? Jesus!"

"Yeah, if he gets pulled over, he's fucked."

"Okay. Keep in touch."

"Let me know if you get a hold of him."

As I searched for Dan's number, the Messenger alert pinged. It was Mona.

He's apparently telling people I was drunk last night & kicked him out. That is absolutely not the case. My only issue is the lie not the relapse. So please support him or help him if you can. I'm going to need to take a break for myself. Love you all. Stay sober.

I called Dan and to my surprise he answered. "Hey," he said.

"What's going on?" I asked, keeping my voice light.

"I'm sure you've heard from Mona."

"I'm not gonna lie, she called Kyle. Are you driving?"

"Yeah, but I'm okay."

He was speaking slow, in a measured deliberate tone, each word carefully enunciated. Like I would do if I'd been drinking. "Okay, but I don't want to talk to you while you're driving. Call me when you get to Iowa City, we'll go to a meeting."

"Maybe. I got stuff to do. You know, she's been drinking. I know she's telling people I'm using, but she's drinking."

"She's saying that's not true."

"Of course she is."

"Okay, well drive safe and I'll talk to you later, okay?"

"Yeah. Okay."

I called Kyle. "I talked to Dan. He sounds weird. He's talking really slow, very measured. His voice sounds flat, no expression. Do you think he's using?"

"Yeah, probably. Did he say anything about Mona drinking? Did you see her message?"

"Yeah, I saw it and he said she is. I told him she's saying it's not true."

"Who the fuck knows? I'm gonna try and get a hold of Roger."

"Roger? Is he the tall guy with white hair from The Abbey?"

"Yeah, he's Dan's sponsor."

"Okay, good. I'm gonna try and get him to a meeting."

"I gotta get back to work. Keep me posted."

"Okay. Keep me posted too."

I talked to him, I posted on Messenger. *Trying to get him to see me. He's being evasive.*

No one responded. An hour later Kyle posted.

Got ahold of Roger. He's going to text Dan now

Good, I replied.

Dan is headed into his moms work right now, Mona messaged. *I'm trying to figure out something for my kids. I might head there.*

*Ok good—*Brandi

A couple of hours later, Brandi texted again. *Any updates on dan?*

I just talked to him. He asked if he can come back tonight.—Mona

Come back where—Kyle

Should he be driving around?—Me

To Des Moines. He's not supposed to drive at all.—Mona

No he already has 3 OWI—Kyle

A 4th would be deep shit—Vape Man

No kidding—Kyle

Oh he would be in prison. He's already a felon.—Mona

Relapses are normal just gotta keep the kid knowing he supported—Kyle

And he must stay safe.—Me

Yea—Kyle

I will. He needs to hear it from everyone though.—Mona

What's his cell?—Vape Man

After I was home from work, I called and texted Dan about going to the 6 o'clock Melrose meeting. No response. After 7, I got a text. *Sorry couldnt make the meeting. Im ok.*

Forty-five minutes later, Messenger pinged. It was Mona.

He just admitted it is Xanax.

Ok—Kyle

We're all in both your courts—Jesse!

Agreed—Kyle

United—Jesse

I am here for both of you.—Me

So he's home tho? I just wonder I used to lie and say it was other shit when it was really adderall just to admit to a lesser evil. Keep watching him—Kyle

Also afraid to text him he might feel attacked—also Kyle

Idk. From what he's told me it's always downers. I'm not sure I'll be sticking this out. Love the guy but lying to my face for two days breaks me. I think if he talks to anyone it will be me. He's trying to save the relationship. He just yelled at his dad to leave him alone because he was talking to me.—Mona

Unfortunately lying is part of the package of addiction, don't take that personal. Easier said than done.—Vape Man

I'm fully aware but we had a deal. We are both addicts. Good or bad never lie to each other. I've never lied to him & never would.—Mona

The chatter ended until the next day, Saturday, around noon.

Any news on Dan?—Marc

I guess he's going to Monas. He's ok—Kyle

Apparently there had been stuff going on last night that I wasn't aware of.

He's using still—Brandi

Huh? Like right now? Or yesterday—Kyle

Right now. Well this morning—Brandi

This morning is right now enough. How do you know that Brandi?—Me

Mona—Brandi

Xanax? He needs to go back to the abbey—Kyle

He is still high. I told him he can't come because I don't want him driving or around my kids high. They have already asked what was wrong with him & why he was acting so weird. As far as I know he's at home with his parents but I've lost track of the lies at this point.—Mona

Did he ever talk to Roger?—Me

I know Roger texted him. Parents need to bring him back—Kyle

I have no idea. He woke me up at 3:55. I have barely slept. I'm beyond exhausted. He refuses to give me their numbers. At this point I would rather talk to them. I can't accomplish anything with him.—Mona

I bet. You have to take care of yourself and your kids. He needs to reach out to someone. But he can't be forced.—Me

I know where he lives lol. The thing if he's driving he will get an OWI—Kyle

& to answer, yes, it's Xanax. He went and bought it before going to his relapse class on Wednesday. He had lunch with his dealer that day as well.—Mona

Is he working? I've never heard of a xanax dealer—Kyle

He's not working. He just was accepted to the electrical program at dmacc so idk where he's going to live for school now. Clyde has about every drug you could want.

He got it from some Ashley chick though. That was the last story I got. It changes by the minute—Mona

Your new pic looks like a xanax dealer.—Me referring to Kyle's Facebook profile photo.

(Laughing emoji) *kinda agree with Lisa on this one Kyle.*—Mona

Bahaha—Kyle

Could xanax usage easily turn to heroin? And how is he getting around? Is he staying with his parents?—Me

Uh yea that's how it happened last time. Either his parents or he has another apartment—Kyle

He's living with them & yes it will lead to heroin.—Mona

Well I know a guy who knows Clyde I'll just rob him—Kyle

What the fuck?! There's an apartment too? Fucking sweet. Awesome. This just gets better by the minute. Clyde is out of town now. I told him I'll personally make his life a living hell.—Mona

Where's the secret apartment? Melrose plays volleyball on Saturdays and I was going to ask Dan if he wanted to go. Somehow I don't think he's in the mood. (Frowning emoji)—Me

I have some other bad news—Kyle

What. Just pile it on me—Mona

Uh oh. What???—Me

Clint is MIA for a few days and last time his parents saw him he was depressed in his room at their house and took off with a bunch of his clothes and stuff in the middle of the night—Kyle

I had a feeling it was about him. They have no idea where he is?—Me

Nope—Kyle

Does he have a car & access to his money?—Mona

Yea I guess he didn't ever give them power of attorney—Kyle

Shit! I'm going to guess he's been using for a while then but I'm pretty negative about everything in general the last few days.—Mona

My phone quieted until later that evening.

Just talked to Dan, Marc messaged. *admitted he used but sounds like he wants to right the ship, Slipped but not tripped.*

That's good to hear.—Me

?????Hopefully—Marc

Yes, hopefully.

The following weekend I traveled to Fort Dodge for my Aunt Lenchie's birthday. I was going to see the sisters! I had texted the Cedar Rapids guys about my plans, suggesting lunch on my way back on Sunday. Kyle couldn't, Dave and Jesse were a tentative yes, and Clint was still MIA. That Saturday morning, my cousin Peggy, Martha, Peggy's daughter Tina, and I accompanied Lenchie to the casino in Jefferson. Suffering from shingles, Paula stayed behind. With Peggy driving, Martha unfortunately was able to observe the landscape from the backseat window. During that hour-long drive, we discovered she likes old barns, and were subjected to her enchantment with these sagging, rotting, decrepit structures. On a two-lane highway, the barns were close to the road.

"Ooo, look at that one, that's a really good one," Martha gushed. "Oh! There's another one! Look at that one!"

After about the fourth barn shout-out, Lenchie, who had just turned 92, couldn't withhold comment any longer. "Martha, what are you doing? Why are you looking at these old barns?" Her voice was lilting and singsong, filled with light and good humor. The rest of us laughed.

"They're cool, they have a lot of character. I like to take pictures of them," Martha explained.

"Do you want me to pull over so you can take pictures?" asked Peggy, who was like our sixth sister and had orchestrated my intervention and first stint in rehab.

"Would you?" Martha implored.

"Not now!" I exclaimed, knowing what a stop would entail, the waiting, the excruciating sight of her slowly circling the barn, taking multiple shots. It would not be a brief stop. "Maybe on the way back. It's not like they're going anywhere."

Martha peered at me. "That sounds like something Mom would've said."

"We can stop on the way back," Peggy offered.

"Yes, let's do that," I said in a fake enthusiastic voice. To my right, Tina, who had been out drinking the night before, chuckled softly, her head against the window, trying to doze. Martha shot me a hostile glare, but I appeased her. "We can go barn hopping on the way home."

"Barn hopping," Tina murmured.

"Yes! We can go barn hopping on the way home," agreed Peggy, grinning and catching my eye in the rearview mirror.

"Bar hopping! What are you talking about? Bar hopping? We can't go bar hopping!" Lenchie trilled.

We all laughed again, including Tina, roused from her snooze. At the casino, Lenchie sat at her favorite slot machines while Martha, Peggy, and I wandered through the gift shop and the restaurant, ending up at a blackjack table where Tina joined us. It was more fun than I had anticipated.

After eating lunch we walked out to the parking lot. "I'll sit on the right side so I can see the barns," Martha announced. "There were more on that side of the road."

Tina and I exchanged a look.

"Oh, get in the car," Martha ordered.

So we barn hopped on the way home, humoring Martha and her passion. And surprisingly, like the casino, it was fun, affectionately making fun of Martha from the vehicle as she skulked around each barn, snapping photos from multiple angles. There was something captivating about the rustic, collapsing structures, once sturdy and useful, now vulnerable to a strong wind. During one of these stops, my phone rang, startling all of us. It was Dave.

"Lisa! What's going on?"

"I'm barn hopping! We went to a casino for my aunt's birthday and now we're barn hopping." I scrambled out of the vehicle knowing I was loud on the phone, magnified in the small confines of a car. His reaction was what I expected.

"Bar hopping? You're bar hopping with your aunt?"

I laughed. "No, no. Bar*nn*, bar*nn* hopping. Martha likes old barns so we're stopping at some on the way back so she can take pictures."

"Oh! BARN hopping. I get it. I was worried for a second. I should've known better." A beat. "Are we still on for lunch tomorrow?"

"Yes, we are! Jesse bailed but I'm still planning on it."

"Good. And you're okay with the Irish Democrat even though it's a bar? Not a barn, a bar."

"Yes, I know exactly where it is. It's fine. It's not a problem."

"They do have good food. They have a great burger. It's not a George's burger but it's still good."

"I'm planning on leaving around 10 but I'll let you know when I'm close."

"Okay. Sounds good. See you tomorrow."

"Yep. See you tomorrow." *See you tomorrow. Yay!* I had been disappointed when Jesse bailed, but now after talking to Dave, I was happy it was going to be just me and him.

I had carefully chosen my outfit for the lunch, my favorite olive skort paired with a coral, short-sleeved top. I wanted to look nice, not for any romantic reason, but because I saw these guys so infrequently and each time was special. Sunday morning, I bid adieu to Peggy and the sisters, the latter telling me to say hello to Dave for them. I think he had the hots for Paula; he always made a flirtatious remark when I mentioned her. "If I weren't a married man..." he'd say.

During my usual pit stop outside Parkersburg, I texted Dave. *At Parkersburg. Should be in CR around 1.* I went to the bathroom, purchased a Diet Pepsi, and was lighting a cigarette in my car when my phone chimed.

See you at the ID, he texted.

At the Irish Democrat, I walked through the darkened pool room into the main bar, unsurprisingly near empty on this summer day except for the bartender and a Bloody Mary drinker. Also unsurprisingly I was here first. A slender, young woman materialized at my side. I ordered a Diet Pepsi and told her I was meeting someone for lunch.

I looked at the Bloody Mary drinker and felt a twinge, not for the drink but for the Sunday drinking. My last year in Wisconsin, I had become a Sunday morning regular at J.J.'s Top of the Swamp, where they served a good breakfast and a stiff vodka and diet Sprite. During football season, breakfast often stretched into the noon Packers game. I always made sure I drove home before I was too hammered. The regulars at J.J.'s knew when I was too far gone to drive. Now, the waitress returned with my Diet Pepsi and a couple of heavy plastic menus, setting them all on the table. I slid one menu across the table and flipped to the lunch items in mine. A familiar shape entering my peripheral vision stirred excitement within me. There he was, tanned and slender. I stood up and we hugged and as soon as we were seated, the waitress reappeared and took his drink order, another Diet Pepsi.

"You look good," he said.

"So do you. You're tan."

"Golf and tennis. The golf is still tough with the drinking that goes along with it."

"I bet. Maybe you shouldn't golf for a while."

"That's what my wife says. How was Fort Dodge?"

"It was nice. The sisters say 'Hi.'" I waited expectantly.

"The sisters..." He grinned. "Is Paula married?"

"Yes, Dave. I've told you that."

"Hmm." He opened his menu.

The burgers were big and messy and yummy. Normally self-conscious about eating in front of others, I was not with Dave, probably because we had shared so many meals. I talked and laughed with my mouth full, requesting extra napkins for dabbing between each bite.

"Do you have cravings?" he asked.

"Not cravings. More like twinges. Like with the nice weather, I'd have twinges." Dave nodded. "One time I was driving down Dodge Street and there were students on their porches drinking and I thought to myself 'It's sure a nice day for drinking.'"

"I know exactly what you mean. They warned us about that—wanting to drink when you're feeling good."

We talked about playing tennis, about Dave wanting to have a cookout for the Abbey gang at his house, and about Dan and Mona. I shared my theory. "I'm pretty good at picking up on stuff like that. Do you think they waited until after we left because they knew we'd disapprove?"

"I thought about that. Maybe not so much disapprove as they knew we'd discourage it. He just doesn't seem like her type."

"I know. The boyish type."

"But actually he was the right type," he mused, his mustache twisting sardonically.

"What do you mean?"

A deliberate, suspenseful beat. "He was vulnerable."

I nodded. "Yeah, you're right."

"And horny. Perfect pickings for an attractive, experienced female. We're pigs, Lisa. Horny, vulnerable pigs."

I grinned and rolled my eyes. "I know Dave. I know."

I was back on the road by three. We never played tennis and Dave never had a cookout. But we did have a reunion, of sorts, two weeks later.

Chapter Twenty-Nine

The summer days hummed along, and I fell into a peaceful routine of work, AA meetings, and the soul-satisfying tasks of tending to flowers and to the backyard creatures. I had several potted plants outside my front door, a couple of larger pots with multiple plants and some smaller pots with single plants. Watering them and watching them grow filled me with quiet happiness. I had a favorite squirrel to whom I fed peanuts before leaving for work. Upon hearing the signature Avelleyra squirrel call—a rapidfire tssking—he would scamper across the courtyard, slowing to a tentative approach at the ten-foot mark, peanut toss distance. Sometimes he was late, showing up just as I was walking to my car, causing me to curse softly but always turning around to hurriedly unlock the door and grab a fistful of peanuts from the bin inside the door. Those times, I'd scatter some peanuts on the sidewalk and toss him a couple, scolding him for his tardiness.

The relaxed carefree summer screeched to a halt one evening on June 17. It started with a text from Kyle.

Dans in the hospital.

What? Which hospital? Did he OD?

Not sure of the details. Mona called me.

I couldn't take it. I called Kyle.

"What happened? What did she say?" I asked.

"That he's in the hospital. She found out from his family. He's been in Iowa City. They were on the rocks again."

"He was in Iowa City? I had no idea."

"You haven't seen him? That's not what he said. I'm gonna send you a screenshot of a text. Just a heads up, I had a lapse."

"You had a what???"

"Don't yell at me. Look at the text."

"You relapsed? Why didn't you call me? Why didn't you let me know?"

"I know, I know, I'm a dumb fuck. Read the text. I'm gonna check with Mona."

My stomach churned as I waited for the text. Dan was in the hospital and hadn't contacted me. Kyle had relapsed and hadn't reached out to me. My phone chimed. Looking at the screenshot, I saw Dan's phone name was "Dan Abbey." Ohhh, Kyle!

June 12, 2017, 11:51 AM.

How's it going—Dan

Pretty good other than I relapsed. Started with a drink. Smh. U?—Kyle

I messed up a couple times but I'm still trying it.

For sure man. No H though bro! Shits deadly around here. Have you seen anyone else from Abbey lately?

I haven't done that again I see pat and Mona a lot and Lisa when im in ic but not a whole bunch.

Not true, Dan. You haven't seen me at all.

Cool cool

My phone dinged, the Messenger alert tone. I switched away from Kyle's text.

I just got a call. Dan overdosed. I'm headed to Iowa city—Mona

Omg! Keep me updated—Brandi

Where are they taking him?—Me

Probably u of I. Is he stable or critical?—Kyle

He's on a respirator now. Pat is going to drive me. Critical—Mona

Jesus—Kyle

I decided not to wait for Pat. I'm driving to Iowa city now—Mona

When did they find him—Brandi

Not sure. I just talked to him 3 hours ago.—Mona

Omg prayers lots of prayers—Brandi

I immediately texted the sisters, then I called the University of Iowa Hospital per the sisters' advice. After asking if he was a patient there, I was placed on hold a few minutes until connected with the ER nurses' station. The nurse I spoke to acknowledged he was there and that "they were working on him," but nothing else. Her voice had sounded taut with urgency. I was torn. I wanted to go to the hospital to offer support but didn't feel comfortable being around his family members. Then there was the Mona factor. I really did not want to witness the distressed girlfriend show. No matter how much I prayed for her, I blamed her for allowing the relationship to happen, blamed her for allowing him to move in with her, blamed her for his relapses.

An hour later, Messenger pinged.

I know who sold him the drugs. My parents are on the way. I'm almost there.—Mona

An hour later, I messaged Mona via The Abbey group.

How is Dan?

I waited and waited for a response. I paced. I went outside to smoke a cigarette. I texted Kyle to see if he'd heard anything. He hadn't. Forty-five minutes later, my phone pinged.

It's not good. It's really touch & go right now—Mona

Prayers from me—Marc

Is he conscious?—Me

Right is he awake or still out—Kyle

No. Very little brain activity.—Mona

I went to bed and tried to read but my mind kept wandering from the words on the page. My phone pinged an hour and a half later.

Any new news on Dan Mona?—Marc

We're waiting to hear from the neurosurgeon right now. He's not responsive at all. On the respirator—Mona

I don't even know what to say. Other than I'm crushed because I know from the short time I got to know him he has a HUGE HEART N VERY COMPASSIONATE!—Marc

Man...I really want the man upstairs to bring him through this right now.—Vape Man

We all do. I'll be staying here for the foreseeable future. My parents are coming in the morning as well.—Mona

Agreed Mona, Jim and the rest of our Abbey brothers n sisters! God give Dan a break please!—Marc

Why did Mona keep mentioning her parents? To remind her audience what a "family" she and Dan were? I pictured Dan lying in a hospital bed, eyes closed, a tube breathing for him, hooked up to machines monitoring his vital signs. For the first time since hearing the horrible news, I cried.

Three hours later, I was awakened by the Messenger ping. I groped around in the dark for my phone on the nightstand. It was Kyle.

Status?

No response, no response, come on Mona, give us something.

Ping!

No change. They sent us home. I'm staying at his parents. He did show signs of discomfort because his heart rate is elevated. That's likely due to being cold. They drop the body temperature to help the swelling of his brain. He is not breathing on his own and there are tons of things attached to his head to monitor brain function. I will update everyone as I can. Kyle, can you get a hold of his sponsor? Anyone have F Jeffs number? Just trying to reach out to anyone that can be there when he hopefully wakes up.—Mona

I'll have to find rogers number again—Kyle

Where in the hospital is he? Can I come up? I have eff Jeff's...—Me

Many thoughts and prayers—Jesse

I texted Roger—Kyle

Hospital just called. He's not doing well. We are headed back.—Mona

Shit—Kyle

No kidding Kyle. Lots of good, positive thoughts.—Jesse

Damn it, come everyone and pray for him!—Marc

It's in gods hands now. Hoping and praying he makes it through the night. Mona I will call you in the morning.—Kyle

I'll need to check with family. This is not a good sign.—Mona

Send any updates you can. I'd be down there now but I have Elijah—Kyle

I fell back to sleep but awoke at 5:30, automatically reaching for my phone to see if I had slept through any messages. I hadn't. But another came through twenty minutes later.

I'm not sure what all I can say right now. We're at university hospital. My parents arrived about an hour ago. He's not going to make it.—Mona

Yes he is prayer hunny—Brandi

No. He's brain dead. They are going to start turning off the machines when we are ready. I just need to hold his hand.—Mona

Wtf Mona I'm so sorry pls tell him I love him that we all do—Brandi

I love you to—Mona

Another hour passed.

Status Mona?—Kyle

Nothing. Another hour and a half later, Mona texted.

He's gone.—Mona

Omg I'm so sorry—Brandi

A horror emoji followed by 3 crying emojis—Kyle

I sat in silence, numb and paralyzed with disbelief. Dan was dead, overcome by his addiction. Why didn't he reach out to us? Why didn't he reach out to me? That damn Mona! If only he hadn't moved to Des Moines, we could have gone to meetings together! I called Dave.

"He's gone."

"I know. I just talked to Kyle. What a tragedy. He was just a kid. His poor parents."

"I blame her."

"I know. But he made his choices. She didn't stick the needle in his arm. But I know. Don't you do anything stupid."

"Don't worry. I feel bad but I don't feel like having a drink. Not at all."

Along with their sorrow for Dan, the sisters were worried about me, too. And I completely understood it. I'd only been sober three months. But turning to drink was not an option. In a weird, twisted way, I felt drinking would dishonor him. Addiction overtook Dan but it wasn't going to overtake me! My phone rang. It was Pat.

"Pat! This is so awful!"

"I know Lisa, it's so sad. I can't believe it. But then I can. I'm coming to Iowa City today and going to his folks' house. Do you want to come with me? I'll pick you up."

This was a lot for my grief-stricken brain to digest. Did I want to see Dan's parents? That also meant seeing Mona. "Yes, I do. I'll go over there with you."

It was nine o'clock. "My place is easy to find. I'll text you the directions."

"Just give me the address. I have GPS."

Even in this sad, tragic situation I had to ask myself the age-old question, "What am I going to wear?" I went with my khaki skort again and a russet top and waited nervously for Pat. Should we be going to his parents this soon? Do they want to see people? Pat must've talked to them. The sisters thought it was a good thing. Pat called when he was on my street, baffled by the four identical buildings. I guided him to the correct building and soon I heard a knock at the door. I opened it and there he was, my first Abbey visitor.

"Oh Lisa, it's so good to see you," he said hurriedly. "I'm sorry, I wouldn't ask to come in, but I really have to use your bathroom."

I moved aside so he could pass. "Come on in!"

He rushed past me and slammed the door shut. I smiled. Pat was here, peeing loudly in my apartment. After flushing, he emerged from the bathroom.

"That was close." He looked around. "Your place is really nice."

"Thanks."

"Are you ready?"

"Yep. Let's go."

We got into Pat's shiny maroon SUV, where he began fiddling with the GPS.

"I have the address," I broached helpfully.

Pat had called in an order for subs, so I directed him down the Benton Street hill to Riverside Drive.

"Do you need any help?" I asked after we parked.

"No. I got it. It's just one platter of sandwiches."

My apprehension flared sitting alone in the vehicle. It was one of my major shortcomings—fretting about something that hasn't even happened yet. I reined myself into the moment, watching Pat through the window with the cashier, then a diligent sparrow on the concrete, pecking at a crumb. Pat pushed open the restaurant door and exited, hoisting a large cellophane-covered platter. Once he was back in the car, the GPS poking resumed.

"I have the address, Pat. I kind of know where it is." I tried not to sound irritated.

"I have it programmed." Poke, poke, punch, punch. "I swear I have it programmed in this goddamn thing."

"Okay, let's just go. I know how to find it."

The GPS poking continued, now a little more aggressively. "But I programmed it. Why isn't the map coming up?"

I grabbed his arm. "Pat, we can find it! Stop!"

He looked at me, a grin replacing his furrowed brow. "Am I driving you crazy?"

I smiled back. "Yes! Stop it! Let's go!"

Any anxiety evaporated as we bickered good-naturedly. I directed Pat out of the parking lot toward Highway 6.

"I think Mona might be pregnant," he announced at a red light.

"What? Pregnant? Seriously?" I sputtered.

"Either that or she's gained weight. Check out her belly when we see her."

"Did she tell you she's pregnant?"

"No, but just look at her. And she's been drinking." A beat. "Maybe that's where the belly came from."

"What? Drinking too?"

"Yeah. They both were." He sighed. "It was just a matter of time before he started using."

"Jesus." Silence as the blame churned. "Turn left at the stoplight." More silent blame. "I really hope you're wrong."

"I could be. What do I know? I can't even get GPS to work."

I grinned as I directed him to turn right onto their street, spurring us to start scrutinizing house numbers.

It was a nice neighborhood, houses about twenty years old, not cookie cutter replicas, each house unique, each nicely landscaped. *Dan grew up here, this was his 'hood, this was the street where he played catch, where he learned how to ride a bike.* A pang of sorrow flared within me, but I focused on the house numbers. "There it is," I said.

Pat pulled over to the curb across from their house and parked the car. They must've been watching for us because by the time Pat pulled out the sandwich platter, Mona and Dan's dad were out in the driveway, warmly greeting us. Tom's engulfing hug was a painful reminder of his son.

"Oh Tom, this is so sad, I can't even imagine," I said, reluctantly breaking away. There stood Mona, blinking back tears. I moved to hug her. Pat caught my eye over her head, a question in his eyes. I frowned and rolled my eyes. Upon first seeing her, I had noted the swell of her stomach. We followed Tom and Mona through the living room and kitchen, where Pat set the platter on the kitchen island, to the porch at the rear of the house. I bypassed checking out the family photos in the living room. Thankfully, Pat did all the talking. Dan's sister was also on the porch, and Mona curled up in a corner chair. I sat in the adjacent corner. "How are you all doing? I know it's a dumb question but how are you?"

"I'm numb, in shock. I can't believe he's gone," Tom said, choking up. Pat moved to give Tom a partial hug.

"He was living here?" Pat asked.

Tom nodded, fighting back tears.

"I knew he was using," Mona interjected. "I couldn't have him around my kids."

Prevent defense. I knew that was coming.

"You did what you had to do, Mona," Tom said.

"Yeah, I knew he was using at the Cubs game," Emily added. "He kept disappearing. I think he was sniffing something."

I recalled a posting on Facebook of Dan and Emily at that game, and thinking his eyes looked weird, glassy and unfocused. "What was he sniffing?" I asked.

"Probably opiates? Right?" Pat asked.

"I think so," Emily replied.

"We found him downstairs," Tom said. "We hadn't seen him for a while, knew he was here, and I went down there and found him. He was unconscious..." His voice trailed off. "Do you want to see where we found him?"

My eyes widened and sought out Pat who returned my startled look.

"Sure. I'll go," he said.

"I'll stay up here," I said.

After they left, Mona asked if I wanted something to eat or drink and got up to lead me to the kitchen. Away from Emily, I suspected. Mona pulled a cheese and sausage tray out of the refrigerator, setting it on the island; she was very much at ease in this kitchen. "Do you want some pasta salad?" she asked, peering into the fridge.

"Sure."

Mona watched as I fixed a plate for myself. "I really feel like drinking," she confessed.

"I'm sure. If anything's gonna make you want to drink, this would be it." A beat. "But it will only make things worse. And you have to think of your kids."

"I know." Another beat as she looked down at the island countertop. "I've drank a couple of times."

A couple of times? That's what we alcoholics always say, a couple times, a couple drinks. "With Dan?"

Still looking down. "Yes."

So he had been telling the truth about her. But now was not the time to beat up on Mona. "Are you drinking now?"

"No," she quickly replied.

"Good." I put on my new AA face. "It would only make things worse," I repeated.

Mona's chin quivered and her eyes filled with tears. I moved around the island and hugged her, genuine sympathy washing away my stirring anger.

Back on the porch, Pat and Tom had returned from downstairs, and Tom was describing how they had found Dan. "I knew he was home, I heard him come in but then I didn't hear anything for a while, so I went down there and listened at the door and still didn't hear anything. I knocked at first then started pounding. My worst fears were coming true. So I went in and there he was, just lying there." Tom covered his face with his hand and Pat moved to comfort him. Tears burned my eyes. *Jesus fucking Christ Dan, why didn't you reach out to me, to Kyle, to someone?*

But I knew full well about not reaching out, about being alone with my drug, about not wanting anything else. I knew. There was a very small window for reaching out nestled between the first thought of taking a drink and the action to procure that drink. I vividly recalled the evening of my return to drinking upon moving back to Iowa City. It was a Friday in January and I had come home from work to find a large box outside my apartment door—the pub table and matching chairs for the kitchen I had ordered. After much deliberation, I had decided on the round, black table on a silver pedestal with two swiveling armless chairs. Assembling them proved to be more challenging than I had anticipated, and the irritation nudged me to consider a drink. It wasn't just a twinge; I knew where I could get it. I had learned at The Abbey that this is when I should have reached out, that this is when a relapse begins. A second nudge that evening occurred after receiving an unsatisfactory text response from my ex. I was still hoping to get back together. Instead of calling someone—a sister, a friend—I had stewed with disappointment, rationalizing that I deserved a drink. As soon as I had picked up my purse, keys in hand, the relapse had begun. Sitting in my car in the dark parking lot outside Hartwig Drugstore, hands gripping the steering wheel, I had *almost* called someone, *almost* averted the twelve-month drunken tumble down the hill toward my kitchen floor. Instead, I had gotten out of the car, walked into the drugstore, down the liquor aisle, past the tequila, past the gin, until I got to the vodka.

The urgency to drink had grown as I hurried to the cashier. I couldn't wait to get home. I wondered when Dan's relapse had started, when had he decided to get drugs, to contact a dealer. It took more planning to get drugs than booze. Or did it? Had he hesitated before making that call or sending that text? Had he considered texting someone for help?

I was ready to go. I caught Pat's eye and held it, tilting my head slightly toward the front door. He frowned, then understanding dawned upon his face and he repeated the head tilt, adding a soft nod.

"Well, Lisa, should we be going? You guys are probably exhausted." Once in the car, I congratulated him. "I wasn't sure you'd get my signal. Good job."

"I didn't at first. But you have very expressive eyes. So do you think she's preggo?"

"I'm not sure. She might've just gained weight. I just don't know. She told me she drank a couple of times."

"A couple of times," he scoffed. "I know it was more than a couple of times."

"Yeah. I figured she was lowballing it."

"Poor Tom. Did you notice he was drinking?"

"Yeah. I don't blame him."

"I can't imagine losing one of my sons. He's gonna be a mess."

I directed Pat to a coffee shop across the street from George's of the infamous burgers. Pat had been texting Dave.

"What's the latest on Dave coming down?" I asked.

"Now it's four o'clock."

"Four!" I glanced at my watch. "That's two hours!"

"Are you sick of being with me?"

"No. It's not you, it's me." I needed to elaborate. "I have a being-with-people threshold and I've passed it. It's not you personally. It's any person." I had become aware of this threshold the past few weeks, and acutely aware one evening while out with ACT people on a Friday after work. It was all good, I was not tempted or bothered by the drinking, but after a couple of hours an inner voice whispered: *"It's time to go."* The fun had run its course. Plus I genuinely just wanted to go home. I heeded the inner voice and left. When I drank, I could be around people for hours. Now, when I start wondering what time it is, it's time to go.

"Do you understand? It's not personal." I didn't want to hurt his feelings.

"I do. You like your alone time."

"I really do. It's become almost..." I groped for a word. "Cherished. Especially with being on the phones all day at work. I just don't want to be around people anymore."

"Let me text Dave and tell him you're getting antsy. I know he wants to see you too."

For once, Dave responded right away. "Okay, he's gonna try and leave in an hour. And he wants you to get a hold of Eff Jeff to see if he can meet us."

An hour was pushing it. I swiped through my contacts, found Eff Jeff and pressed call. To my surprise, he answered. Anymore, I always expect voicemail. "Jeff! It's Lisa. Lisa from The Abbey!" I wondered how many Lisa's from The Abbey he knew.

"Lisa! How are you? So sad about Dan."

"I know. We were just at his parents' house. I'm sitting here with Pat at Higher Ground and Dave is coming down. What are you doing? Do you want to get together?"

"I'm just working around the house. Do you guys want to come over?"

I looked at Pat. "He wants us to come over. Is that okay with you?"

"Sure. That's fine with me. Do you know where he lives?'

"Kind of. It's not far from here." To Eff Jeff. "You live over by the cemetery on Governor, right?"

"Yeah, it's easy to find. I'll give you the address."

Eff Jeff had talked about living near the Black Angel, a well-known Iowa City monument in the old cemetery. The statue was constructed in 1912 and over time blackened with oxidation. Commissioned by a Czech-Bohemian immigrant, the towering angel's head droops, looking down upon the grave of the immigrant's son. Approaching the cemetery on Governor Street, we turned onto Church Street before passing it. Pat's vehicle rumbled noisily over the uneven brick surface.

"Brick streets. Cool," Pat commented. "He's in an old neighborhood."

At the end of Church, we turned left. Eff Jeff's house was the last on the right, a long driveway leading up to it, red bricks glimpsed through the thick trees.

"This is it?" Pat asked.

"According to his directions it is. That's the number on the mailbox." The mailbox was on a post at the end of the driveway.

Pat turned his vehicle into the one-lane driveway. "It's kind of spooky.

Would you want to live next to a cemetery?"

"I'm not sure."

Pat pulled up next to the house, a beautiful century-old structure with stately tall windows. Next to the house was a smaller building, like a garage but large enough to have living quarters on the second floor. We walked up to the back door and I knocked. Standing there, we heard thuds and a crash from within. We looked at each other.

"What the hell's going on in there?" Pat asked.

I giggled and the door opened, Eff Jeff standing there, grinning. "Hi! Come in, come in!"

We followed him into the kitchen, a beautiful open space with exposed brick walls and expansive light flooding through the tall windows. "Pat, it's good to see you!" Eff Jeff waved me off. "I see you all the time."

"It's good to see you too!" Pat replied. "This is a really cool house."

"I'll give you a tour. Is Dave coming?"

"He should be on his way," I said. "I'll text him."

"Did you redo the kitchen yourself?" Pat asked. "I'm guessing it wasn't this big originally."

As I texted Dave, Eff Jeff explained how he had removed the pantry walls and built the island.

"Who knew you were so talented," I said with a grin.

"Yeah, who knew?" he grinned back. "How are you two doing? This is rough. I know. I've been through it."

"I'm doing fine," I said. "Honestly, I have not considered taking a drink."

"Oh, I've considered it," Pat admitted, "but I haven't come close to doing it."

My phone rang, it was Dave calling. "Where are you?" I asked.

"Lost. What street am I looking for?" He sounded testy.

"Church. Did you come in on Dodge?"

"Yeah, but I think I've gone too far. I just passed the street that goes to George's."

"You've gone too far. Turn left on Iowa then left on Governor and come back this way. Turn right on Church, right before the cemetery."

"Church. I knew it was a building name. I was thinking House or School."

"Okay," I smiled. "We'll see you soon."

"Doesn't he have GPS?" Pat smirked.

"GPS," I scoffed. "Dave still has a flip phone!"

Pat filled in Eff Jeff on our visit to Dan's parents, though neither of us mentioned Mona's possible condition. A few minutes later, there was a knock at the door. Eff Jeff let Dave in, and the room shimmered with the bonafide affection between these men. This was the first time Pat and Dave had seen Eff Jeff since The Abbey. Observing their reunion melted some of my underlying sadness. Next, Eff Jeff led us to the other parts of the house, where the rooms were their original sizes. In the living room, built-in bookshelves overflowed with books, cozy chairs arranged for reading and conversation, a comfortable, lived-in clutter scattered about. Next to the living room was his office, a large wooden desk in front of a tall window with a view of the expansive lawn.

"I'm leaving The Abbey in July and starting counseling here full-time," he informed us.

"You're leaving The Abbey?" Pat asked.

"Yes. Things are changing there. Andrew's gone and there's more change in the works."

I wanted to know more but I could tell he was done talking about it.

Dave was looking at me. "You want to know more, don't you?" he said.

"Well, yeah," I admitted.

Eff Jeff grinned at me and didn't miss a beat, smoothly changing the subject. "I need to rewire the electric in here so I can get internet and I just need more outlets."

"I'm an electrician!" Pat said. "I can help you with that!"

As they discussed paths for rewiring, I quietly watched them again, my insides opening with warmth and love. I smiled softly and Dave caught it, responding with a slight upturn of his mustache. He knew what I was thinking. Or at least close to it. I felt so comfortable with these guys. Granted, I had bared my soul before them, stood spiritually naked in front of them, but it was more than that. I refused to analyze it too closely. I just wanted to bask in it, enfold myself in it like one of Dan's hugs. Tour over, we once again circled the kitchen island, reluctant to end the visit. So we didn't.

"Why don't we go to George's, get some burgers?" Dave suggested.

I was enjoying their company, but we were way over my people threshold. It must have shown on my face.

"What's wrong? You have somewhere you need to be?" Dave asked.

"She's past her time of wanting to be with people," Pat chimed in.

I shot Pat a look.

"It's one night out of your life. You're going to George's," Dave ordered.

It was like when he had hounded me about going to church, but I succumbed this time. "Alright. Let's go to George's," I agreed, mock grudgingly.

"Great. Three drunks and an addict going to George's," Eff Jeff said. "Fucking perfect."

We all laughed.

George's was a classic dive bar, located in a two-story standalone brick building, defying the gentrification going on around it. It was dark, no soft mood lighting here, most of the illumination coming from behind the bar, primarily from the infamous vintage Hamm's beer sign, a relic from the 60s, a bucolic river slowly looping over and over and over, a red tent and red canoe on its bank. A scene from the land of sky-blue waters. The lingering aroma of grilled meat hung in the air. In my college days, the bar had been populated by pseudo-intellectuals and aging hippies discussing current events in a haze of cigarette smoke. It hadn't been one of our regular haunts—it wasn't the best place to meet guys—but we'd frequent it occasionally to get away from the college crowd. Squeezed into a wooden booth, we were the only customers along with a sprinkling of hipsters and an older regular at the bar chatting with the bartender.

"Burgers? Everyone getting a burger?" Dave asked.

We all assented to burgers as the bartender came out from behind the bar and over to our booth. We ordered our non-alcoholic beverages and cheeseburgers, then talk turned to the unavoidable subject of Dan.

"I saw it in his eyes at The Abbey," Eff Jeff said.

"What do you mean? You saw what?" I asked.

"He knew he wasn't going to make it. He knew it was gonna kill him."

We sat in silence a moment, each of us with our own recollections.

"He did talk a lot about his fears of still wanting to get high, how much he liked it," I recalled.

"Heroin is a powerful drug," Eff Jeff said.

"Yeah, and powerfully deadly," Pat added.

Our burgers arrived, simply wrapped in wax paper, the greasy aroma sublime.

"They aren't very big," Pat groused.

"They're perfect," I mumbled, the first bite already in my mouth.

"Get another one!" exclaimed Dave, the George's burger pusher man. "Do you want me to order another one?"

"No, it's fine," pouted Pat, devouring a third of his with one bite.

Smushed in next to Eff Jeff, I felt him chuckle. After we ate, I brought the conversation back to Dan. "Why did he have to get with Mona? Why?"

"Yeah, I was surprised by that," Dave said.

"She's got it. Opens doors with just a smile," Eff Jeff recited.

I looked at Eff Jeff. "What's that from? Isn't that from a song?"

"Eagles, 'Lyin' Eyes,'" Dave answered.

"Ain't no way to hide your lyin' eyes..." Pat sang off-key.

"Sex is also a powerful drug," Dave said.

I sighed.

"Another sad ending," Eff Jeff said.

Conversation turned to happier topics, the dongs, Eff Jeff mooching food, Dave telling me he had a hot tub in his room, new to Eff Jeff having never heard it before. We laughed and joked, our sober booth boisterous. *Could I actually have fun without drinking? Is it possible?* As if reading my mind, Eff Jeff turned to me. "Who knew a bunch of fucking drunks could have fun at a bar without drinking?"

Who knew, indeed.

Chapter Thirty

Thankfully, that week I worked at the warehouse with Grace, checking in international materials, not having to deal with hapless test coordinators on the phone. The unpacking of boxes and matching up of tests was perfect for my frame of mind, the waves of grief free to flow, unhindered by forced politeness.

Kyle picked me up for the visitation on Thursday evening, with Dave in the front seat. The visitation was at a newly built Catholic church on the far east side of Iowa City, east of the Buddha. I don't like these modern churches. My hometown parish was doing the same thing, building a brand spanking-new church next to the high school, abandoning the old majestic, historical structures. The rationale was centralizing the Catholic community because of the declining number of priests, unable to oversee all the separate parishes. Instead of addressing the priest shortage by letting women be priests or allowing priests to marry, they abandoned the older churches and built new. I directed Kyle down Melrose to Burlington Street through downtown and to the near east side, where Burlington merged into Muscatine Avenue.

"Why didn't we take Rochester?" Kyle asked. "We could've taken Rochester."

I always forgot that Kyle used to live in Iowa City. "What's wrong with this way?" I bristled. "I like this neighborhood. I want to live over here."

"There's a lot of child molesters in this neighborhood," Kyle stated matter-of-factly.

"How do you know that?" I exclaimed, noticing Dave shaking his head.

"After you told me you were looking at places over here, I looked it up," he replied, catching me in the rearview mirror shaking my head. "What?"

We crossed Scott Boulevard into a neighborhood of newly constructed homes and townhouses, following the street to an open, as of yet, undeveloped space, except for the church off to our left, a lone sprawling structure topped by a cross.

"We could've taken Rochester," Kyle repeated.

"Geezus, just park the car," I said.

"There's a lot of cars here," Dave commented.

Kyle parked and we walked into a spacious foyer. Upon entering the parish center, we encountered a long line of mourners along the wall, waiting to pay their respects.

"I gotta pee," I said, realizing it was going to be a while. I ducked into a restroom off the foyer and when I rejoined the guys, they had only moved a couple of spaces. Dave pulled something out of his wallet, a scapular, stamp-sized, cloth portraits of saints on both ends of a narrow ribbon, worn over the shoulders with a saint in the front and another in the back. I had one as a young girl but disliked wearing it, the laminated saints always sticking to my skin. Dave held the scapular gently in his hands. He noticed me looking at it.

"I asked Dan's parents if I could give it to him, if he could be buried with it and they said yes," he said.

My throat tightened and my eyes stung. "That's really beautiful, Dave."

"What is that?" Kyle asked.

"You wear it over your shoulders under your shirt," Dave explained, "one saint in the front, one in the back. Obviously Dan will be wearing it on the outside."

"That's really cool," said Kyle, a catch in his voice.

I looked out the window as we moved a few more feet, an onrush of emotion stirring inside me. Suddenly, Kyle grabbed my arm.

"Don't look now but Vape Man is here," he hissed in my ear.

"Shit," I muttered. Dave had heard but was carefully looking straight ahead.

"Hey guys, good to see you," Vape Man greeted us. "Wish it was under different circumstances."

Kyle got stuck talking to him while Dave stood by silently and I eavesdropped, struggling to control my facial expressions. It was all about him. "I've done ninety meetings in ninety days. I got a sponsor and I'm chairing meetings," Vape Man bragged. No questions for Kyle about how he was doing. Thankfully, Mona's sister walked up, asking to speak to me. We stepped away from the line. She got right to the point. "We're worried that Mona's been drinking. I know it's kind of weird to ask but could you see, when you go through the line, if she has been today?"

"Sure, I can do that," I said. "I'll be discreet." I returned to my place in line.

"What was that about?" Dave asked. Vape Man was still talking about himself to Kyle.

"She wants me to check to see if Mona's been drinking," I murmured.

Dave's mustache twitched quizzically. "Hmmm. They must have concerns."

We were now just a few people away from Dan, close enough to see him lying in the casket. We stood in silence, even Vape Man. This was so wrong, Dan lying there motionless, eyes closed, lifeless, makeup caked on that beautiful, boyish face. He didn't look good, not at all. He looked fake, like a department store mannequin. I watched with a tightening throat as Dave lowered himself onto the padded kneeler and crossed himself, scapular clutched in his right hand, swinging back and forth with each point of the cross. After a few moments, he rose and gently placed the scapular over Dan's head, carefully arranging it on his chest. I gasped as tears rushed to my eyes, taken aback by the simple beauty of the gesture. Behind me, I heard Kyle sniffling. It was my turn.

Kneeling before Dan, but not really Dan, I continued to scold him as I had been all week. *We should be going to meetings together! Why didn't you reach out to one of us?* I recalled what Eff Jeff had said, that Dan had known he wasn't going to make it. If that was so, then now he was at peace.

I got up and moved on to offer my condolences to his parents and sisters, and Kyle replaced me at the kneeler. I moved on to Mona, who stood forlornly at the end of the line. I sniffed her right before we hugged and during. I didn't smell anything. Vodka is not odorless as falsely rumored, it's just not as strong as the brown liquors or beer. I looked over at her sister and shook my head, to which she mouthed "thank you."

Dave was with Pat at another table, where Kyle and Vape Man eventually joined us. Luckily, Vape Man had to get back to Mason City—a four-hour drive—and wasn't able to stay for the funeral. Joni had taught me to halt any mean-spirited thoughts with a prayer, so I half-heartedly prayed he had a safe drive back to Mason City.

"Why don't we go to George's?" Dave suggested after Vape Man's departure. "I'm hungry."

"George's again?" I protested.

"Kyle hasn't been there. And we had fun there the other night," Dave countered.

"It's gonna be more crowded on a Thursday," I said.

"So what?" Dave countered again.

"Famous burgers George's?" Kyle chimed in. "I wanna go." Looking straight at me. "And we're gonna take Rochester to get there."

I rolled my eyes. "Alright. George's it is."

"I'm getting two burgers this time," Pat said.

At George's we scored the big table in the front window and the woman who waited on us was someone I knew from Ragbrai and through Brian and his brothers.

"You know Lisa?" Dave asked. "Have you worked here long? I used to come here in the 80s."

"Over thirty years," she replied. "You do look kind of familiar."

"I came here a lot with my brother during law school."

Again we ordered non-alcoholic beverages and cheeseburgers, two for Pat, and again they were delicious.

"You guys weren't kidding," Kyle said. "These are the best. The grease to bun size ratio is perfect."

"You're not right," Dave said.

We discussed the plan for the next day. Pat was staying overnight with Dave and had left his vehicle at the church, and I wanted to drive so I wasn't held hostage all day, so we decided to meet at the church before the service. Regretfully, Kyle was unable to attend because of work. As Kyle drove back to my apartment, Dave found a classic rock radio station and when Bachman Turner Overdrive's "Takin' Care of Business," came on, we all broke into song, the lyrics and key level manageable for all caliber of singers. The chorus was especially tailor made for a singalong. *"Takin' care of business, every day. Takin' care of business, every way. Takin' care of business. It's alright! Takin' care of business. I'm workin' overtime."* In the midst of one of these choruses, my phone rang, or rather drummed, Martha's latest ring tone.

"What is that noise?" Pat shouted over the singing.

"It's Martha. That's her ring tone," I said, digging around in my purse for the phone. I found it and pressed to answer. "Hey Sissy!"

"Martha!" Dave shouted.

"Martha!" Pat echoed. "We're kidnapping your sister!"

"What is going on?" she asked, laughter in her voice.

"We're singing 'Takin' Care of Business,'" I said.

"Every day!" Kyle called out.

"Where are you?" she asked.

"In Kyle's car! We're just about to my place!" I had to speak loudly over the singing.

"We're not taking her there! We're kidnapping her!" Pat shouted.

"See you tomorrow, Martha!" Dave yelled.

"I'll call you when I get home! Turn here, Kyle!" I ended the call, laughing helplessly. Once home, I sat in the dark wondering how I could feel so happy, even though Dan was gone forever. It didn't seem right, but somehow I knew he would approve of our laughter and hijinks. And in a tragic, heartbreaking turn of events, he was responsible for bringing us together. I hoped he was able to see us, to *feel* us and share our laughter.

The next day was sunny and without humidity, a blessed gift for a June day in Iowa. Since I was driving myself, I could set my own pace for getting ready, focusing on each task and not allowing myself to contemplate why I was getting gussied up. I chose a flared black skirt with a black and white animal print top, lightly scattered with sequins, and comfortable black Mary Janes. The church parking lot was as full as the night before but unlike last night the foyer was filled with mourners. I spotted Dave and Pat and wound my way through the crowd toward them. And I saw Dan. They had moved him out here, near the entrance to the church nave. I hurried toward my guys.

"Did you know Pat's a pall bearer?" Dave asked.

"No. Oh Pat, that's wonderful," I said, crossing myself. "Why didn't you say anything?"

He humbly shrugged. "I don't know. I figured you'd find out eventually. You know, like when I walk up with the casket."

"You just crossed yourself," Dave pointed out.

"It's a reflex like when I'm thankful or I'm saying a quick prayer," I explained. "Don't get excited. I'm not gonna start going to mass or anything."

I spied Martha through the crowd and waved at her. Once she reached us, the guys warmly greeted her. "We didn't kidnap her last night," Pat said.

"That's good," Martha smiled.

"Pat's a pall bearer!" I said.

Martha lightly touched Pat's arm. "I love that so much."

I blinked away tears.

"I don't like these new churches," Martha said. "Aren't there older ones here in Iowa City?"

"I know," I said. "There's a couple in the downtown area but this is the eastside church."

She shook her head. "Just like Fort Dodge."

Through an opening in the crowd, I saw Eff Jeff, dressed in cargo shorts and a bright Madras shirt. I watched him as he looked around, waiting for him to glance our way and when he finally did, I waved. "Eff Jeff's here." His face broke into a big grin as he threaded his way toward us. I waited as greetings were exchanged.

"That's Eff Jeff?" Martha asked.

I got his attention, never an easy feat, and steered it toward Martha. "This is my sister Martha. Martha, this is Eff Jeff."

"I've heard a lot about you," she said. "It's so nice to finally meet you."

"It's nice to meet you too," he said, looking over at me like, *So what the fuck have you been saying about me?*

As we talked about how many people were there and Eff Jeff asked if we'd seen anyone else from The Abbey, Martha stealthily pulled me aside. "He's not how I pictured him at all," she murmured.

I was intrigued by this revelation. "Eff Jeff? How did you picture him?"

She paused thoughtfully. "Rough. Big. With long hair and a beard. I pictured him like a biker guy."

I giggled. "He's not like that at all."

"I see that. It was because of all the swearing and the wild stories," she explained.

"Karen's here," said Dave.

I spotted her neatly coiffed head above the fray, those wise warm eyes calmly scanning the crowd. Dave waved and she glided over.

"How is everyone doing?" she asked, meeting all of our eyes with her steady gaze.

"As well as could be expected," Dave replied.

After a brief catch-up with everyone, Karen turned to Martha and me. "It's so nice to see you two," she said.

On impulse, I hugged her, a wave of emotion swelling up inside me. "Oh Karen..." was all I could say.

"I know," she whispered. "I love you all so much."

After that, I retreated to the bathroom to be alone with my churning emotions, to get away from the group. Looking at myself in the bathroom mirror, all gussied up, that recurring thought returned: *This is so wrong, being here at Dan's funeral. This should not be happening.* Upon returning to the foyer, I noticed that no one was at the casket, so I veered over to it. I stood over him and said goodbye to the earthly Dan, lamenting again that we wouldn't be spending our sobriety together. I wished him peace and crossed myself. Walking back to the group, a wave of sorrow engulfed me, unexpected like a sudden, strong wind before a storm. Pat stepped in front of me, his eyes glistening behind his glasses.

"Oh no," he said, "not you, Lisa. I can't stand to see you cry." He hugged me through the gulping sobs, which quickly subsided. We pulled apart and I wiped away the tears.

"Okay. I'll be fine now. Whew! That came out of nowhere."

"That's going to happen," said Karen.

Pat left us to fulfill his pallbearer duties. Karen led us into the chapel, choosing a pew halfway down into which she was followed by Eff Jeff, Dave, Martha, and me. A couple of Melrose meeting guys sat down on the other side of Dave. The interior of the church was bright, airy, and beautiful, not what I wanted for a solemn Catholic service. Give me dark, filtered stain-glassed window lighting, ominous towering statues any day. It was nice sitting next to Dave, showing him that indeed, I did know how to participate in Mass. The gospel reading from the New Testament was the one about Lazarus rising from the dead, Martha and Mary discovering his empty tomb. I nudged my Martha, figuring she wasn't paying attention.

"The reading has Martha in it," I whispered. "Of all the readings to pick..." I liked to believe the universe was offering comfort.

Following the priest's sermon, Mona and her two pre-teen children got up from their pew in front with Dan's family and walked up to the lectern on the altar. Martha and I exchanged a careful look. And what the hell was Mona thinking, wearing a spaghetti-strapped sundress to her boyfriend's funeral? Dan's dad placed his arm around Mona's bare shoulders as her daughter proceeded to read something Mona had shared with us on Messenger, a letter to her "dad." This was a travesty. Mona had been with him three months. But who was I to judge? The family had obviously agreed to this. The daughter was poised and a good reader, no easy feat in these circumstances, but the words left me cold. Martha and I exchanged a look of dismay.

The rest of the mass continued, the Holy Eucharist, the sign of peace, then Communion and with it, the Communion dilemma—should I or shouldn't I? I hadn't gone to confession since college. I had over thirty years of sin built up, plus I was twice divorced. But I had taken Communion over the years and nothing catastrophic had ever occurred. Martha with her unconfessed sins chose to stay behind while Dave and I stepped out of the pew. I always felt a little naughty after receiving the wafer, walking back to the pew unscathed. Back in the pew, we proceeded with the last segment of the mass, the downhill slide when I always felt a surge of energy knowing it was almost over. Some congregants, usually those sitting in the rear pews, snuck out at this point, unseen by the judging eyes of their fellow parishioners. If Dad could've, he would have been one of those sneaks, but Mom wouldn't allow it. Instead, he hustled us out as soon as the last note of the closing song was sung. No post-Mass chit chat for the Avelleyras. We had to beat the traffic!

After the family followed out the casket, we regrouped in the parking lot, where we were joined by Abbey Jeffrey. It was so nice to see him! We said our goodbyes to Karen, and Dave offered to drive to the cemetery so Eff Jeff, Martha and I piled into his car.

"You know, Martha pictured you a lot differently," I tattled to Eff Jeff.

"Lisa!" Martha cried from the front seat.

"How did she picture me?" Eff Jeff grinned, clearly intrigued.

"Rough, because of all the swearing, like a biker guy."

"Oh Lisa," Martha groaned.

"And big. Big and scary with a beard."

"I never said scary," she corrected.

"Hey! It's okay! I love it!" Eff Jeff reassured her. Ever unflappable, he proceeded to show me photos on his phone of himself in waders fishing in the middle of a river.

"Where is this?" I asked.

"Wyoming. This is where I find peace, where I feel closest to my Higher Power."

"Shee-it," I said, recalling the moniker for his Higher Power.

"Shee-it?" Martha repeated.

"He, she, it. Shee-it," he explained. "My Higher Power."

"I get it," Martha said. And I knew she did.

We entered the cemetery from Dodge Street. Dave pulled onto the grass near the awning where mourners were gathering. Our jocularity set aside, we stood at the gravesite, the warm June sun heating up the day. The priest solemnly recited final prayers before Dan's remains were lowered into the ground. It was all so soul crushing when you boiled it down. Dan was gone, his spirit forever extinguished to the living. Platitudes brought me no comfort at this point, but the steadying presence of my Abbey cohorts and my sister provided solace.

"Do you want to say good-bye?" Dave asked me after the prayers, the mourners drifting away to their cars.

I nodded and followed him up to the canopy. I touched the shiny surface of the casket, silently telling Dan that I loved him and I would stay sober for him. Upon returning to our group, we found Martha acting as social director, planning the next get together.

"You could all meet in Cedar Rapids," she said. "I'd come down for it."

"You could meet in North Liberty at the Tin Roost where I work," Jeffrey offered.

"Are you talking about getting together?" I interjected. To Jeffrey. "I thought you worked at that steak place downtown."

"Joseph's. I did but I just started at the Tin Roost. We just opened."

"That would be fun!" I really liked the idea of seeing each other soon. "We could meet at Jeffrey's restaurant. North Liberty is kind of centralized. What kind of food do you have there?"

We continued to plan until Pat left with the other pallbearers. Back in Dave's car, the jocularity resumed, a hungry Eff Jeff wondering about the food.

"What do you think they'll have? Real food? Or just something like cheese and crackers?"

"What do you care? It's free!" Dave joked.

"How long do you think before Mona gets into another relationship?" I asked.

"Six months. Tops," Eff Jeff answered immediately.

"Oh, I'd say three months," Dave added. "It won't be long. She's hot." He grinned at me in the rear-view mirror, catching my eyeroll.

Martha withheld comment but I noticed her shaking her head. Her phone beeped, prompting her to look at it. "Oh, no."

"What is it?" I asked.

"It's Mangera. She said, 'Call me ASAP.' I'll wait until we get to the church."

"Do you not know what ASAP means?" Dave prodded. "Call her!"

Eff Jeff leaned over to me. "Who's Madeira?"

"Mangera. A college friend."

"I don't want to be rude," Martha fretted.

"Call her! It's not rude. We're like family," Dave said.

My heart soared. We *are* like family. From Martha's end of the conversation, we learned that another college friend had been moved down to the university hospital from Dubuque. Martha would go see her after lunch. Eff Jeff and I exchanged a look.

"Well?" Dave inquired.

"You know, if you're going to take a phone call in front of other people, the least you can do is tell them about it," Eff Jeff added.

We all laughed, and I felt another twinge of remorse that Dan would never again participate in moments like this, in this precious camaraderie, unexpected gems popping up out of nowhere, like finding a five-dollar bill in the pocket of a winter coat after not wearing it for a year. Once the laughter subsided, Martha filled us in on her friend, who had cancer and had just started chemo this past week. She had been feeling sick, Martha explained, and they discovered she was filling up with fluid. They decided to move her down here because her surgeon was here and because this is where you brought people when you really didn't know what was going on.

"Wow, good thing you just happen to be in Iowa City," I said to my sister.

"Yeah, funny how that worked out." We smiled knowingly at each other, acknowledging our shared belief in serendipity.

The room where the visitation had taken place was set up for lunch. Seated with my cohorts, I shared another meal with those whom I had shared so many. Even though he wasn't part of what I considered the core group, I was glad Jeffrey had joined us, a quiet observer amidst our boisterous crew. "You know who he reminds me of?" Martha said, looking at Jeffrey who was in earshot.

I looked at him, the receding hairline, the hint of a five o'clock shadow, the sensitive eyes. "Chris Murphy," I replied without hesitation.

"Who's Chris Murphy?" he asked. "Is that a good thing?"

"Our cousin in Denver," I said. "One of our favorite cousins."

"And we have a lot of cousins," Martha added.

Martha and I looked at him, then back at each other. "He really does," Martha repeated.

Mona came over to our table and thanked us for being there. I fought to keep my face expressionless. After she left, I caught Dave smirking at me, mustache set in mischievous position. "You did really well, Lisa. I'm impressed with your performance."

I rolled my eyes. "I just can't..." I sputtered.

"And the Oscar goes to..." Martha said.

"Me!" I completed.

Jeffrey also deserved an award, I thought, recalling his altercation with Mona.

Basking in the warmth and ease of this fellowship, I decided to divulge something I had been pondering for a while. "Why do they not allow mixed sponsorships, a man and a woman?" I asked. "I mean, my sponsor is gay and it's just fine. I'd rather sponsor a young guy than a woman."

Pat, Dave and Eff Jeff exchanged looks, not quite lascivious but in that ballpark.

"Step Thirteen," Eff Jeff answered as Pat and Dave snickered.

"What is Step Thirteen?" Martha asked.

I had never heard of Step Thirteen before, but I had a guess. "I'm pretty sure I know."

"Well Martha, when a man and a woman spend a lot of time together..." Pat started.

"Things happen," Dave continued.

"Sexual things," Eff Jeff clarified.

"Oh, come on!" Martha exclaimed. "It doesn't have to!"

"But it will!" said Pat gleefully.

Eff Jeff raised his plastic glass of lemonade in a toast. "To Step Thirteen!"

"To Step Thirteen!" cheered the other two mischief makers.

"We're in a Catholic church," Martha reproached.

I couldn't help but join their laughter.

Jeffrey was smiling at me. "I can see you doing it."

Soon thereafter, my inner barometer was telling me I needed to be alone. Pat made another attempt to extend the threshold, but it failed.

"No Pat, I don't want to look at Harleys," I said to him.

"You can't afford a Harley!" Dave admonished him.

"I know," Pat said sheepishly. "But I can still look."

Alone in my apartment, I allowed all the emotions from the day to flow through me. Although I savored my alone time, I was comforted knowing that Martha was staying over and soon would be walking through the door.

The next morning, I awoke and did the same thing, lying in my bed, replaying some of the scenes from the week, most warming me, a couple bringing quick tears to my eyes. Then something happened that prompted me to grab my phone and start furiously typing.

Facebook post:

"I awoke to the bright chirping of a cardinal. I parted the curtains and there he was, hopping merrily around the feeder. I hadn't seen him in a while. Hello Dan. I will never forget you my dear, sweet, beautiful friend. And rightfully so."

The post got 46 reactions, including from Kyle and Jesse. Dan would've liked that.